QA 351 BEL

SPECIAL FUNCTIONS
FOR
SCIENTISTS AND ENGINEERS

SPECIAL
FUNCTIONS
FOR
SCIENTISTS AND ENGINEERS

W. W. BELL
Lecturer in Engineering
University of Aberdeen

VAN NOSTRAND REINHOLD COMPANY
LONDON
NEW YORK CINCINNATI TORONTO MELBOURNE

VAN NOSTRAND REINHOLD COMPANY LTD
Windsor House, 46 Victoria Street, London S.W.1

INTERNATIONAL OFFICES
New York, Cincinnati, Toronto, Melbourne

Printed in Great Britain by
Butler & Tanner Ltd, Frome and London

PREFACE

This book is primarily intended for use in undergraduate courses by physics and engineering students in universities and technical colleges. It should, however, also prove useful to those working in other sciences, since it does not contain any specific examples drawn from the fields of physics, engineering, chemistry, etc. We believe it to be preferable to give here the principal results concerning special functions likely to be encountered in applications, and to leave the applications themselves to the particular context in which they arise. The book is designed for those who, although they have to use mathematics, are not mathematicians themselves, and may not even have any great mathematical aptitude or ability. Hence an attempt has been made, especially in the earlier chapters, to sacrifice brevity for completeness of argument. The level of mathematical knowledge required of the reader is no more than that of an elementary calculus course; in particular, no use is made of complex variable theory. Equally, no attempt is made to attain a high level of mathematical rigour; for example, we use results like $1/0 = \infty$, $1/\infty = 0$, which, to be rigorous, should really be written in terms of limits.

In Chapter 1 we discuss the solution of second-order differential equations in terms of power series, a topic of crucial importance for the following chapters. This is because very often in applications we have a partial differential equation for some quantity of interest, and this equation may, by the method of separation of variables, be split into several ordinary differential equations whose solutions we thus require. If, as is often the case, these equations do not have solutions in terms of elementary functions, we have to investigate these solutions, and this is best done by the method of series solutions. These solutions lead to the definitions of new functions, and it is the study of the properties of such 'special' functions which is the main subject-matter of this book.

Chapter 2 is devoted to the gamma and beta functions, two functions defined by integrals and closely related to one another; these functions are not only used in later chapters, but are also encountered in many other contexts.

Chapter 3 is concerned with a study of the Legendre polynomials.

They are introduced as solutions of Legendre's equation, which very often arises when a problem possesses spherical symmetry. Such problems can occur, for example, in quantum mechanics, electromagnetic theory, hydrodynamics and heat conduction.

Chapter 4 is devoted to Bessel functions. These functions occur in a very wide range of applications, such as loudspeaker design, optical diffraction, the vibration of circular membranes and plates, the scattering of sound by circular cylinders, and in general in many problems in both classical and quantum physics involving circular or cylindrical boundaries of some kind. Kelvin's functions, introduced in Section 4.9, are of most interest to the electrical engineer, while the spherical Bessel functions of Section 4.10 are of prime importance in quantum mechanical scattering theory.

The Hermite polynomials, discussed in Chapter 5, have their main application in the quantum-mechanical harmonic oscillator, but other applications do occur. Likewise, the Laguerre polynomials of Chapter 6 are most useful in the quantum mechanical study of the hydrogen atom, but they also find applications in, for example, transmission line theory and seismological investigations.

Chapter 7 treats the Chebyshev polynomials which not only are of interest for their use in polynomial approximations to arbitrary functions, but also occur in electrical circuit theory.

Chapter 8 is devoted to two generalisations of the Legendre polynomials —the Gegenbauer and Jacobi polynomials. These occur less frequently than the functions mentioned above, but they do have application in various branches of physics and engineering, e.g., transformation of spherical harmonics under co-ordinate rotations.

In Chapter 9 we discuss the hypergeometric function. This is the most general of all the special functions considered. Indeed, all the other special functions considered, and many elementary functions, are just special cases of the hypergeometric function.

Chapter 10 contains a brief summary of various other functions which occur in applications. These are often defined by integrals which cannot be evaluated in terms of known functions, and very often all the useful information concerning these integrals is contained in a table of values of the integral.

Appendix 1 is concerned with the definition of Euler's constant, encountered in the chapter on Bessel functions, and Appendix 2 treats explicitly the convergence of the solutions to Legendre's equation found in Chapter 3. The remaining appendices summarise certain properties of the special functions which have been proved throughout the book.

The problems at the end of each chapter should be considered as an integral part of the text: every reader is urged to attempt most, if not all, of the questions. Hints and solutions are provided for all but the easiest of the problems, but the reader should not seek help from the hints before he has made an effort to solve the problem for himself.

The proofs of certain theorems are indicated as being able to be omitted at a first reading. This does not mean to imply that the proofs of such theorems are difficult, but rather that they are fairly lengthy and that inclusion of such a proof on a first reading would tend to destroy the continuity of presentation of the material.

W. W. B.

Aberdeen, 1967

LIST OF SYMBOLS

Symbol	Function	Section in which symbol first appears
$B(x, y)$	Beta function	2.1
$\mathrm{ber}_n x$, $\mathrm{bei}_n x$	Kelvin's functions	4.10
$C(x)$	Fresnel integral	10.3
$C_n^\lambda(x)$	Gegenbauer polynomial or ultraspherical polynomial	8.1
$\mathrm{Ci}(x)$	Cosine integral	10.2
$D_n(x)$	Debye functions	10.5
$E(k, \phi)$	Elliptic integral of second kind	10.6
$E(k)$	Complete elliptic integral of second kind	10.6
$\mathrm{Ei}(x)$, $E_1(x)$	Exponential integrals	10.2
$E_n(x)$	Generalised error function	10.3
$\mathrm{erf}\, x$	Error function	10.3
$F(k, \phi)$	Elliptic integral of first kind	10.6
$_mF_n(\alpha_1, \alpha_2, \ldots \alpha_m; \beta_1, \beta_2, \ldots \beta_n; x)$	Hypergeometric function	9.1
$H_n(x)$	Hermite polynomial	5.1
$H_n^{(1)}(x)$, $H_n^{(2)}(x)$	Hankel functions or Bessel functions of the third kind	4.5
$h_n^{(1)}(x)$, $h_n^{(2)}(x)$	Spherical Hankel functions	4.11
$I_n(x)$	Modified Bessel function	4.7
$J_n(x)$	Bessel function of the first kind	4.1
$j_n(x)$	Spherical Bessel function	4.11
$K(k)$	Complete elliptic integral of first kind	10.6
$K_n(x)$	Modified Bessel function	4.7
$\mathrm{ker}_n x$, $\mathrm{kei}_n x$	Kelvin's functions	4.10
$L_n(x)$	Laguerre polynomial	6.1
$L_n^k(x)$	Associated Laguerre polynomial	6.7
$\mathrm{li}\,(x)$	Logarithmic integral	10.2
$M(\alpha, \beta, x)$	Confluent hypergeometric function	9.1
$M_{k,m}(x)$	Whittaker's confluent hypergeometric function	9.3
$N_n(x)$	Neumann function or Bessel function of the second kind	4.1

Symbol	Function	Section in which symbol first appears
$P_l(x)$	Legendre polynomial	3.1
$P_l^m(x)$	Associated Legendre function	3.8
$P_n^{(\alpha, \beta)}(x)$	Jacobi polynomial	8.2
$Q_l(x)$	Legendre function of the second kind	3.10
$S(x)$	Fresnel integral	10.3
$\mathrm{si}(x), \mathrm{Si}(x)$	Sine integrals	10.2
$T_n(x)$	Chebyshev polynomial of the first kind	7.1
$U_n(x)$	Chebyshev polynomial of the second kind	7.1
$Y_l^m(\theta, \phi)$	Spherical harmonic	3.11
$Y_n(x)$	Bessel function of the second kind	4.1
$y_n(x)$	Spherical Bessel function	4.11
$\Gamma(x)$	Gamma function	2.1
$\Gamma(x, \alpha), \gamma(x, \alpha)$	Incomplete gamma functions	10.1
γ	Euler's constant	4.1
$\zeta(x)$	Riemann's zeta function	10.4
$\Pi(k, \phi, a)$	Elliptic integral of third kind	10.6
$\Pi(k, a)$	Complete elliptic integral of third kind	10.6
$\Psi_n(x)$	Weber-Hermite function	5.7

CONTENTS

PREFACE   v

LIST OF SYMBOLS   ix

CHAPTER 1   SERIES SOLUTION OF DIFFERENTIAL EQUATIONS

1.1 Method of Frobenius   1
1.2 Examples   8
     Problems   21

CHAPTER 2   GAMMA AND BETA FUNCTIONS

2.1 Definitions   23
2.2 Properties of the beta and gamma functions   24
2.3 Definition of the gamma function for negative values of the
     argument   30
2.4 Examples   37
     Problems   40

CHAPTER 3   LEGENDRE POLYNOMIALS AND FUNCTIONS

3.1 Legendre's equation and its solution   42
3.2 Generating function for the Legendre polynomials   46
3.3 Further expressions for the Legendre polynomials   48
3.4 Explicit expressions for and special values of the Legendre
     polynomials   50
3.5 Orthogonality properties of the Legendre polynomials   52
3.6 Legendre series   55
3.7 Relations between the Legendre polynomials and their deriva-
     tives; recurrence relations   58
3.8 Associated Legendre functions   62
3.9 Properties of the associated Legendre functions   65
3.10 Legendre functions of the second kind   70
3.11 Spherical harmonics   78
3.12 Graphs of the Legendre functions   82
3.13 Examples   85
     Problems   90

CHAPTER 4   BESSEL FUNCTIONS

4.1   Bessel's equation and its solutions; Bessel functions of the first
      and second kind   92
4.2   Generating function for the Bessel functions   99
4.3   Integral representations for Bessel functions   101
4.4   Recurrence relations   104
4.5   Hankel functions   107
4.6   Equations reducible to Bessel's equation   108
4.7   Modified Bessel functions   110
4.8   Recurrence relations for the modified Bessel functions   113
4.9   Integral representations for the modified Bessel functions   116
4.10 Kelvin's functions   120
4.11 Spherical Bessel functions   121
4.12 Behaviour of the Bessel functions for large and small values of
      the argument   127
4.13 Graphs of the Bessel functions   133
4.14 Orthonormality of the Bessel functions; Bessel series   137
4.15 Integrals involving Bessel functions   141
4.16 Examples   148
      Problems   154

CHAPTER 5   HERMITE POLYNOMIALS

5.1   Hermite's equation and its solution   156
5.2   Generating function   157
5.3   Other expressions for the Hermite polynomials   158
5.4   Explicit expressions for, and special values of, the Hermite
      polynomials   160
5.5   Orthogonality properties of the Hermite polynomials   161
5.6   Relations between Hermite polynomials and their derivatives;
      recurrence relations   162
5.7   Weber-Hermite functions   163
5.8   Examples   164
      Problems   166

CHAPTER 6   LAGUERRE POLYNOMIALS

6.1   Laguerre's equation and its solution   168
6.2   Generating function   169
6.3   Alternative expression for the Laguerre polynomials   170
6.4   Explicit expressions for, and special values of, the Laguerre
      polynomials   171

6.5   Orthogonality properties of the Laguerre polynomials   172
6.6   Relations between Laguerre polynomials and their derivatives;
     recurrence relations   173
6.7   Associated Laguerre polynomials   176
6.8   Properties of the associated Laguerre polynomials   177
6.9   Notation   182
6.10 Examples   182
      Problems   185

CHAPTER 7   CHEBYSHEV POLYNOMIALS

7.1   Definition of Chebyshev polynomials; Chebyshev's equation   187
7.2   Generating function   190
7.3   Orthogonality properties   192
7.4   Recurrence relations   193
7.5   Examples   194
      Problems   196

CHAPTER 8   GEGENBAUER AND JACOBI POLYNOMIALS

8.1   Gegenbauer polynomials   197
8.2   Jacobi polynomials   198
8.3   Examples   200
      Problems   201

CHAPTER 9   HYPERGEOMETRIC FUNCTIONS

9.1   Definition of hypergeometric functions   203
9.2   Properties of the hypergeometric function   207
9.3   Properties of the confluent hypergeometric function   210
9.4   Examples   212
      Problems   216

CHAPTER 10   OTHER SPECIAL FUNCTIONS

10.1 Incomplete gamma functions   218
10.2 Exponential integral and related functions   218
10.3 The error function and related functions   221
10.4 Riemann's zeta function   223
10.5 Debye functions   224
10.6 Elliptic integrals   224
10.7 Examples   225
      Problems   228

APPENDICES

1	Convergence of Legendre series	230
2	Euler's constant	231
3	Differential equations	233
4	Orthogonality relations	234
5	Generating functions	236

HINTS AND SOLUTIONS TO PROBLEMS   237

BIBLIOGRAPHY   243

INDEX   245

1

SERIES SOLUTION
OF DIFFERENTIAL EQUATIONS

1.1 METHOD OF FROBENIUS

Many special functions arise in the consideration of the solutions of equations of the form

$$P(x)\frac{d^2y}{dx^2} + Q(x)\frac{dy}{dx} + R(x)y = 0. \tag{1.1}$$

We shall restrict ourselves to equations of the type

$$x^2 \frac{d^2y}{dx^2} + xq(x)\frac{dy}{dx} + r(x)y = 0, \tag{1.2}$$

where $q(x)$ and $r(x)$ may be expanded as power series in x,

$$q(x) = \sum_{m=0}^{\infty} q_m x^m \tag{1.3}$$

$$r(x) = \sum_{m=0}^{\infty} r_m x^m, \tag{1.4}$$

convergent for some range of x including the point $x = 0$.

The basis of Frobenius' method is to try for a solution of equation (1.2) of the form

$$z(x,s) = x^s(a_0 + a_1x + a_2x^2 + \ldots + a_nx^n + \ldots) = \sum_{n=0}^{\infty} a_nx^{s+n} \tag{1.5}$$

with $a_0 \neq 0$. (We may always take $a_0 \neq 0$, since otherwise we should just have another series of the type (1.5) with a different value of s, the first coefficient of which we could now call a_0.)

From equation (1.5) we have

$$\frac{dz}{dx} = \sum_{n=0}^{\infty} a_n(s+n)x^{s+n-1}$$

and

$$\frac{d^2z}{dx^2} = \sum_{n=0}^{\infty} a_n(s+n)(s+n-1)x^{s+n-2},$$

so that if we require z to satisfy equation (1.2) we must have

$$x^2\frac{d^2z}{dx^2} + xq(x)\frac{dz}{dx} + r(x)z = 0,$$

and this reduces to

$$\sum_{n=0}^{\infty} a_n(s+n)(s+n-1)x^{s+n} + q(x)\sum_{n=0}^{\infty} a_n(s+n)\,x^{s+n}$$

$$+ r(x)\sum_{n=0}^{\infty} a_n x^{s+n} = 0$$

which, on using equations (1.3) and (1.4) for $q(x)$ and $r(x)$ and cancelling a common factor of x^s, becomes

$$\sum_{n=0}^{\infty} a_n(s+n)(s+n-1)x^n + \sum_{n=0}^{\infty}\sum_{m=0}^{\infty} a_n q_m(s+n)x^{n+m}$$

$$+ \sum_{n=0}^{\infty}\sum_{m=0}^{\infty} a_n r_m x^{n+m} = 0. \qquad (1.6)$$

For the infinite series on the left-hand side of equation (1.6) to be zero for all values of x in some range, we must have the coefficient of each power of x equal to zero. This requirement gives rise to a set of equations as follows.

Requiring that the coefficient of x^0 be zero, and noting that x^0 arises only from the choice $m = 0$, $n = 0$, gives

$$a_0 s(s-1) + a_0 q_0 s + a_0 r_0 = 0. \qquad (1.7)$$

Requiring that the coefficient of x^1 be zero, and noting that x^1 arises in equation (1.6) by choosing in the first term $n = 1$, and in the second and third terms $n + m = 1$ (i.e., $m = 0$, $n = 1$ or $m = 1$, $n = 0$) gives

$$a_1(s+1)s + \{a_1 q_0(s+1) + a_0 q_1 s\} + \{a_1 r_0 + a_0 r_1\} = 0. \qquad (1.8)$$

We may now write down a general equation from the requirement that the coefficient of x^i should be zero. Remembering that in equation (1.6) x^i arises in the first term by choosing $n = i$ and in the second and third terms by choosing $n + m = i$ (i.e., $n = i$, $m = 0$ or $n = i - 1$, $m = 1$ or $n = i - 2$, $m = 2$, etc., up to $n = 0$, $m = i$) we obtain

$$a_i(s + i)(s + i - 1)$$
$$+ \{a_i q_0(s + i) + a_{i-1} q_1(s + i - 1) + a_{i-2} q_2(s + i - 2) + \ldots + a_0 q_i s\}$$
$$+ \{a_i r_0 + a_{i-1} r_1 + \ldots + a_0 r_i\} = 0 \qquad (i \geqslant 1). \qquad (1.9)$$

Thus

$$a_i f(s + i)$$
$$+ \{a_{i-1} q_1(s + i - 1) + a_{i-2} q_2(s + i - 2) + \ldots + a_0 q_i s\}$$
$$+ \{a_{i-1} r_1 + a_{i-2} r_2 + \ldots + a_0 r_i\} = 0 \qquad (i \geqslant 1) \qquad (1.10)$$

where we have collected all the terms in a_i together and denoted their coefficient by

$$f(s + i) \equiv (s + i)(s + i - 1) + q_0(s + i) + r_0. \qquad (1.11)$$

We now see that equation (1.7) reduces to

$$a_0\{s^2 + (q_0 - 1)(s + r_0)\} = 0$$

which, with the given assumption that $a_0 \neq 0$, becomes

$$s^2 + (q_0 - 1)(s + r_0) = 0. \qquad (1.12)$$

This is called the indicial equation; it is quadratic in s and hence will yield two roots which we shall denote by s_1 and s_2. In many cases of interest these roots will be real; this we shall henceforth assume, together with the fact that $s_2 \geqslant s_1$.

Noting that equation (1.12) is just $f(s) = 0$, we have immediately

$$f(s) = (s - s_1)(s - s_2). \qquad (1.13)$$

We might now expect that these two values of s would lead to the two independent solutions of the original differential equation. We shall see that this is true apart from certain exceptional cases, viz. when

(a) the two roots of the indicial equation are equal; or
(b) the two roots of the indicial equation differ by an integer.

The set of equations (1.10) can now be used to determine the coefficients $a_1, a_2, \ldots$ in terms of a_0.

Equation (1.10) with $i = 1$ gives

$$a_1 f(s + 1) + a_0 q_1 s + a_0 r_1 = 0$$

so that we have

$$a_1 = \frac{-a_0(q_1 s + r_1)}{f(s + 1)}$$
$$= \frac{a_0 h_1(s)}{f(s + 1)} \qquad (1.14)$$

where $h_1(s) = -(q_1 s + r_1)$ is a polynomial of first degree in s.

Equation (1.10) with $i = 2$ gives

$$a_2 f(s + 2) + \{a_1 q_1 (s + 1) + a_0 q_2 s\} + \{a_1 r_1 + a_0 r_2\} = 0,$$

which, when we use equation (1.14) for a_1, becomes

$$a_2 f(s + 2) + \left\{ \frac{a_0 h_1(s)}{f(s + 1)} q_1(s + 1) + a_0 q_2 s \right\} + \left\{ \frac{a_0 h_1(s)}{f(s + 1)} r_1 + a_0 r_2 \right\} = 0,$$

yielding

$$a_2 = \frac{-a_0 \{ q_1 (s + 1) h_1(s) + q_2 s f(s + 1) + r_1 h_1(s) + r_2 f(s + 1) \}}{f(s + 1) f(s + 2)}$$

$$= a_0 \frac{h_2(s)}{f(s + 1) f(s + 2)} \tag{1.15}$$

where $h_2(s) = -\{ q_1 (s + 1) h_1(s) + q_2 s f(s + 1) + r_1 h_1(s) + r_2 f(s + 1) \}$ is a polynomial in s.

In general it is not difficult to see that we obtain

$$a_i = a_0 \frac{h_i(s)}{f(s + 1) f(s + 2) \ldots f(s + i)} \tag{1.16}$$

where $h_i(s)$ is a polynomial in s.

If in equation (1.16) we now substitute $s = s_1$ we shall obtain expressions for a_i in terms of a_0, leading to a solution with a_0 as an arbitrary multiplicative constant; similarly we may substitute $s = s_2$, so that we have the two solutions required. This will work, however, only if the denominator of equation (1.16) is never zero, i.e., provided

$$f(s_1 + i) \neq 0$$

and $f(s_2 + i) \neq 0$ for i equal to any positive integer. $\tag{1.17}$

Now, equation (1.13) tells us that

$$f(s) = (s - s_1)(s - s_2)$$

so that

$$f(s + i) = (s + i - s_1)(s + i - s_2)$$

and hence

$$f(s_1 + i) = i(s_1 - s_2 + i)$$

and $f(s_2 + i) = (s_2 - s_1 + i)i,$ $\tag{1.18}$

so that equation (1.17) will be satisfied if, and only if, $s_2 - s_1$ is not a positive integer, i.e., provided the roots of the indicial equation do not differ by an integer. (We recall that we have labelled the roots so that $s_2 \geqslant s_1$.)

If the roots do differ by an integer, the procedure given above will work for the larger root: if $s_2 - s_1 = r$ (a positive integer), then from equations (1.18) we have

$$f(s_1 + i) = i(-r + i) \tag{1.19}$$

$$f(s_2 + i) = i(r + i), \tag{1.20}$$

and we see that $f(s_1 + i) = 0$ for $i = r$, while $f(s_2 + i) \neq 0$ for any positive integral i. Hence the procedure will work with $s = s_2$ but not with $s = s_1$. How, in fact, do we find the second solution? If we use the relationship (1.16) before fixing the value of s we have the series

$$z(x, s) = a_0 x^s \left\{ 1 + \frac{h_1(s)}{f(s + 1)} x + \frac{h_2(s)}{f(s + 1) f(s + 2)} x^2 \right.$$
$$\left. + \ldots + \frac{h_i(s)}{f(s + 1) f(s + 2) \ldots f(s + i)} x^i + \ldots \right\}. \tag{1.21}$$

We know by the method of construction of $a_1, a_2, \ldots$ that if all the terms on the right-hand side are well defined, then this must satisfy

$$x^2 \frac{d^2 z}{dx^2} + xq(x)\frac{dz}{dx} + r(x)z = a_0 f(s)x^s$$

(since equations (1.10) are satisfied, the coefficient of each power x^{s+i} with $i \geqslant 1$ must vanish, and the coefficient of x^s is, by equations (1.7) and (1.11) just $a_0 f(s)$). This equation may be rewritten in the form

$$\left\{ x^2 \frac{d^2}{dx^2} + xq(x)\frac{d}{dx} + r(x) \right\} z(x, s) = a_0 f(s)x^s. \tag{1.22}$$

Unfortunately, all the terms on the right-hand side of equation (1.21) are not well defined for $s = s_1$; there are zeros in the denominators for $i \geqslant r$. However, if we multiply $z(x, s)$ by $f(s + r)$ we shall just cancel the factor in the denominators of the later terms which vanishes when $s = s_1$. And since $f(s + r) = (s + r - s_1)(s + r - s_2) = (s + s_2 - 2s_1)(s - s_1)$ we might just as well multiply by $(s - s_1)$. Also, since this factor is independent of x, equation (1.22) now takes the form

$$\left\{ x^2 \frac{d^2}{dx^2} + xq(x)\frac{d}{dx} + r(x) \right\}(s - s_1)z(x, s) = a_0(s - s_1)f(s)x^s$$
$$= a_0(s - s_1)^2(s - s_2)x^s, \tag{1.23}$$
$$\text{using equation (1.13).}$$

Setting $s = s_2$, we have

$$\left\{ x^2 \frac{d^2}{dx^2} + xq(x)\frac{d}{dx} + r(x) \right\}(s_2 - s_1)z(x, s_2) = 0$$

which shows that $z(x, s_2)$ is a solution, a fact we already know.

Similarly, setting $s = s_1$ gives $[(s - s_1)z(x, s)]_{s=s_1}$ as a solution. In fact it turns out that this series is not independent of $z(x, s_2)$ but is just a multiple of it. This comes about as follows. The factor $s - s_1$ cancels zeros in the denominator for terms with $i \geq r$, but will provide zero in the numerator for all terms with $i < r$, thus the first power in the series is just $x^{s_1+r} = x^{s_2}$, which is just the first term in $z(x, s_2)$. And since we use the same rules for calculating any coefficient in terms of preceding ones in the two cases, we must just obtain the same series in both cases, apart from a constant multiplicative factor.

If we differentiate both sides of equation (1.23) with respect to s, we obtain

$$\left\{ x^2 \frac{d^2}{dx^2} + xq(x)\frac{d}{dx} + r(x) \right\} \left[\frac{d}{ds} \{(s - s_1)z(x, s)\} \right]$$

$$= a_0 \left[(s - s_1)^2 \frac{d}{ds}\{(s - s_2)x^s\} + 2(s - s_1)(s - s_2)x^s \right] \qquad (1.24)$$

and we see that the right-hand side of this equation is zero when $s = s_1$, so that we must have $[(d/ds)\{(s - s_1)z(x, s)\}]_{s=s_1}$ as a solution of the differential equation. It may be proved that this solution is in fact independent of the first solution (i.e., it is not merely a constant multiple of the first solution), but we shall not do so here.

Thus we can take as independent solutions

$$[(s - s_1)z(x, s)]_{s=s_1} \qquad (1.25)$$

and

$$\left[\frac{d}{ds}\{(s - s_1)z(x, s)\} \right]_{s=s_1}. \qquad (1.26)$$

Another type of situation may arise when the roots of the indicial equation differ by an integer. As well as $f(s + i) = 0$ for $s = s_1$ and $i = r$, it may happen that $h_r(s_1) = 0$. In this case a_r is indeterminate (since it has a zero in both numerator and denominator) so that we may in fact use it as another arbitrary constant, thus obtaining the two independent solutions from the one series. We shall see in detail how this happens when we come to consider particular examples.

The one remaining case is when the indicial equation has equal roots, say $s = s_1$. Here $f(s) = (s - s_1)^2$, and if we make use of equation (1.22) we obtain

$$\left\{ x^2 \frac{d^2}{dx^2} + xq(x)\frac{d}{dx} + r(x) \right\} z(x, s) = a_0(s - s_1)^2 x^s. \qquad (1.27)$$

Setting $s = s_1$ makes the right-hand side zero, so that $z(x, s_1)$ is a solution. But if we differentiate both sides with respect to s, we obtain

$$\left\{x^2 \frac{d^2}{dx^2} + xq(x)\frac{d}{dx} + r(x)\right\}\left[\frac{d}{ds}z(x, s)\right]$$

$$= a_0\left\{2(s - s_1)x^s + (s - s_1)^2 \frac{d}{ds}x^s\right\}. \quad (1.28)$$

Again the right-hand side is zero when $s = s_1$, so that we have for a solution $[(d/ds)\{z(x, s)\}]_{s=s_1}$. This, in fact, may be shown to be independent from $z(x, s_1)$, so that in this case we have the two independent solutions

$$z(x, s_1)$$

and
$$\left[\frac{d}{ds}z(x, s)\right]_{s=s_1}. \quad (1.29)$$

Let us now summarise briefly the methods of obtaining independent solutions which have been described above.

Form the series $z(x, s)$ by the use of the relations (1.10). Then there are four distinct cases.

(1) If the roots s_1 and s_2 of the indicial equation are distinct and do not differ by an integer, then the two independent solutions are given by

$$z(x, s_1)$$
and
$$z(x, s_2).$$

(2) If the roots s_1 and s_2 $(s_2 > s_1)$ differ by an integer and one of the coefficients in the series for $z(x, s)$ is infinite when $s = s_1$, the two independent solutions are given by

$$[(s - s_1)z(x, s)]_{s=s_1}$$

and
$$\left[\frac{d}{ds}\{(s - s_1)z(x, s)\}\right]_{s=s_1}.$$

(3) If the roots s_1 and s_2 $(s_2 > s_1)$ differ by an integer and one of the coefficients in the series for $z(x, s)$, say a_r, is indeterminate when $s = s_1$, the two independent solutions are obtained from $z(x, s_1)$, keeping a_0 and a_r as arbitrary constants.

(4) If the roots of the indicial equation are equal, say, $s = s_1$, then the two independent solutions are given by

$$z(x, s_1)$$

and
$$\left[\frac{d}{ds}z(x, s)\right]_{s=s_1}.$$

The question of convergence of the series obtained must, of course, be considered. It may be proved (although we shall not do so here) that the range of values of x for which the solution is convergent is at least as large as the range of values of x for which both $q(x)$ and $r(x)$ may be expanded as convergent power series.

In certain cases $q(x)$ or $r(x)$ may not be expanded as power series in x for any range of x (e.g., $1/x$ or $\exp(1/x)$). It may perhaps then be possible to make a change of variable, such as $x' = x - a$, or $x' = 1/x$, so that $q(x)$ and $r(x)$ may be expanded in powers of x' and a solution found in the form (1.5) with x' replacing x.

Finally, let us remark that when carrying out the actual solution of a differential equation of type (1.1), it is not usually profitable to transform it to an equation of the type (1.2); all that we require for the above results to hold is that this transformation should be possible.

Let us now illustrate the above methods by means of some examples.

1.2 EXAMPLES

Example 1

$$2x\frac{d^2y}{dx^2} + \frac{dy}{dx} + y = 0.$$

We must first verify that this equation is of the form

$$x^2\frac{d^2y}{dx^2} + xq(x)\frac{dy}{dx} + r(x)y = 0$$

where $q(x)$ and $r(x)$ may be expanded as power series. Multiplied by $x/2$, the given equation becomes

$$x^2\frac{d^2y}{dx^2} + x\cdot\frac{1}{2}\cdot\frac{dy}{dx} + \frac{1}{2}x\cdot y = 0$$

so that $q(x) = \frac{1}{2}$, $r(x) = \frac{1}{2}x$ and the required condition is obviously satisfied.

Since $q(x)$ and $r(x)$ are already in power series form, valid for all values of x, it follows from the remarks made at the end of the previous section that any series solutions obtained will be convergent for all values of x.

We now revert to the original equation.

Set
$$z = x^s \sum_{n=0}^{\infty} a_n x^n = \sum_{n=0}^{\infty} a_n x^{s+n}$$

so that
$$\frac{dz}{dx} = \sum_{n=0}^{\infty} a_n(s+n)x^{s+n-1}$$

and
$$\frac{d^2z}{dx^2} = \sum_{n=0}^{\infty} a_n(s+n)(s+n-1)x^{s+n-2}.$$

Then we have

$$2x\frac{d^2z}{dx^2} + \frac{dz}{dx} + z$$

$$= \sum_{n=0}^{\infty} 2a_n(s+n)(s+n-1)x^{s+n-1} + \sum_{n=0}^{\infty} a_n(s+n)x^{s+n-1}$$

$$+ \sum_{n=0}^{\infty} a_n x^{s+n}$$

$$= \sum_{n=0}^{\infty} 2a_n(s+n)(s+n-1)x^{s+n-1} + \sum_{n=0}^{\infty} a_n(s+n)x^{s+n-1}$$

$$+ \sum_{n=1}^{\infty} a_{n-1}x^{s+n-1}, \tag{1.30}$$

where in the last summation we have replaced the label n by the label $n-1$ in order that the general power should look the same in all terms.

In order that z should satisfy the differential equation, we must have the coefficient of each power of x in (1.30) equal to zero. The power with $n = 0$ appears only in the first two terms; thereafter the powers with $n \geqslant 1$ appear in all three terms. Hence we have the equations:

$$2a_0(s+0)(s+0-1) + a_0(s+0) = 0 \tag{1.31}$$

and

$$2a_n(s+n)(s+n-1) + a_n(s+n) + a_{n-1} = 0 \quad (n \geqslant 1). \tag{1.32}$$

These equations simplify to

$$a_0 s(2s-1) = 0 \tag{1.33}$$

and

$$a_n(s+n)\{2(s+n)-1\} + a_{n-1} = 0. \tag{1.34}$$

Equation (1.33) gives the indicial equation

$$s(2s-1) = 0$$

with roots $s = 0$ and $s = \frac{1}{2}$. Since these are distinct and do not differ by an integer, we know that we may proceed according to prescription (1) on page 7.

Equation (1.34) gives the recurrence relation for the coefficients in $z(x, s)$:

$$a_n = -\frac{a_{n-1}}{(s+n)\{2(s+n)-1\}} \tag{1.35}$$

and hence

$$a_1 = -\frac{a_0}{(s+1)(2s+1)},$$

$$a_2 = -\frac{a_1}{(s+2)(2s+3)} = \frac{a_0}{(s+1)(s+2)(2s+1)(2s+3)},$$

$$a_3 = -\frac{a_2}{(s+3)(2s+5)} = -\frac{a_0}{(s+1)(s+2)(s+3)(2s+1)(2s+3)(2s+5)}$$

and in general

$$a_n = (-1)^n \frac{a_0}{(s+1)(s+2)\ldots(s+n)(2s+1)(2s+3)\ldots(2s+2n-1)}.$$

Thus we have the series $z(x, s)$ given by

$$z(x, s) = a_0 x^s \Big\{ 1 - \frac{x}{(s+1)(2s+1)} + \frac{x^2}{(s+1)(s+2)(2s+1)(2s+3)} + \cdots$$

$$+ (-1)^n \frac{x^n}{(s+1)(s+2)\ldots(s+n)(2s+1)(2s+3)\ldots(2s+2n-1)} + \cdots \Big\}.$$

$$(1.36)$$

Since the roots of the indicial equation are $s = 0$ and $s = \frac{1}{2}$, the two independent solutions are given by $z(x, 0)$ and $z(x, \frac{1}{2})$ which, by equation (1.36), are

$$z(x, 0) = a_0 \Big\{ 1 - \frac{x}{1.1} + \frac{x^2}{1.2.1.3} - \frac{x^3}{1.2.3.1.3.5} + \cdots$$

$$+ (-1)^n \frac{x^n}{1.2.3\ldots n.1.3.5\ldots(2n-1)} + \cdots \Big\} \quad (1.37)$$

and $\qquad z(x, \tfrac{1}{2}) = a_0 x^{\frac{1}{2}} \Big\{ 1 - \frac{x}{\frac{3}{2}.2} + \frac{x^2}{\frac{3}{2}.\frac{5}{2}.2.4} + \cdots$

$$+ (-1)^n \frac{x^n}{\frac{3}{2}.\frac{5}{2}\ldots\frac{2n+1}{2}.2.4.6\ldots 2n} + \cdots \Big\}. \quad (1.38)$$

We may rewrite these series more compactly if we note the following results:

$$1.2.3.\ldots.n = n!, \quad (1.39)$$

$$1.3.5\ldots(2n-1) = \frac{1.2.3.4\ldots(2n-1).2n}{2.4\ldots(2n-2).2n}$$

$$= \frac{(2n)!}{2.1.2.2.2.3\ldots 2(n-1).2n}$$

$$= \frac{(2n)!}{2^n n!}, \quad (1.40)$$

$$\frac{3}{2} \cdot \frac{5}{2} \cdot \frac{7}{2} \cdots \frac{2n+1}{2} = \frac{1}{2^n} 3.5.7 \ldots (2n+1)$$

$$= \frac{1}{2^n} \frac{2.3.4.5.6.7 \ldots (2n+1)}{2.4.6. \ldots 2n}$$

$$= \frac{1}{2^n} \frac{(2n+1)!}{2^n.n!} = \frac{(2n+1)!}{2^{2n}n!}, \tag{1.41}$$

and $$2.4.6 \ldots 2n = 2^n n!. \tag{1.42}$$

Using these results we see that equation (1.37) reduces to

$$z(x, 0) = a_0 \sum_{n=0}^{\infty} (-1)^n \frac{x^n}{n!\{(2n)!/(2^n n!)\}}$$

$$= a_0 \sum_{n=0}^{\infty} (-1)^n \frac{(2x)^n}{(2n)!} \tag{1.43}$$

while equation (1.38) becomes

$$z(x, \tfrac{1}{2}) = a_0 x^{1/2} \sum_{n=0}^{\infty} (-1)^n \frac{x^n}{\{(2n+1)!/(2^{2n}n!)\}2^n n!}$$

$$= a_0 x^{1/2} \sum_{n=0}^{\infty} (-1)^n \frac{(2x)^n}{(2n+1)!}. \tag{1.44}$$

Thus the general solution is given by the general linear combination of $z(x, 0)$ and $z(x, \tfrac{1}{2})$, viz.

$$y = A \sum_{n=0}^{\infty} (-1)^n \frac{(2x)^n}{(2n)!} + Bx^{1/2} \sum_{n=0}^{\infty} (-1)^n \frac{(2x)^n}{(2n+1)!}$$

where A and B are arbitrary constants.

Example 2

$$x(1-x)\frac{d^2y}{dx^2} + (1-x)\frac{dy}{dx} - y = 0.$$

We first verify that this equation is of the form

$$x^2 \frac{d^2y}{dx^2} + xq(x)\frac{dy}{dx} + r(x)y = 0$$

where $q(x)$ and $r(x)$ may be expanded as power series in x.

The given equation is obviously equivalent to

$$x^2 \frac{d^2y}{dx^2} + x\frac{dy}{dx} - \frac{x}{1-x}y = 0.$$

Hence $q(x) = 1$ and $r(x) = -x/(1 - x)$. $q(x)$ is already in power series form, convergent for all values of x, but $r(x)$ is not. However, it may be expanded as a power series in x by the binomial theorem, and this series will be convergent for those values of x such that $|x| < 1$.

It follows from the remarks at the end of the previous section that any series solutions which we obtain will be convergent for at least the same values of x, viz. $|x| < 1$.

We now revert to the original equation.

Set
$$z = \sum_{n=0}^{\infty} a_n x^{s+n}$$

so that
$$\frac{dz}{dx} = \sum_{n=0}^{\infty} a_n(s + n)x^{s+n-1}$$

and
$$\frac{d^2z}{dx^2} = \sum_{n=0}^{\infty} a_n(s + n)(s + n - 1)x^{s+n-2}.$$

Hence,

$$(x-x^2)\frac{d^2z}{dx^2} + (1-x)\frac{dz}{dx} - z$$

$$= \sum_{n=0}^{\infty} a_n(s+n)(s+n-1)x^{s+n-1} - \sum_{n=0}^{\infty} a_n(s+n)(s+n-1)x^{s+n}$$

$$+ \sum_{n=0}^{\infty} a_n(s+n)x^{s+n-1} - \sum_{n=0}^{\infty} a_n(s+n)x^{s+n} - \sum_{n=0}^{\infty} a_n x^{s+n}$$

$$= \sum_{n=0}^{\infty} a_n(s+n)(s+n-1)x^{s+n-1} - \sum_{n=1}^{\infty} a_{n-1}(s+n-1)(s+n-2)x^{s+n-1}$$

$$+ \sum_{n=0}^{\infty} a_n(s+n)x^{s+n-1} - \sum_{n=1}^{\infty} a_{n-1}(s+n-1)x^{s+n-1} - \sum_{n=1}^{\infty} a_{n-1}x^{s+n-1}.$$

For z to be a solution, we require the coefficient of each power of x to be zero, so that we have

$$a_0 s(s - 1) + a_0 s = 0 \qquad (1.45)$$

and

$$a_n(s + n)(s + n - 1) - a_{n-1}(s + n - 1)(s + n - 2) + a_n(s + n)$$
$$-a_{n-1}(s + n - 1) - a_{n-1} = 0 \quad (n \geqslant 1). \qquad (1.46)$$

These equations simplify to

$$a_0 s^2 = 0 \qquad (1.47)$$

and
$$a_n(s + n)^2 - a_{n-1}\{(s + n - 1)^2 + 1\}. \tag{1.48}$$

Equation (1.47) gives the indicial equation
$$s^2 = 0 \tag{1.49}$$

while equation (1.48) gives the recurrence relation
$$a_n = a_{n-1} \frac{\{(s + n - 1)^2 + 1\}}{(s + n)^2}. \tag{1.50}$$

Equation (1.49) has coincident roots $s = 0$; so we know (by prescription (4) on page 7) that the two independent solutions are given by $z(x, 0)$ and $[(d/ds)z(x, s)]_{s=0}$.

Equation (1.50) gives
$$a_1 = a_0 \frac{(s^2 + 1)}{(s + 1)^2},$$

$$a_2 = a_1 \frac{\{(s + 1)^2 + 1\}}{(s + 2)^2} = a_0 \frac{\{s^2 + 1\}\{(s + 1)^2 + 1\}}{(s + 1)^2(s + 2)^2},$$

and in general
$$a_n = a_0 \frac{\{s^2 + 1\}\{(s + 1)^2 + 1\}\{(s + 2)^2 + 1\}\ldots\{(s + n - 1)^2 + 1\}}{(s + 1)^2(s + 2)^2\ldots(s + n)^2}$$

so that
$$z(x, s) = a_0 x^s \left[1 + \sum_{n=1}^{\infty} \frac{\{s^2+1\}\{(s+1)^2+1\}\ldots\{(s+n-1)^2+1\}}{(s+1)^2(s+2)^2\ldots(s+n)^2} x^n\right]. \tag{1.51}$$

The first solution is then
$$z(x, 0) = a_0\left[1 + \sum_{n=1}^{\infty} \frac{1\{1^2+1\}\{2^2+1\}\{3^2+1\}\ldots\{(n-1)^2+1\}}{1^2.2^2.3^2\ldots n^2} x^n\right]$$

$$= a_0\left[1 + \sum_{n=1}^{\infty} \frac{1.2.5.10.17\ldots\{(n-1)^2+1\}}{(n!)^2} x^n\right]$$

$$= a_0 y_1(x), \text{ say.} \tag{1.52}$$

For the second solution we require $(d/ds)z(x, s)$. Now, from equation (1.51) we have

$$\frac{d}{ds}z(x, s)$$

$$= a_0\left(\frac{d}{ds}x^s\right)\left[1 + \sum_{n=1}^{\infty} \frac{\{s^2+1\}\{(s+1)^2+1\}\ldots\{(s+n-1)^2+1\}}{(s+1)^2(s+2)^2\ldots(s+n)^2} x^n\right]$$

$$+ a_0 x^s \sum_{n=1}^{\infty} \frac{d}{ds}\left[\frac{\{s^2+1\}\{(s+1)^2+1\}\ldots\{(s+n-1)^2+1\}}{(s+1)^2(s+2)^2\ldots(s+n)^2}\right] x^n. \tag{1.53}$$

For the first term we note that

$$\frac{d}{ds}x^s = \frac{d}{ds}(e^{\ln x})^s = \frac{d}{ds}e^{s \ln x} \dagger$$

$$= (\ln x) \, e^{s \ln x} = (\ln x)x^s \tag{1.54}$$

and hence

$$\left[\frac{d}{ds}x^s\right]_{s=0} = \ln x. \tag{1.55}$$

The second term we evaluate by the technique of logarithmic differentiation.

If we denote the term in square brackets by $f_n(s)$ we have

$$\frac{d}{ds}\ln f_n(s) = \frac{1}{f_n(s)}\frac{d}{ds}f_n(s)$$

so that

$$\frac{d}{ds}f_n(s) = f_n(s)\frac{d}{ds}\ln f_n(s). \tag{1.56}$$

But

$$\ln f_n(s) = \ln\{s^2 + 1\} + \ln\{(s+1)^2 + 1\} + \ldots + \ln\{(s+n-1)^2 + 1\}$$
$$- \ln(s+1)^2 - \ln(s+2)^2 \ldots - \ln(s+n)^2$$

$$= \sum_{m=1}^{n} \ln\{(s+m-1)^2 + 1\} - \sum_{m=1}^{n} \ln(s+m)^2.$$

Hence

$$\frac{d}{ds}\ln f_n(s) = \sum_{m=1}^{n}\frac{2(s+m-1)}{(s+m-1)^2 + 1} - \sum_{m=1}^{n}\frac{2}{s+m}$$

$$= 2\sum_{m=1}^{n}\left\{\frac{s+m-1}{(s+m-1)^2 + 1} - \frac{1}{s+m}\right\}$$

so that

$$\frac{d}{ds}f_n(s)$$

$$= \frac{2\{s^2 + 1\}\ldots\{(s+n-1)^2 + 1\}}{(s+1)^2 \ldots (s+n)^2}\sum_{m=1}^{n}\left\{\frac{s+m-1}{(s+m-1)^2 + 1} - \frac{1}{s+m}\right\}$$

and

$$\left[\frac{d}{ds}f_n(s)\right]_{s=0}$$

$$= \frac{2\{1\}\{1^2 + 1\}\{2^2 + 1\}\ldots\{(n-1)^2 + 1\}}{1^2 . 2^2 \ldots n^2}\sum_{m=1}^{n}\left\{\frac{m-1}{(m-1)^2 + 1} - \frac{1}{m}\right\}.$$

† We recall that $x = e^{\ln x}$, where we are using the notation $\ln x \equiv \log_e x$.

Denoting this expression by c_n, we have

$$c_n = \frac{2.1.2.5.10.17\ldots\{(n-1)^2+1\}}{(n!)^2} \sum_{m=1}^{n} \frac{m-2}{m\{(m-1)^2+1\}}. \qquad (1.57)$$

Thus, setting $s = 0$ in equation (1.53) gives the second solution

$$\left[\frac{\mathrm{d}}{\mathrm{d}s}z(x,s)\right]_{s=0}$$

$$= a_0 \ln x\left[1 + \sum_{n=1}^{\infty} \frac{\{1\}\{1^2+1\}\{2^2+1\}\ldots\{(n-1)^2+1\}x^n}{1^2.2^2\ldots n^2}\right]$$

$$+ a_0 \sum_{n=1}^{\infty} c_n x^n$$

$$= a_0 y_1(x) \ln x + a_0 \sum_{n=1}^{\infty} c_n x^n$$

$$= a_0 y_2(x), \text{ say,}$$

where

$$y_2(x) = y_1(x)\ln x + \sum_{n=1}^{\infty} c_n x^n. \qquad (1.58)$$

Then the general solution is given by

$$y = A y_1(x) + B y_2(x)$$

where A and B are arbitrary constants.

Example 3

$$x^2 \frac{\mathrm{d}^2 y}{\mathrm{d}x^2} - 3x\frac{\mathrm{d}y}{\mathrm{d}x} + (3-x)y = 0.$$

We see immediately that this is of the form (1.2) with $q(x) = -3$, $r(x) - 3 - x$, which are already in power series form, so that they have a power series expansion valid for all values of x.

It follows from the remarks at the end of the previous section that any series solutions obtained will be convergent for all values of x.

Writing $z = \sum_{n=0}^{\infty} a_n x^{s+n}$ leads in the same manner as in the previous examples to the following equations, which have to be satisfied if z is to be a solution of the given equation:

$$a_0(s-1)(s-3) = 0 \qquad (1.59)$$

$$a_n(s+n-1)(s+n-3) - a_{n-1} = 0 \quad (n \geqslant 1). \qquad (1.60)$$

Equation (1.59) gives the indicial equation

$$(s - 1)(s - 3) = 0 \qquad (1.61)$$

with roots $s = 1$, $s = 3$. These differ by an integer, so that we know that we are dealing with an exceptional case.

Equation (1.60) gives the recurrence relation

$$a_n = \frac{a_{n-1}}{(s + n - 1)(s + n - 3)} \qquad (n > 1) \qquad (1.62)$$

so that we have

$$a_1 = \frac{a_0}{s(s - 2)},$$

$$a_2 = \frac{a_1}{(s + 1)(s - 1)} = \frac{a_0}{s(s + 1)(s - 2)(s - 1)}$$

and in general

$$a_n = \frac{a_0}{s(s + 1)(s + 2) \ldots (s + n - 1)(s - 2)(s - 1)s \ldots (s + n - 3)}. \qquad (1.63)$$

We see explicitly from equation (1.63) that when $s = 1$ all the a_n with $n \geqslant 2$ are infinite, so that we have to apply method (2) described above on page 7.

We have

$$z(x, s) = a_0 x^s \left\{ 1 + \sum_{n=1}^{\infty} \frac{x^n}{s(s+1) \ldots (s+n-1)(s-2)(s-1) \ldots (s+n-3)} \right\}$$

so that

$$(s - 1)z(x, s) = a_0 x^s \left\{ (s - 1) + \frac{(s - 1)}{s(s - 2)} x \right.$$

$$\left. + \sum_{n=2}^{\infty} \frac{x^n}{s(s + 1) \ldots (s + n - 1)(s - 2)s(s + 1) \ldots (s + n - 3)} \right\}. \qquad (1.64)$$

The first solution is given by

$$[(s - 1)z(x, s)]_{s=1}$$

$$= a_0 x \sum_{n=2}^{\infty} \frac{x^n}{1.2 \ldots n(-1).1.2 \ldots (n - 2)}$$

$$= a_0 \sum_{n=2}^{\infty} - \frac{x^{n+1}}{n!(n - 2)!}$$

$$= a_0 y_1(x), \text{ say.}$$

The second solution is given by $[(d/ds)\{(s - 1)z(x, s)\}]_{s=1}$.

From equation (1.64) we have

$$\frac{d}{ds}\{(s-1)z(x,s)\}$$

$$= a_0\left(\frac{d}{ds}x^s\right)\left\{(s-1) + \frac{(s-1)}{s(s-2)}x\right.$$

$$+ \sum_{n=2}^{\infty} \frac{x^n}{s(s+1)\ldots(s+n-1)(s-2)s(s+1)\ldots(s+n-3)}\right\}$$

$$+ a_0 x^s \left\{1 + \frac{d}{ds}\frac{(s-1)}{s(s-2)}x\right.$$

$$+ \sum_{n=2}^{\infty} x^n \frac{d}{ds} \frac{1}{s(s+1)\ldots(s+n-1)(s-2)s(s+1)\ldots(s+n-3)}\right\}.$$

$$(1.65)$$

To evaluate the last derivatives we use logarithmic differentiation: denoting

$$\frac{1}{s(s+1)\ldots(s+n-1)(s-2)s(s+1)\ldots(s+n-3)}$$

by $f_n(s)$, we have again

$$\frac{d}{ds}f_n(s) = f_n(s)\frac{d}{ds}\ln f_n(s)$$

and since

$$\ln f_n(s) = -\ln s - \ln(s+1) - \ln(s+2)\ldots -\ln(s+n-1)$$
$$- \ln(s-2) - \ln s - \ln(s+1)\ldots -\ln(s+n-3)$$

we have

$$\frac{d}{ds}\ln f_n(s)$$

$$= -\left\{\frac{2}{s} + \frac{2}{s+1} + \ldots + \frac{2}{s+n-3} + \frac{1}{s-2}\right.$$

$$+ \frac{1}{s+n-2} + \frac{1}{s+n-1}\right\}$$

so that

$$\left[\frac{d}{ds}\ln f_n(s)\right]_{s=1}$$

$$= -\left\{2\left(1 + \frac{1}{2} + \frac{1}{3} + \ldots \frac{1}{n-2}\right) - 1 + \frac{1}{n-1} + \frac{1}{n}\right\}$$

$$= -\left\{2\sum_{m=1}^{n-2}\frac{1}{m} - 1 + \frac{1}{n-1} + \frac{1}{n}\right\}$$

and
$$[f_n(s)]_{s=1} = \frac{1}{1.2.\ \ldots\ n.(-1).1.2 \ldots (n-2)}$$
$$= -\frac{1}{n!(n-2)!}$$

so that

$$\left[\frac{d}{ds}f_n(s)\right]_{s=1} = \frac{1}{n!\,(n-2)!}\left\{2\sum_{m=1}^{n-2}\frac{1}{m} - 1 + \frac{1}{n-1} + \frac{1}{n}\right\}$$
$$= c_n, \text{ say.}$$

It is also easy to show that

$$\left[\frac{d}{ds}\frac{(s-1)}{s(s-2)}\right]_{s=1} = -1$$

and, as before, we have

$$\frac{d}{ds}x^s = (\ln x)x^s.$$

Thus, finally, we have from equation (1.65)

$$\left[\frac{d}{ds}\{(s-1)z(x,\,s)\}\right]_{s=1} = a_0(\ln x)y_1(x) + a_0x\left\{1 - x + \sum_{n=2}^{\infty}c_n x^n\right\}$$
$$= a_0 y_2(x), \text{ say,}$$

and the general solution is then

$$y = Ay_1(x) + By_2(x)$$

where A and B are arbitrary constants.

Example 4

$$x^2\frac{d^2y}{dx^2} + (x^3 - 2x)\frac{dy}{dx} - 2y = 0.$$

Again this is of the form (1.2) with $q(x) = -2 + x^2$ and $r(x) = -2$, so that the series solutions to be obtained will be valid for all values of x.

Writing $z = x^s\sum_{n=0}^{\infty}a_n x^n$ and requiring z to be a solution of the given equation leads, as before, to the system of equations:

$$a_0(s-2)(s-1) = 0 \qquad (1.66)$$
$$a_1(s-1)s = 0 \qquad (1.67)$$
$$a_n(s+n-2)(s+n-1) + a_{n-2}(s+n-2) = 0 \quad (n \geqslant 2). \quad (1.68)$$

Equation (1.66) gives the indicial equation

$$(s - 2)(s - 1) = 0$$

with roots $s = 2$, $s = 1$. These differ by an integer, so we are dealing with an exceptional case. When $s = 1$, equation (1.67) is satisfied irrespective of the value of a_1; i.e., a_1 is indeterminate, so that we are dealing with case (3) of page 7. We then know that the two independent solutions are obtained from the one value of s, namely $s = 1$.

Equation (1.68) gives the recurrence relation

$$a_n = - \frac{a_{n-2}}{(s + n - 1)} \quad (n \geqslant 2) \tag{1.69}$$

(the factor $s + n - 2$ may be cancelled since it is non-zero for $n \geqslant 2$ and $s = 1$ or $s = 2$), which with $s = 1$ becomes

$$a_n = - \frac{a_{n-2}}{n} \quad (n \geqslant 2). \tag{1.70}$$

Thus

$$a_2 = - \frac{a_0}{2}, \quad a_4 = - \frac{a_2}{4} = \frac{a_0}{2.4},$$

$$a_3 = - \frac{a_1}{3}, \quad a_5 = - \frac{a_3}{5} = \frac{a_1}{3.5},$$

and in general

$$a_{2n} = (-1)^n \frac{a_0}{2.4.6 \ldots 2n}$$

and

$$a_{2n+1} = (-1)^n \frac{a_1}{3.5.7 \ldots (2n + 1)},$$

so that we have

$$z(x, 1) = x \left[a_0 \left\{ 1 + \sum_{n=1}^{\infty} (-1)^n \frac{x^{2n}}{2.4 \ldots 2n} \right\} \right.$$

$$\left. + a_1 \sum_{n=0}^{\infty} (-1)^n \frac{x^{2n+1}}{1.3.5 \ldots (2n + 1)} \right].$$

That is, we have the general solution given by

$$y = A y_1(x) + B y_2(x)$$

where

$$y_1(x) = x + \sum_{n=1}^{\infty} (-1)^n \frac{x^{2n+1}}{2.4.6 \ldots 2n},$$

$$y_2(x) = \sum_{n=0}^{\infty} (-1)^n \frac{x^{2n+2}}{1.3.5 \ldots (2n + 1)}$$

and A and B are arbitrary constants.

SF—C

In the examples given so far, it has always been relatively easy to write down the general term of any series appearing in the solutions. This is by no means always so; it may be impossible for us to find in any simple manner an expression for the general coefficient from the recurrence relation. This is so, in general, when the recurrence relation contains three or more terms instead of the two they have had up till now. All that we can do in such a situation is to give the first few terms of the power series solution, and hope that this will be of some use. We illustrate by the following example.

Example 5

$$(x^2 - 1)\frac{d^2y}{dx^2} + 3x\frac{dy}{dx} + xy = 0.$$

Rewriting this in the form

$$x^2\frac{d^2y}{dx^2} + x.\frac{3x^2}{x^2 - 1}\frac{dy}{dx} + \frac{x^3}{x^2 - 1}y = 0,$$

we see that it is of the form (1.2) with $q(x) = (3x^2)/(x^2 - 1)$ and $r(x) = x^3/(x^2 - 1)$. Both $q(x)$ and $r(x)$ may be expanded as power series in x (by the binomial theorem) convergent for $|x| < 1$. Hence any series solutions we obtain will be convergent for at least this range of values of x.

We now revert to the original equation, and trying for a solution of the form

$$z = \sum_{n=0}^{\infty} a_n x^{s+n}$$

leads, in the same manner as in previous examples, to the set of equations

$$a_0 s(s - 1) = 0 \qquad\qquad (1.71)$$

$$a_1(s + 1)s = 0 \qquad\qquad (1.72)$$

$$a_0 s(s + 2) - a_2(s + 2)(s + 1) = 0 \qquad\qquad (1.73)$$

$$a_{n-3} + a_{n-2}(s + n - 2) - a_n(s + n)(s + n - 1) = 0 \quad (n \geqslant 3). \quad (1.74)$$

Equation (1.71) gives the indicial equation

$$s(s - 1) = 0$$

with roots $s = 0$ and $s = 1$. Equation (1.72) then shows that a_1 is indeterminate if $s = 0$, so that we are dealing with case (3) above—the two independent solutions may both be obtained from the root $s = 0$, taking a_0 and a_1 as arbitrary constants.

With $s = 0$, equation (1.73) gives

$$a_2 = 0$$

and equation (1.74) becomes

$$a_{n-3} + n(n-2)a_{n-2} - n(n-1)a_n = 0,$$

giving

$$a_n = \frac{a_{n-3} + n(n-2)a_{n-2}}{n(n-1)} \quad (n > 3). \tag{1.75}$$

It is impossible for us to use the recurrence relation (1.75) to obtain a general expression for a_n; but we may proceed to calculate as many terms as we please.

Thus

$$a_3 = \frac{a_0 + 3a_1}{6}$$

$$= \tfrac{1}{6}a_0 + \tfrac{1}{2}a_1,$$

$$a_4 = \frac{a_1 + 8a_2}{12}$$

$$= \tfrac{1}{12}a_1,$$

$$a_5 = \frac{a_2 + 15a_3}{20}$$

$$= \tfrac{1}{8}a_0 + \tfrac{3}{8}a_1$$

and so on as far as we please.

We have calculated the series solution up to terms in x^5:

$$y = a_0 + a_1 x + (\tfrac{1}{6}a_0 + \tfrac{1}{2}a_1)x^3 + \tfrac{1}{12}a_1 x^4$$
$$+ (\tfrac{1}{8}a_0 + \tfrac{3}{8}a_1)x^5 + \ldots$$
$$= a_0\{1 + \tfrac{1}{6}x^3 + \tfrac{1}{8}x^5 + \ldots\}$$
$$+ a_1\{x + \tfrac{1}{2}x^3 + \tfrac{1}{12}x^4 + \tfrac{3}{8}x^5 + \ldots\}.$$

PROBLEMS

(1) Obtain solutions of the following differential equations in ascending powers of x, stating for what values of x the series are convergent:

(i) $4x\dfrac{d^2y}{dx^2} + \dfrac{dy}{dx} - y = 0$;

(ii) $x\dfrac{d^2y}{dx^2} + (x+1)\dfrac{dy}{dx} + y = 0$;

(iii) $x\dfrac{d^2y}{dx^2} - 2\dfrac{dy}{dx} + y = 0$;

(iv) $9x(1 - x)\dfrac{d^2y}{dx^2} - 12\dfrac{dy}{dx} + 4y = 0$;

(v) $(1 - x^2)\dfrac{d^2y}{dx^2} + 2x\dfrac{dy}{dx} + y = 0$;

(vi) $x^2\dfrac{d^2y}{dx^2} + (x^2 - 3x)\dfrac{dy}{dx} + (4 - 2x)y = 0$;

(vii) $(1 - x^2)\dfrac{d^2y}{dx^2} + x\dfrac{dy}{dx} - y = 0$;

(viii) $x^2\dfrac{d^2y}{dx^2} - 3x\dfrac{dy}{dx} + (x^3 - 5)y = 0$;

(ix) $\dfrac{d^2y}{dx^2} - x^2\dfrac{dy}{dx} - y = 0$.

(2) Determine whether or not it is possible to obtain solutions of the following equations in terms of ascending powers of x:

(i) $x^3\dfrac{d^2y}{dx^2} + x^2\dfrac{dy}{dx} + y = 0$;

(ii) $x^2\dfrac{d^2y}{dx^2} + \dfrac{dy}{dx} + x^2y = 0$;

(iii) $x^2\dfrac{d^2y}{dx^2} + x^2\dfrac{dy}{dx} + y = 0$.

(3) Obtain solutions of the following equations in terms of ascending powers of $1/x$:

(i) $2x^2(x - 1)\dfrac{d^2y}{dx^2} + x(3x + 1)\dfrac{dy}{dx} - 2y = 0$;

(ii) $2x^3\dfrac{d^2y}{dx^2} + (2x + x^2)\dfrac{dy}{dx} + 2y = 0$.

2

GAMMA AND BETA FUNCTIONS

2.1 DEFINITIONS

We define the gamma and beta functions respectively by:

$$\Gamma(x) = \int_0^{\infty} e^{-t}t^{x-1}\,dt \tag{2.1}$$

$$B(x, y) = \int_0^1 t^{x-1}(1 - t)^{y-1}\,dt. \tag{2.2}$$

The first definition is valid only for $x > 0$, and the second only for $x > 0$ and $y > 0$, because it is for just these values of x and y that the above integrals are convergent. We shall not prove this statement, but shall at least make it plausible.

Consider the integral in definition (2.1). It is known that at infinity the behaviour of an exponential dominates the behaviour of any power, so that $e^{-t}\,t^{x-1} \rightarrow 0$ as $t \rightarrow \infty$ for any value of x, and hence no trouble is expected from the upper limit of the integral. Near the lower limit of the integral we have $e^{-t} \simeq 1$; hence if this approximation is good between $t = 0$ and $t = c$, we may write equation (2.1) in the form

$$\Gamma(x) \simeq \int_0^c t^{x-1}\,dt + \int_c^{\infty} e^{-t}t^{x-1}\,dt$$

$$= \left[\frac{1}{x}t^x\right]_0^c + \int_c^{\infty} e^{-t}t^{x-1}\,dt,$$

so that if the first term is to remain finite at the lower limit we must have $x > 0$.

A similar argument applies to the beta function, the behaviour at $t = 0$ leading to the restriction on x and at $t = 1$ to the restriction on y.

2.2 PROPERTIES OF THE BETA AND GAMMA FUNCTIONS

Theorem 2.1

$$\Gamma(1) = 1.$$

PROOF

We have, from the definition (2.1),

$$\begin{aligned}
\Gamma(1) &= \int_0^\infty e^{-t} t^{1-1}\, dt \\
&= \int_0^\infty e^{-t}\, dt \\
&= \left[-e^{-t} \right]_0^\infty \\
&= 1.
\end{aligned}$$

Theorem 2.2

$$\Gamma(x + 1) = x\Gamma(x). \quad (x > 0)$$

PROOF

$$\Gamma(x + 1) = \int_0^\infty e^{-t} t^x\, dt$$

(by the definition (2.1))

$$= \left[(-e^{-t}) t^x \right]_0^\infty - \int_0^\infty (-e^{-t}) x t^{x-1}\, dt$$

(on integrating by parts)

$$= 0 + x \int_0^\infty e^{-t} t^{x-1}\, dt$$

(where the first term vanishes at the upper limit since the exponential dominates the power, and at the lower limit since $x > 0$)

$$= x\Gamma(x)$$

(using definition (2.1) again).

Theorem 2.3

If x is a non-negative integer, then $\Gamma(x + 1) = x!$

PROOF

$$\Gamma(x + 1) = x\Gamma(x)$$

(by theorem 2.2)

$$= x(x - 1)\Gamma(x - 1)$$

(using theorem 2.2 again)

$$= x(x - 1)(x - 2)\Gamma(x - 2)$$

(by further use of theorem 2.2)

$$= x(x - 1)(x - 2)(x - 3) \ldots 3.2.1\Gamma(1)$$

(by repeated use of theorem 2.2, and remembering that x is integral, so that continued subtraction of unity will eventually lead to 1)

$$= x!\Gamma(1)$$
$$= x!$$

(by theorem 2.1).

Theorem 2.4

$$\Gamma(x) = 2 \int_0^\infty e^{-t^2} t^{2x-1} \, dt.$$

PROOF

In definition (2.1) substitute u^2 for t: $t = u^2$, so that $dt = 2u \, du$; when $t = 0$, $u = 0$ and when $t = \infty$, $u = \infty$, so that we have

$$\Gamma(x) = \int_0^\infty e^{-u^2}(u^2)^{x-1} . 2u \, du$$

$$= 2 \int_0^\infty e^{-u^2} u^{2x-1} \, du$$

$$= 2 \int_0^\infty e^{-t^2} t^{2x-1} \, dt$$

(since in a definite integral we may choose the variable of integration to be anything we please).

Theorem 2.5

$$\int_0^{\pi/2} \cos^{2x-1} \theta \, \sin^{2y-1} \theta \, d\theta = \frac{\Gamma(x)\Gamma(y)}{2\Gamma(x + y)}.$$

PROOF

We prove this result by considering in two different ways the double integral

$$I = \iint_R \exp\left(-t^2 - u^2\right) t^{2x-1} u^{2y-1} \, dt \, du$$

(where R is the first quadrant of the tu-plane, shown unshaded in Fig. 2.1).

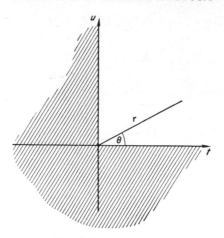

FIG. 2.1   The tu-plane

Firstly, we have

$$I = \int_{t=0}^{\infty}\int_{u=0}^{\infty} \exp\left(-t^2 - u^2\right) t^{2x-1} u^{2y-1} \, dt \, du$$

$$= \int_{0}^{\infty} e^{-t^2} t^{2x-1} \, dt . \int_{0}^{\infty} e^{-u^2} u^{2y-1} \, du$$

$$= \tfrac{1}{2}\Gamma(x).\tfrac{1}{2}\Gamma(y)$$

(using theorem 2.4)

$$= \tfrac{1}{4}\Gamma(x)\Gamma(y). \tag{2.3}$$

Next we change variables to plane polar co-ordinates r and θ in the tu-plane so that $t = r \cos\theta$, $u = r \sin\theta$ and the element of area $dt \, du$ is replaced by the element of area $r \, dr \, d\theta$. Then we shall have

$$I = \iint_{R} \exp\left(-r^2 \cos^2\theta - r^2 \sin^2\theta\right)(r\cos\theta)^{2x-1}(r\sin\theta)^{2y-1} r \, dr \, d\theta$$

$$= \int_{r=0}^{\infty}\int_{\theta=0}^{\pi/2} e^{-r^2} r^{2x-1} \cos^{2x-1}\theta \; r^{2y-1} \sin^{2y-1}\theta \; r \, dr \, d\theta$$

$$= \int_{0}^{\infty} e^{-r^2} r^{2(x+y)-1} \, dr \int_{0}^{\pi/2} \cos^{2x-1}\theta \sin^{2y-1}\theta \, d\theta$$

$$= \tfrac{1}{2}\Gamma(x+y) \int_{0}^{\pi/2} \cos^{2x-1}\theta \sin^{2y-1}\theta \, d\theta \tag{2.4}$$

(using theorem 2.4 again).

Equating the two expressions (2.3) and (2.4) for I leads immediately to the required result, which will be true for $x > 0$ and $y > 0$, since it is for this range of values that the gamma functions involved are defined.

Theorem 2.6

$$\Gamma(\tfrac{1}{2}) = \sqrt{\pi}.$$

PROOF

Put $x = y = \tfrac{1}{2}$ in theorem 2.5, and we obtain

$$\int_0^{\pi/2} d\theta = \frac{\Gamma(\tfrac{1}{2})\Gamma(\tfrac{1}{2})}{2\Gamma(1)}$$
$$= \tfrac{1}{2}\{\Gamma(\tfrac{1}{2})\}^2,$$

(using the fact that $\Gamma(1) = 1$).

Performing the integration on the left-hand side gives

$$\frac{\pi}{2} = \tfrac{1}{2}\{\Gamma(\tfrac{1}{2})\}^2$$

and hence
$$\Gamma(\tfrac{1}{2}) = \pm\sqrt{\pi}.$$

But from the definition (2.1) we see that $\Gamma(x)$ must be positive (since the integrand is positive), so that we can discard the negative square root and obtain $\Gamma(\tfrac{1}{2}) = \sqrt{\pi}$ as required.

COROLLARY

$$\int_0^\infty e^{-t^2}\, dt = \tfrac{1}{2}\sqrt{\pi}.$$

PROOF

Setting $x = \tfrac{1}{2}$ in theorem 2.4 gives $\Gamma(\tfrac{1}{2}) = 2\int_0^\infty e^{-t^2}\, dt$, so that the required result follows immediately on the use of theorem 2.6.

Theorem 2.7

$$B(x, y) = \frac{\Gamma(x)\Gamma(y)}{\Gamma(x + y)}.$$

PROOF

Substitute $t = \cos^2\theta$ in the definition (2.2) of $B(x, y)$: $t = \cos^2\theta$ so that $dt = -2\cos\theta\sin\theta\, d\theta$; also, when $t = 0$, $\cos\theta = 0$ so that $\theta = \pi/2$ and when $t = 1$, $\cos\theta = 1$ so that $\theta = 0$.

Hence we have:

$$B(x, y) = \int_{\pi/2}^0 (\cos^2\theta)^{x-1}(\sin^2\theta)^{y-1}. -2\cos\theta\sin\theta\, d\theta$$
$$= 2\int_0^{\pi/2} \cos^{2x-1}\theta\,\sin^{2y-1}\theta\, d\theta$$

$$= 2 \frac{\Gamma(x)\Gamma(y)}{2\Gamma(x+y)}$$

$$\text{(by theorem 2.5)}$$

$$= \frac{\Gamma(x)\Gamma(y)}{\Gamma(x+y)}.$$

Theorem 2.8

$$B(x, y) = B(y, x).$$

PROOF

This result follows immediately from theorem 2.7.

Theorem 2.9

(i) $B(x + 1, y) = \dfrac{x}{x+y} B(x, y).$

(ii) $B(x, y + 1) = \dfrac{y}{x+y} B(x, y).$

PROOF

(i) We have

$$B(x + 1, y) = \frac{\Gamma(x+1)\Gamma(y)}{\Gamma(x+1+y)}$$

$$\text{(by theorem 2.7)}$$

$$= \frac{x\Gamma(x)\Gamma(y)}{(x+y)\Gamma(x+y)}$$

$$\text{(by theorem 2.2)}$$

$$= \frac{x}{x+y} \cdot \frac{\Gamma(x)\Gamma(y)}{\Gamma(x+y)}$$

$$= \frac{x}{x+y} B(x, y)$$

$$\text{(by theorem 2.7)}.$$

(ii) Exactly similar to (i).

Theorem 2.10 (Legendre Duplication Formula)

$$\Gamma(2x) = \frac{2^{2x-1}}{\sqrt{\pi}}\Gamma(x)\Gamma(x + \tfrac{1}{2}).$$

PROOF

We have, by theorem 2.7,

$$\frac{\Gamma(x)\Gamma(x)}{\Gamma(x + x)} = B(x, x)$$

$$= \int_0^1 t^{x-1}(1 - t)^{x-1}\, dt$$

(by definition (2.2))

$$= \int_{-1}^1 \frac{1}{2^{x-1}}(1 + s)^{x-1}\frac{1}{2^{x-1}}(1 - s)^{x-1}\frac{1}{2}\, ds$$

(on making the substitution $t = \tfrac{1}{2}(1 + s)$)

$$= \frac{1}{2^{2x-1}}\int_{-1}^1 (1 - s^2)^{x-1}\, ds$$

$$= \frac{2}{2^{2x-1}}\int_0^1 (1 - s^2)^{x-1}\, ds$$

$$= 2^{-2x+2}\int_0^1 (1 - u)^{x-1}\tfrac{1}{2}u^{-1/2}\, du$$

(on making the substitution $u = s^2$)

$$= 2^{-2x+1}\int_0^1 (1 - u)^{x-1}u^{-1/2}\, du$$

$$= 2^{-2x+1}B(\tfrac{1}{2}, x)$$

$$= 2^{-2x+1}\frac{\Gamma(\tfrac{1}{2})\Gamma(x)}{\Gamma(\tfrac{1}{2} + x)}$$

(by theorem 2.7).

Hence, using theorem (2.6),

$$\frac{\Gamma(x)}{\Gamma(2x)} = \frac{2^{-2x+1}}{\Gamma(x + \tfrac{1}{2})}\sqrt{\pi}$$

and thus

$$\Gamma(2x) = \frac{2^{2x-1}}{\sqrt{\pi}}\,\Gamma(x)\Gamma(x + \tfrac{1}{2}).$$

COROLLARY

If x is a positive integer

$$\Gamma(x + \tfrac{1}{2}) = \frac{(2x)!}{2^{2x}x!}\sqrt{\pi}.$$

PROOF

In the theorem we may use theorem 2.3 to rewrite $\Gamma(2x)$ as $(2x - 1)!$ and $\Gamma(x)$ as $(x - 1)!$ Hence we have

$$(2x - 1)! = \frac{2^{2x-1}}{\sqrt{\pi}}(x - 1)!\Gamma(x + \tfrac{1}{2}),$$

which, on multiplying both sides by $2x$, becomes

$$2x(2x - 1)! = \frac{2^{2x}}{\sqrt{\pi}}x(x - 1)!\Gamma(x + \tfrac{1}{2});$$

this equation may be expressed more simply in the form

$$(2x)! = \frac{2^{2x}}{\sqrt{\pi}}x!\Gamma(x + \tfrac{1}{2})$$

and thus

$$\Gamma(x + \tfrac{1}{2}) = \frac{(2x)!}{2^{2x}x!}\sqrt{\pi}.$$

2.3 DEFINITION OF THE GAMMA FUNCTION FOR NEGATIVE VALUES OF THE ARGUMENT

From theorem 2.2 we have

$$\Gamma(x) = \frac{1}{x}\Gamma(x + 1). \tag{2.5}$$

Apart from $x = 0$, where the denominator vanishes, the right-hand side of this equation is well defined for those values of x such that the argument of the gamma function is positive (since this was the condition for definition (2.1) to hold), that is, for $x + 1 > 0$, i.e. for $x > -1$. We also note that we may say that $\Gamma(0)$ is infinite, for as $x \to 0$ we have $\Gamma(x + 1) \to \Gamma(1) = 1$, and hence $\Gamma(x) = (1/x)\Gamma(x + 1) \to \infty$. So far the left-hand side is only defined for $x > 0$, but we can now use the right-hand side to extend this definition to $x > -1$. The argument we are using is as follows:

(i) Equation (2.5) was proved true for $x > 0$;
(ii) Right-hand side is well defined for $x > -1$, left-hand side for $x > 0$;
(iii) Use right-hand side to define left-hand side for $x > -1$.

This means that we now have $\Gamma(x)$ defined for $x > -1$, so that the right-hand side of equation (2.5) is well defined for $x + 1 > -1$, i.e. $x > -2$; we may thus use it to define the left-hand side for $x > -2$; and this process may be repeated to define $\Gamma(x)$ for all negative values of x.

Theorem 2.11

$\Gamma(m) = \infty$, *if m is zero or a negative integer.*

PROOF

We have already remarked above that $\Gamma(0) = \infty$. From equation (2.5) we have

$$\Gamma(-1) = \frac{1}{-1}\Gamma(0) = \infty$$

and

$$\Gamma(-2) = \frac{1}{-2}\Gamma(-1) = \infty,$$

etc.

It is now possible to draw a graph of $\Gamma(x)$. Plotting of points combined with information from the various theorems leads to a graph as shown in Fig. 2.2.

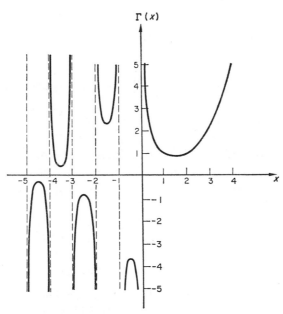

FIG. 2.2   The gamma function

Theorem 2.12

$$\Gamma(x)\Gamma(1-x) = \frac{\pi}{\sin \pi x}.$$

Proof†

We shall prove this result in three stages:

(i) We shall prove the infinite product expansion for $\sin \theta$, viz.

$$\sin \theta = \prod_{n=1}^{\infty} \{1 - (\theta^2/n^2\pi^2)\};$$

(ii) We shall show that this implies that

$$\frac{1}{\sin \theta} = \sum_{n=-\infty}^{\infty} \frac{(-1)^n}{\theta - n\pi};$$

(iii) We shall use result (ii) to prove the required result.

(i) We know that

$$\sin \theta = 2 \sin \frac{\theta}{2} \cos \frac{\theta}{2}$$

$$= 2 \sin \frac{\theta}{2} \sin \left(\frac{\pi}{2} + \frac{\theta}{2}\right) \tag{2.6}$$

and hence, by applying this result to both factors on the right-hand side, we obtain

$$\sin \theta = 2\left\{2 \sin \frac{\theta}{4} \sin \left(\frac{\pi}{2} + \frac{\theta}{4}\right)\right\}\left\{2 \sin \left(\frac{\pi}{4} + \frac{\theta}{4}\right) \sin \left(\frac{\pi}{2} + \frac{\pi}{4} + \frac{\theta}{4}\right)\right\}$$

$$= 2^3 \sin \frac{\theta}{2^2} \sin \frac{\pi + \theta}{2^2} \sin \frac{2\pi + \theta}{2^2} \sin \frac{3\pi + \theta}{2^2}. \tag{2.7}$$

It is left to the reader to verify that applying the result (2.6) to each of the factors on the right-hand side of equation (2.7) gives us

$$\sin \theta = 2^7 \sin \frac{\theta}{2^3} \sin \frac{\pi + \theta}{2^3} \sin \frac{2\pi + \theta}{2^3} \sin \frac{3\pi + \theta}{2^3} \sin \frac{4\pi + \theta}{2^3}$$

$$\sin \frac{5\pi + \theta}{2^3} \sin \frac{6\pi + \theta}{2^3} \sin \frac{7\pi + \theta}{2^3}. \tag{2.8}$$

If this process is carried out n times altogether, the general result will be

---

† The proof of this theorem may be omitted on a first reading; alternatively, parts (i) and (ii), which are standard trigonometric identities, may be assumed and used to prove the result in part (iii).

$$\sin \theta = 2^{p-1} \sin \frac{\theta}{p} \sin \frac{\pi + \theta}{p} \sin \frac{2\pi + \theta}{p} \ldots \sin \frac{(p-1)\pi + \theta}{p} \qquad (2.9)$$

with $p = 2^n$.

The form of this equation is plausible as the correct generalization of equations (2.6), (2.7) and (2.8); if desired it may be proved by the method of induction.

The last factor in equation (2.9) is

$$\sin \frac{(p-1)\pi + \theta}{p} = \sin \left\{ \pi - \frac{(\pi - \theta)}{p} \right\}$$
$$= \sin \left(\frac{\pi - \theta}{p} \right).$$

Similarly, the second last factor is

$$\sin \frac{(p-2)\pi + \theta}{p} = \sin \left\{ \pi - \frac{(2\pi - \theta)}{p} \right\}$$
$$= \sin \left(\frac{2\pi - \theta}{p} \right),$$

and in general the rth factor before the end is

$$\sin \left(\frac{r\pi - \theta}{p} \right).$$

We now regroup the factors appearing in equation (2.9) by taking together the second and the last, the third and the second last, and so on. Then equation (2.9) becomes

$$\sin \theta = 2^{p-1} \sin \frac{\theta}{p} \left\{ \sin \frac{\pi + \theta}{p} \sin \frac{\pi - \theta}{p} \right\} \left\{ \sin \frac{2\pi + \theta}{p} \sin \frac{2\pi - \theta}{p} \right\} \ldots$$
$$\left\{ \sin \frac{(\frac{1}{2}p - 1)\pi + \theta}{p} \sin \frac{(\frac{1}{2}p - 1)\pi - \theta}{p} \right\} \sin \frac{\frac{1}{2}p\pi + \theta}{p}. \qquad (2.10)$$

The factor inside each curly bracket is of the form

$$\sin (A + B) \sin (A - B) = \tfrac{1}{2}\{\cos 2B - \cos 2A\}$$
$$= \sin^2 A - \sin^2 B$$

and hence equation (2.10) becomes

$$\sin \theta = 2^{p-1} \sin \frac{\theta}{p} \left\{ \sin^2 \frac{\pi}{p} - \sin^2 \frac{\theta}{p} \right\} \left\{ \sin^2 \frac{2\pi}{p} - \sin^2 \frac{\theta}{p} \right\} \ldots$$
$$\left\{ \sin^2 \frac{(\frac{1}{2}p - 1)\pi}{p} - \sin^2 \frac{\theta}{p} \right\} \cos \frac{\theta}{p}. \qquad (2.11)$$

Dividing both sides by $\sin (\theta/p)$, letting $\theta \to 0$ and remembering that $\lim_{x \to 0} (\sin x/x) = 1$ so that

$$\lim_{\theta \to 0} \frac{\sin \theta}{\sin (\theta/p)} = \lim_{\theta \to 0} \frac{\sin \theta}{\theta} \cdot \frac{\theta/p}{\sin (\theta/p)} \cdot p$$
$$= p,$$

we obtain
$$p = 2^{p-1} \sin^2 \frac{\pi}{p} \sin^2 \frac{2\pi}{p} \dots \sin^2 \frac{(\frac{1}{2}p - 1)\pi}{p}. \qquad (2.12)$$

If we now divide equation (2.11) by equation (2.12), we obtain

$$\frac{\sin \theta}{p} = \sin \frac{\theta}{p} \left\{ 1 - \frac{\sin^2 (\theta/p)}{\sin^2 (\pi/p)} \right\} \left\{ 1 - \frac{\sin^2 (\theta/p)}{\sin^2 (2\pi/p)} \right\} \dots$$
$$\left\{ 1 - \frac{\sin^2 (\theta/p)}{\sin^2 \frac{(\frac{1}{2}p - 1)\pi}{p}} \right\} \cos \frac{\theta}{p}. \quad (2.13)$$

We now let $p \to \infty$. We take into account the three results

(a) $\lim_{p \to \infty} p \sin \dfrac{\theta}{p} = \lim_{p \to \infty} \dfrac{\sin (\theta/p)}{\theta/p} \cdot \theta$
$$= \theta,$$

(b) $\lim_{p \to \infty} \dfrac{\sin^2 (\theta/p)}{\sin^2 (r\pi/p)} = \lim_{p \to \infty} \left\{ \dfrac{\sin (\theta/p)}{\theta/p} \right\}^2 \left(\dfrac{\theta}{p} \right)^2 \left\{ \dfrac{r\pi/p}{\sin (r\pi/p)} \right\}^2 \dfrac{1}{(r\pi/p)^2}$
$$= \theta^2/r^2\pi^2,$$

(c) $\lim_{p \to \infty} \cos \dfrac{\theta}{p} = 1$

and see that therefore equation (2.13) gives

$$\sin \theta = \theta \left(1 - \frac{\theta^2}{\pi^2} \right) \left(1 - \frac{\theta^2}{2^2\pi^2} \right) \left(1 - \frac{\theta^2}{r^2\pi^2} \right) \dots$$
$$= \theta \prod_{n=1}^{\infty} \left(1 - \frac{\theta^2}{n^2\pi^2} \right).$$

(ii) It is trivial to verify the result that

$$\frac{1}{\sin \theta} = \frac{d}{d\theta} \ln \tan \frac{\theta}{2}.$$

Hence

$$\frac{1}{\sin \theta} = \frac{d}{d\theta} \ln \frac{\sin (\theta/2)}{\cos (\theta/2)}$$
$$= \frac{d}{d\theta} \ln \frac{2 \sin^2 (\theta/2)}{2 \sin (\theta/2) \cos (\theta/2)}$$
$$= \frac{d}{d\theta} \ln \frac{2 \sin^2 (\theta/2)}{\sin \theta}$$

$$= \frac{d}{d\theta}\{\ln 2 + \ln \sin^2(\theta/2) - \ln \sin \theta\}$$

$$= \frac{d}{d\theta}\{2 \ln \sin(\theta/2) - \ln \sin \theta\}$$

$$= \frac{d}{d\theta}\left\{2 \ln \prod_{n=1}^{\infty} \theta\left(1 - \frac{\theta^2}{4n^2\pi^2}\right) - \ln \prod_{n=1}^{\infty} \theta\left(1 - \frac{\theta^2}{n^2\pi^2}\right)\right\}$$

$$= \frac{d}{d\theta}\left\{2 \ln \theta + 2 \sum_{n=1}^{\infty} \ln\left(1 - \frac{\theta}{2n\pi}\right) + 2 \sum_{n=1}^{\infty} \ln\left(1 + \frac{\theta}{2n\pi}\right)\right.$$

$$\left. - \ln \theta - \sum_{n=1}^{\infty} \ln\left(1 - \frac{\theta}{n\pi}\right) - \sum_{n=1}^{\infty} \ln\left(1 + \frac{\theta}{n\pi}\right)\right\}$$

$$= \frac{d}{d\theta}\left\{\ln \theta + 2 \sum_{n=1}^{\infty} \ln(2n\pi - \theta) + 2 \sum_{n=1}^{\infty} \ln(2n\pi + \theta)\right.$$

$$\left. - \sum_{n=1}^{\infty} \ln(n\pi - \theta) - \sum_{n=1}^{\infty} \ln(n\pi + \theta)\right\}$$

$$= \frac{1}{\theta} + 2 \sum_{n=1}^{\infty} \frac{-1}{2n\pi - \theta} + 2 \sum_{n=1}^{\infty} \frac{1}{2n\pi + \theta} - \sum_{n=1}^{\infty} \frac{-1}{n\pi - \theta} - \sum_{n=1}^{\infty} \frac{1}{n\pi + \theta}$$

$$= \frac{1}{\theta} + \left\{2 \sum_{n=1}^{\infty} \frac{1}{\theta - 2n\pi} - \sum_{n=1}^{\infty} \frac{1}{\theta - n\pi}\right\}$$

$$+ \left\{2 \sum_{n=1}^{\infty} \frac{1}{\theta + 2n\pi} - \sum_{n=1}^{\infty} \frac{1}{\theta + n\pi}\right\}$$

$$= \frac{1}{\theta} + \sum_{n=1}^{\infty} \frac{(-1)^n}{\theta - n\pi} + \sum_{n=1}^{\infty} \frac{(-1)^n}{\theta + n\pi}$$

$$= \sum_{n=-\infty}^{\infty} \frac{(-1)^n}{\theta - n\pi}.$$

(iii) Let us first assume that $0 < x < 1$.
Then

$$\Gamma(x)\Gamma(1 - x) = B(x, 1 - x)\Gamma(x + 1 - x)$$

$$\text{(by theorem 2.7)}$$

$$= B(x, 1 - x)$$

$$= \int_0^1 t^{x-1}(1 - t)^{-x}\, dt$$

$$\text{(by definition (2.2)).}$$

ʃF—D

We now make the substitution $t = 1/(1 + u)$; then
$$dt = \{-1/(1 + u)^2\} \, du \text{ and } u = (1 - t)/t.$$

Also when $t = 0$, $u = \infty$ and when $t = 1$, $u = 0$.

Then $\Gamma(x)\Gamma(1 - x) = \displaystyle\int_\infty^0 \frac{1}{(1 + u)^{x-1}} \left(\frac{u}{1 + u}\right)^{-x} \left(-\frac{1}{(1 + u)^2} \, du\right)$

$$= \int_0^\infty \frac{u^{-x}}{1 + u} \, du$$

$$= \int_0^1 \frac{u^{-x}}{1 + u} \, du + \int_1^\infty \frac{u^{-x}}{1 + u} \, du.$$

In the second integral we make the substitution $u = 1/v$. Then $du = (-1/v^2) \, dv$; also when $u = 1$, $v = 1$ and when $u = \infty$, $v = 0$.

Thus $\displaystyle\int_1^\infty \frac{u^{-x}}{1 + u} \, du = \int_1^0 \frac{v^x}{1 + (1/v)} \left(-\frac{1}{v^2} \, dv\right)$

$$= \int_0^1 \frac{v^{x-1}}{1 + v} \, dv$$

$$= \int_0^1 \frac{u^{x-1}}{1 + u} \, du.$$

Hence, from equation (2.14) we have

$$\Gamma(x)\Gamma(1 - x) = \int_0^1 \frac{(u^{-x} + u^{x-1})}{1 + u} \, du$$

$$= \int_0^1 (u^{-x} + u^{x-1}) \sum_{n=0}^\infty (-1)^n u^n \, du$$

$$= \sum_{n=0}^\infty (-1)^n \int_0^1 \{u^{n-x} + u^{n+x-1}\} \, du$$

$$= \sum_{n=0}^\infty (-1)^n \left[\frac{1}{n - x + 1} u^{n-x+1} + \frac{1}{n + x} u^{n+x}\right]_0^1$$

$$= \sum_{n=0}^\infty (-1)^n \left\{\frac{1}{n - x + 1} + \frac{1}{n + x}\right\}$$

(remembering that $0 < x < 1$)

$$= \sum_{n=-\infty}^\infty \frac{(-1)^n}{x - n}$$

$$= \sum_{n=-\infty}^{\infty} \frac{(-1)^n \pi}{(x\pi) - (n\pi)}$$

$$= \frac{\pi}{\sin \pi x}$$

(by part (ii) of the proof).

We now remove the restriction $0 < x < 1$. Suppose that $x = y + N$ where N is an integer and that $0 < y < 1$.

Then

$$\Gamma(x)\Gamma(1 - x) = \Gamma(N + y)\Gamma(1 - y - N)$$
$$= (N + y - 1)(N + y - 2) \ldots y\Gamma(y)$$
$$\frac{1}{1 - y - N} \cdot \frac{1}{2 - y - N} \cdots \frac{1}{y}\Gamma(1 - y)$$

(by repeated use of the result $\Gamma(x + 1) = x\Gamma(x)$)

$$= (-1)^N \Gamma(y)\Gamma(1 - y)$$

$$= (-1)^N \frac{\pi}{\sin \pi y}$$

(since we know this result to be true for $0 < y < 1$)

$$= \frac{\pi}{\sin (N\pi + \pi y)}$$

$$= \frac{\pi}{\sin \pi x}$$

as required.

2.4   EXAMPLES

Example 1

Express each of the following integrals in terms of gamma or beta functions and simplify where possible.

(i) $\int_0^{\pi/2} \sqrt{(\tan \theta)} \, d\theta.$ (ii) $\int_0^1 \frac{dx}{\sqrt[3]{(1 - x^3)}}.$

(iii) $\int_0^{\infty} t^{-3/2}(1 - e^{-t}) \, dt.$ (iv) $\int_{-1}^1 \left(\frac{1 + x}{1 - x}\right)^{1/2} dx.$

(i) We use theorem 2.5 where, in order to get $\sqrt{(\tan \theta)} = \sin^{1/2} \theta \cos^{-1/2} \theta$ as integrand, we take $2x - 1 = -\frac{1}{2}$ and $2y - 1 = +\frac{1}{2}$, i.e. $x = \frac{1}{4}$ and $y = \frac{3}{4}$.

Thus $\displaystyle\int_0^{\pi/2} \sqrt{(\tan\theta)}\,\mathrm{d}\theta = \frac{\Gamma(\frac{1}{4})\Gamma(\frac{3}{4})}{2\Gamma(\frac{1}{4}+\frac{3}{4})}$

$\qquad\qquad = \frac{1}{2}\Gamma(\frac{1}{4})\Gamma(\frac{3}{4})$

$\qquad\qquad\qquad\qquad$ (by theorem 2.1)

$\qquad\qquad = \dfrac{1}{2}\,\dfrac{\pi}{\sin(\pi/4)}$

$\qquad\qquad\qquad\qquad$ (by theorem 2.12)

$\qquad\qquad = \dfrac{1}{2}\,\dfrac{\pi}{1/\sqrt{2}}$

$\qquad\qquad = \pi/\sqrt{2}.$

(ii) $\qquad \displaystyle\int_0^1 \frac{\mathrm{d}x}{\sqrt[3]{(1-x^3)}} = \int_0^1 (1-x^3)^{-1/3}\,\mathrm{d}x.$

We change the variable to $t = x^3$. When $x = 0$, $t = 0$ and when $x = 1$, $t = 1$. Also $\mathrm{d}t = 3x^2\,\mathrm{d}x$, i.e., $\mathrm{d}x = \frac{1}{3}t^{-2/3}\,\mathrm{d}t.$

Hence $\qquad \displaystyle\int_0^1 \frac{\mathrm{d}x}{\sqrt[3]{(1-x^3)}} = \int_0^1 (1-t)^{-1/3}\cdot\frac{1}{3}t^{-2/3}\,\mathrm{d}t$

$\qquad\qquad = \frac{1}{3}B(\frac{1}{3},\frac{2}{3})$

$\qquad\qquad\qquad\qquad$ (by definition (2.2))

$\qquad\qquad = \frac{1}{3}\Gamma(\frac{1}{3})\Gamma(\frac{2}{3})$

$\qquad\qquad\qquad\qquad$ (by theorems 2.7 and 2.8)

$\qquad\qquad = \dfrac{1}{3}\,\dfrac{\pi}{\sin(\pi/3)}$

$\qquad\qquad\qquad\qquad$ (by theorem 2.12)

$\qquad\qquad = \dfrac{1}{3}\,\dfrac{\pi}{(\sqrt{3})/2}$

$\qquad\qquad = \dfrac{2\pi}{3(\sqrt{3})}.$

(iii) $\qquad \displaystyle\int_0^\infty t^{-3/2}(1 - e^{-t})\,\mathrm{d}t.$

We cannot relate this immediately to the gamma function; we must first integrate by parts:

$\displaystyle\int_0^\infty t^{-3/2}(1 - e^{-t})\,\mathrm{d}t = \left[-2t^{-1/2}(1 - e^{-t})\right]_0^\infty - \int_0^\infty -2t^{-1/2}\cdot e^{-t}\,\mathrm{d}t$

$$= 0 + 2 \int_0^\infty t^{-1/2} e^{-t} \, dt \, \dagger$$

$$= 2\Gamma(\tfrac{1}{2})$$

(by definition (2.1))

$$= 2\sqrt{\pi},$$

(by theorem 2.6).

(iv) $\displaystyle \int_{-1}^1 \left(\frac{1+x}{1-x} \right)^{1/2} dx.$

In order to change this into a form resembling the beta function it is necessary that the range of integration be changed to 0 to 1. This is accomplished by the change of variable $t = \tfrac{1}{2}(1 + x)$. Then $x = 2t - 1$, $dx = 2dt$ and we have

$$\int_{-1}^1 \left(\frac{1+x}{1-x} \right)^{1/2} dx = \int_0^1 \left(\frac{1 + 2t - 1}{1 - 2t + 1} \right)^{1/2} 2 \, dt$$

$$- 2 \int_0^1 \left(\frac{t}{1-t} \right)^{1/2} dt$$

$$= 2 \int_0^1 t^{1/2} (1 - t)^{-1/2} \, dt$$

$$= 2B(\tfrac{3}{2}, \tfrac{1}{2})$$

(by definition (2.2))

$$= 2 \frac{\Gamma(\tfrac{3}{2})\Gamma(\tfrac{1}{2})}{\Gamma(2)}$$

(by theorem 2.7)

$$= 2 \frac{\tfrac{1}{2}\Gamma(\tfrac{1}{2}) . \Gamma(\tfrac{1}{2})}{1!}$$

(by theorems 2.2 and 2.3)

$$= \pi \quad \text{(by theorem 2.6).}$$

---

† The behaviour of $t^{-1/2}(1 - e^{-t})$ at $t = 0$ requires some explanation. We recall l'Hôpital's rule which states that if $f(a) = g(a) = 0$, then

$$\lim_{t \to a} \frac{f(t)}{g(t)} = \frac{f'(a)}{g'(a)}$$

provided $f'(a)$ and $g'(a)$ are not both zero (or infinite). Hence we have

$$\lim_{t \to 0} \frac{(1 - e^{-t})}{t^{1/2}} = \frac{[e^{-t}]_{t=0}}{[\tfrac{1}{2}t^{-1/2}]_{t=0}} = \frac{1}{\infty} = 0.$$

Example 2

Show that $B(n, n + 1) = \dfrac{1}{2}\dfrac{\{\Gamma(n)\}^2}{\Gamma(2n)}$ and hence deduce that

$$\int_0^{\pi/2} \left(\frac{1}{\sin^3 \theta} - \frac{1}{\sin^2 \theta}\right)^{1/4} \cos \theta \, d\theta = \frac{\{\Gamma(\frac{1}{4})\}^2}{2\sqrt{\pi}}.$$

We have

$$B(n, n + 1) = \frac{\Gamma(n)\Gamma(n + 1)}{\Gamma(2n + 1)}$$

$$\text{(by theorem 2.7)}$$

$$= \frac{\Gamma(n).n\Gamma(n)}{2n\Gamma(2n)}$$

$$\text{(by theorem 2.2)}$$

$$= \frac{\{\Gamma(n)\}^2}{2\Gamma(2n)}.$$

Setting $n = \frac{1}{4}$ gives

$$B(\tfrac{1}{4}, \tfrac{5}{4}) = \frac{\{\Gamma(\frac{1}{4})\}^2}{2\Gamma(\frac{1}{2})},$$

which, on using definition (2.2) and theorem 2.6 becomes

$$\int_0^1 t^{-3/4}(1 - t)^{1/4} \, dt = \frac{\{\Gamma(\frac{1}{4})\}^2}{2\sqrt{\pi}}.$$

Now set $t = \sin \theta$ in the integral on the left-hand side. When $t = 0$, $\theta = 0$ and when $t = 1$, $\theta = \pi/2$; also $dt = \cos \theta \, d\theta$. Hence we have

$$\int_0^1 t^{-3/4}(1 - t)^{1/4} \, dt = \int_0^{\pi/2} (\sin \theta)^{-3/4}(1 - \sin \theta)^{1/4} \cos \theta \, d\theta$$

$$= \int_0^{\pi/2} \left(\frac{1 - \sin \theta}{\sin^3 \theta}\right)^{1/4} \cos \theta \, d\theta$$

$$= \int_0^{\pi/2} \left(\frac{1}{\sin^3 \theta} - \frac{1}{\sin^2 \theta}\right)^{1/4} \cos \theta \, d\theta,$$

so that we have proved the required result.

PROBLEMS

(1) Prove that

(i) $\displaystyle\int_0^\infty e^{-ax}x^n \, dx = \frac{1}{a^{n+1}}\Gamma(n + 1)$

$$(n > -1, a > 0);$$

(ii) $\displaystyle\int_0^\infty x^m\, e^{-x^n}\, dx = \frac{1}{n}\, \Gamma\,\{(m+1)/n\}$

$$(m > -1,\, n > 0).$$

(iii) $\displaystyle\int_a^\infty \exp\,(2ax - x^2)\, dx = \tfrac{1}{2}\sqrt{\pi}\,\exp\,(a^2).$

(2) Prove that $\displaystyle\int_0^{\pi/2} \tan^n \theta\, d\theta = \tfrac{1}{2}\Gamma\{(1+n)/2\}\,\Gamma\{(1-n)/2\}$ if $|n| < 1$.

(3) Prove that $\displaystyle\int_0^{\pi/2} \sin^n \theta\, d\theta = \int_0^{\pi/2} \cos^n \theta\, d\theta = \frac{\sqrt{\pi}}{2}\,\frac{\Gamma\{(1+n)/2\}}{\Gamma\{(2+n)/2\}}$

(4) Express each of the following integrals in terms of the gamma or beta functions and simplify when possible:

(i) $\displaystyle\int_0^1 \left(\frac{1}{x} - 1\right)^{1/4} dx$;

(ii) $\displaystyle\int_0^1 \left(\ln \frac{1}{x}\right)^{a-1} dx$, $(a > 0)$;

(iii) $\displaystyle\int_a^b (b-x)^{m-1}(x-a)^{n-1}\, dx$, $(b > a,\, m > 0,\, n > 0)$;

(iv) $\displaystyle\int_0^1 x^m(1-x^n)^p\, dx$, $(m > -1,\, p > -1,\, n > 0)$;

(v) $\displaystyle\int_0^1 \frac{dx}{\sqrt{(1-x^n)}}$, $(n > 0)$;

(vi) $\displaystyle\int_0^\infty \frac{dt}{(\sqrt{t})(1+t)}$.

(5) Show that the area enclosed by the curve $x^4 + y^4 = 1$ is $\{\Gamma(\tfrac{1}{4})\}^2/2\sqrt{\pi}$.

(6) Evaluate $\Gamma(-\tfrac{1}{2})$ and $\Gamma(-\tfrac{7}{2})$.

(7) Show that

(i) $\displaystyle\Gamma(x)\Gamma(-x) = \frac{-\pi}{x \sin \pi x}$;

(ii) $\displaystyle\Gamma(\tfrac{1}{2} + x)\Gamma(\tfrac{1}{2} - x) = \frac{\pi}{\cos \pi x}$.

3

LEGENDRE POLYNOMIALS AND FUNCTIONS

3.1 LEGENDRE'S EQUATION AND ITS SOLUTIONS

Legendre's differential equation is

$$(1 - x^2)\frac{d^2y}{dx^2} - 2x\frac{dy}{dx} + ky = 0. \tag{3.1}$$

We shall write k in the form $l(l + 1)$ for reasons which will become clear as we proceed.

This equation,

$$(1 - x^2)\frac{d^2y}{dx^2} - 2x\frac{dy}{dx} + l(l + 1)y = 0, \tag{3.2}$$

is of the form of equation (1.2) with $q(x) = -2x^2/(1 - x^2)$ and $r(x) = \{l(l + 1)x^2\}/(1 - x^2)$. The binomial theorem may be used to expand these as power series in x for values of x such that $x^2 < 1$, i.e., such that $-1 < x < 1$. Thus the methods of Chapter 1 will be applicable to the solution of this equation, any power series obtained being valid for at least $-1 < x < 1$.

Writing $z(x, s) = x^s \sum_{n=0}^{\infty} a_n x^n$ and requiring z to be a solution of equation (3.2) leads, as in Chapter 1, to the system of equations

$$a_0 s(s - 1) = 0, \tag{3.3}$$

$$a_1(s + 1)s = 0 \tag{3.4}$$

and

$$a_{n+2}(s + n + 2)(s + n + 1) - a_n\{(s + n)(s + n + 1) - l(l + 1)\}$$
$$= 0 \quad (n \geqslant 0). \quad (3.5)$$

Equation (3.3) gives the indicial equation $s(s - 1) = 0$ with roots $s = 0$ and $s = 1$ (which differ by an integer, so that we know we are dealing with one of the exceptional cases).

Equation (3.4), with $s = 0$, is satisfied irrespective of the value of a_1; this means that a_1 is indeterminate and hence the one root of the indicial equation ($s = 0$) leads to two independent solutions with the two arbitrary constants a_0 and a_1.

Equation (3.5) with $s = 0$ becomes

$$a_{n+2} = a_n \frac{n(n + 1) - l(l + 1)}{(n + 1)(n + 2)} \quad (3.6)$$

which, since

$$n(n + 1) - l(l + 1) = n^2 + n - l^2 - l$$
$$= (n^2 - l^2) + (n - l)$$
$$= (n - l)(n + l) + (n - l)$$
$$= (n - l)(n + l + 1),$$

may be written in the form

$$a_{n+2} = -a_n \frac{(l - n)(l + n + 1)}{(n + 1)(n + 2)}. \quad (3.7)$$

Thus we have

$$a_2 = -a_0 \frac{l(l + 1)}{1.2}, \qquad a_3 = -a_1 \frac{(l - 1)(l + 2)}{2.3},$$

$$a_4 = -a_2 \frac{(l - 2)(l + 3)}{3.4} \qquad a_5 = -a_3 \frac{(l - 3)(l + 4)}{4.5}$$

$$= a_0 \frac{l(l - 2)(l + 1)(l + 3)}{1.2.3.4}, \qquad = a_1 \frac{(l - 1)(l - 3)(l + 2)(l + 4)}{2.3.4.5}$$

and in general

$$a_{2n} = (-1)^n a_0$$
$$\frac{l(l-2)(l-4) \ldots (l-2n+2)(l+1)(l+3) \ldots (l+2n-1)}{(2n)!} \quad (3.8)$$

and

$$a_{2n+1} = (-1)^n a_0$$
$$\frac{(l - 1)(l-3) \ldots (l-2n+1)(l+2)(l+4) \ldots (l+2n)}{(2n + 1)!}. \quad (3.9)$$

Therefore

$$z(x, 0) = a_0 \left\{ 1 + \sum_{n=1}^{\infty} (-1)^n \right.$$

$$\left. \frac{l(l-2) \ldots (l-2n+2)(l+1)(l+3) \ldots (l+2n-1)}{(2n)!} x^{2n} \right\}$$

$$+ a_1 \left\{ x + \sum_{n=1}^{\infty} (-1)^n \right.$$

$$\left. \frac{(l-1)(l-3) \ldots (l-2n+1)(l+2)(l+4) \ldots (l+2n)}{(2n+1)!} x^{2n+1} \right\}$$

$$= a_0 y_1(x) + a_1 y_2(x), \text{ say,}$$

so that $y_1(x)$ and $y_2(x)$ are the linearly independent solutions.

We know already that $y_1(x)$ and $y_2(x)$ will be convergent for $-1 < x < 1$. For many applications, solutions to Legendre's equation are required which are finite for $-1 \leqslant x \leqslant 1$. The theorem quoted at the end of Section 1.1 guarantees convergence only for $-1 < x < 1$, and says nothing at all about convergence for $x = \pm 1$. In fact standard methods of convergence theory may be used to show that the series above are divergent for $x = \pm 1$ (see Appendix 1). How then is it possible to obtain solutions which are finite for $x = \pm 1$? The only way is to make the infinite series reduce to finite series, and this will happen for any positive integral value of l. For, from equation (3.8) we see that if $l = 2n$ (an even positive integer) we have $a_{2n} \neq 0$ but $a_{2n+2} = 0$, and hence all subsequent even coefficients must also equal zero. Similarly equation (3.9) shows that if $l = 2n + 1$ (an odd positive integer) then $a_{2n+1} \neq 0$ but a_{2n+3} and all subsequent odd coefficients are zero. Thus we see that if l is an even integer $y_1(x)$ reduces to a polynomial, and hence is finite for all finite x, while if l is an odd integer the same occurs for $y_2(x)$.† In both cases the highest power of x appearing is x^l, so that since equation (3.7) applies to the series for both $y_1(x)$ and $y_2(x)$, we may obtain a single series valid for both even and odd l if we write it in descending powers of x. The

---

† When we consider integral values of l, we need consider only positive values of l, since the constant appearing in the equation was $l(l + 1)$ and if l were a negative integer we could write $m = -(l + 1)$ and use the easily verified fact that $m(m + 1) = l(l + 1)$.

This arrival at integral values of l is, of course, the reason for writing the original constant k in the form $l(l + 1)$.

first term is $a_l x^l$ and subsequent terms are given by equation (3.7) written in the form

$$a_n = -a_{n+2} \frac{(n+2)(n+1)}{(l-n)(l+n+1)}, \qquad (3.10)$$

so that

$$a_{l-2} = -a_l \frac{l(l-1)}{2(2l-1)},$$

$$a_{l-4} = -a_{l-2} \frac{(l-2)(l-3)}{4(2l-3)}$$

$$= a_l \frac{(l-1)(l-2)(l-3)}{2.4.(2l-1)(2l-3)}$$

and, in general,

$$a_{l-2r} = (-1)^r a_l \frac{l(l-1)(l-2) \ldots (l-2r+1)}{2.4 \ldots 2r(2l-1)(2l-3) \ldots (2l-2r+1)}. \qquad (3.11)$$

Thus for l even, $y_1(x)$ reduces to the following expression, while for l odd, $y_2(x)$ reduces to the same expression:

$$y(x) = a_l x^l + a_{l-2} x^{l-2} + a_{l-4} x^{l-4} + \ldots + \begin{cases} a_0 \text{ for } l \text{ even} \\ a_1 x \text{ for } l \text{ odd} \end{cases}$$

$$= \sum_{r=0}^{[\frac{1}{2}l]} a_{l-2r} x^{l-2r}$$

$$\text{(where } [\tfrac{1}{2}l] = \begin{cases} \tfrac{1}{2}l \text{ for } l \text{ even} \\ \tfrac{1}{2}(l-1) \text{ for } l \text{ odd}, \end{cases} \qquad (3.12)$$

i.e., $[\tfrac{1}{2}l]$ is the largest integer less than or equal to $\tfrac{1}{2}l$)

$$= a_l \sum_{r=0}^{[l/2]} (-1)^r \frac{l(l-1) \ldots (l-2r+1)}{2.4 \ldots 2r(2l-1)(2l-3) \ldots (2l-2r+1)} x^{l-2r} \qquad (3.13)$$

from equation (3.11).

We may rewrite this series more compactly if we note the following results:

$$l(l-1) \ldots (l-2r+1)$$

$$= l(l-1) \ldots (l-2r+1) . \frac{(l-2r)(l-2r-1) \ldots 3.2.1}{(l-2r)(l-2r-1) \ldots 3.2.1}$$

$$= \frac{l!}{(l-2r)!}, \qquad (3.14)$$

$$2.4.6 \ldots 2r = (2.1)(2.2)(2.3) \ldots (2.r)$$
$$= 2^r . 1.2.3 \ldots r$$
$$= 2^r r! \qquad (3.15)$$

and

$$(2l - 1)(2l - 3) \ldots (2l - 2r + 1)$$

$$= \frac{2l(2l-1)(2l-2)(2l-3) \ldots (2l-2r+1)}{2l(2l-2)(2l-4) \ldots (2l-2r+2)} \cdot \frac{(2l-2r)!}{(2l-2r)!}$$

$$= \frac{(2l)!}{2^r l(l - 1) \ldots (l - r + 1)(2l - 2r)!}$$

$$= \frac{(2l)!(l - r)!}{2^r(2l - 2r)!l!}. \tag{3.16}$$

Using equations (3.14), (3.15) and (3.16) in equation (3.13) gives us

$$y(x) = a_l \sum_{r=0}^{[l/2]} (-1)^r \frac{l!}{(l - 2r)!} \cdot \frac{1}{2^r r!} \cdot \frac{2^r(2l - 2r)!l!}{(2l)!(l - r)!} x^{l - 2r}$$

$$= a_l \sum_{r=0}^{[l/2]} (-1)^r \frac{(l!)^2(2l - 2r)!}{r!(l - 2r)!(l - r)!(2l)!} x^{l - 2r}.$$

This is a solution for any value of a_l. If we choose $a_l = (2l)!/\{2^l(l!)^2\}$ we obtain the solution which we denote by $P_l(x)$ and call the Legendre polynomial of order l:

$$P_l(x) = \sum_{r=0}^{[l/2]} (-1)^r \frac{(2l - 2r)!}{2^l r!(l - r)!(l - 2r)!} x^{l - 2r}. \tag{3.17}$$

Thus this is the solution of Legendre's equation which is finite for $-1 \leqslant x \leqslant 1$; it is the only such solution, apart from an arbitrary multiplicative constant.

3.2   GENERATING FUNCTION FOR THE LEGENDRE POLYNOMIALS

Theorem 3.1

$$\frac{1}{\sqrt{(1 - 2tx + t^2)}} = \sum_{l=0}^{\infty} t^l P_l(x) \quad if \mid t \mid < 1 \text{ and } \mid x \mid \leqslant 1.$$

This means that when $(1 - 2tx + t^2)^{-1/2}$ *is expanded in powers of t, the co-efficient of* t^l *is* $P_l(x)$; $(1 - 2tx + t^2)^{-1/2}$ *is called the generating function of the Legendre polynomials.*

PROOF

Expand $(1 - 2tx + t^2)^{-1/2}$ by the binomial theorem:

$$(1 - 2tx + t^2)^{-1/2} = \{1 - t(2x - t)\}^{-1/2}$$

$$= 1 + (-\tfrac{1}{2})\{-t(2x - t)\} + \frac{(-\tfrac{1}{2})(-\tfrac{3}{2})}{2!}\{-t(2x - t)\}^2$$

$$+ \ldots + \frac{(-\tfrac{1}{2})(-\tfrac{3}{2}) \ldots \{-(2r - 1)/2\}}{r!}\{-t(2x - t)\}^r + \ldots$$

$$= \sum_{r=0}^{\infty} (-1)^r \frac{1.3.5 \ldots (2r - 1)}{2^r r!}(-1)^r t^r (2x - t)^r$$

$$= \sum_{r=0}^{\infty} \frac{(2r)!}{2^{2r}(r!)^2} t^r (2x - t)^r.$$

Now expand $(2x - t)^r$ by the binomial theorem (remembering that r is integral):

$$(2x - t)^r = \sum_{p=0}^{r} {}^r C_p (2x)^{r-p}(-t)^p$$

where ${}^r C_p$ is the binomial coefficient $\dfrac{r!}{p!(r - p)!}.$

Hence we now have

$$(1 - 2tx + t^2)^{-1/2} = \sum_{r=0}^{\infty} \frac{(2r)!}{2^{2r}(r!)^2} \sum_{p=0}^{r} {}^r C_p (-1)^p t^{r+p}(2x)^{r-p}. \qquad (3.18)$$

We wish to find the coefficient of t^l, so we must take $r + p = l$, and hence for a fixed value of r we must take $p = l - r$. But p only takes on values such that $0 \leqslant p \leqslant r$, so we must only consider those values of r satisfying $0 \leqslant l - r \leqslant r$, i.e. $\tfrac{1}{2}l \leqslant r \leqslant l$. Hence if l is even, r can take on values between $\tfrac{1}{2}l$ and l, while if l is odd, r can take on values between $\tfrac{1}{2}(l + 1)$ and l. For any of these values of r the coefficient of t^l in equation (3.18), obtained by taking $p = l - r$, is

$$\frac{(2r)!}{2^{2r}(r!)^2} {}^r C_{l-r}(-1)^{l-r}(2x)^{r-(l-r)}$$

and the total coefficient of t^l is obtained by summing over all appropriate values of r so that we obtain

$$\text{coefficient of } t^l \ = \ \sum_{r=\begin{cases} l/2 \ (l \text{ even}) \\ (l + 1)/2 \ (l \text{ odd}) \end{cases}}^{l} \frac{(2r)!}{2^{2r}(r!)^2} {}^r C_{l-r}(-1)^{l-r}(2x)^{2r-l}.$$

If we now change the variable of summation from r to $k = l - r$, we obtain

coefficient of t^l

$$= \sum_{k=\{{}^{l/2\ (l\ \text{even})}_{(l-1)/2\ (l\ \text{odd})}}^{0} \frac{(2l-2k)!}{2^{2l-2k}\{(l-k)!\}^2}\,{}^{l-k}C_k(-1)^k(2x)^{l-2k}$$

$$= \sum_{k=0}^{[l/2]} \frac{(2l-2k)!}{2^{2l-2k}\{(l-k)!\}^2}\,\frac{(l-k)!}{(l-2k)!k!}(-1)^k 2^{l-2k}x^{l-2k}$$

(where $[l/2]$ is as defined above in equation (3.12))

$$= \sum_{k=0}^{[l/2]} (-1)^k \frac{(2l-2k)!}{2^l(l-k)!(l-2k)!k!} x^{l-2k}$$

$$= P_l(x)$$

(by the definition (3.17)).

Hence the required result is proved.

The restriction on the values of x comes from the condition for convergence of the binomial expansion of $\{1 - t(2x - t)\}^{-1/2}$, viz. $|t(2x - t)| < 1$. When $|x| \leqslant 1$ this condition may be shown to be equivalent to $|t| < 1$.

3.3 FURTHER EXPRESSIONS FOR THE LEGENDRE POLYNOMIALS

Theorem 3.2 (Rodrigues' Formula)

$$P_l(x) = \frac{1}{2^l l!}\frac{d^l}{dx^l}(x^2 - 1)^l.$$

PROOF

We may expand $(x^2 - 1)^l$ by the binomial theorem:

$$(x^2 - 1)^l = \sum_{r=0}^{l} {}^lC_r(-1)^r x^{2(l-r)}.$$

Hence,

$$\frac{1}{2^l l!}\frac{d^l}{dx^l}(x^2 - 1)^l = \frac{1}{2^l l!}\frac{d^l}{dx^l}\sum_{r=0}^{l} {}^lC_r(-1)^r x^{2l-2r}. \qquad (3.19)$$

But the lth derivative of a power of x less than l is zero, so that

$$\frac{d^l}{dx^l}x^{2l-2r} = 0 \text{ if } 2l - 2r < l, \text{ i.e., if } r > l/2.$$

Thus we may replace $\sum\limits_{r=0}^{l}$ by $\sum\limits_{r=0}^{l/2}$ if l is even and by $\sum\limits_{r=0}^{(l-1)/2}$ if l is odd, i.e.,

by $\sum\limits_{r=0}^{[l/2]}$ where $[l/2]$ is as defined above.

Also,

$$\frac{d^l}{dx^l}x^p = p(p-1)(p-2)\ldots(p-l+1)x^{p-l}$$

$$= \frac{p!}{(p-l)!}x^{p-l}$$

so that

$$\frac{d^l}{dx^l}x^{2l-2r} = \frac{(2l-2r)!}{(l-2r)!}x^{l-2r}$$

and hence, substituting into equation (3.19), we have

$$\frac{1}{2^l l!}\frac{d^l}{dx^l}(x^2-1)^l = \frac{1}{2^l l!}\sum_{r=0}^{[l/2]}\frac{l!}{r!(l-r)!}(-1)^r\frac{(2l-2r)!}{(l-2r)!}x^{l-2r}$$

$$= \sum_{r=0}^{[l/2]}(-1)^r\frac{(2l-2r)!}{2^l r!(l-r)!(l-2r)!}x^{l-2r}$$

$$= P_l(x) \qquad \text{(by the definition (3.17))}.$$

Theorem 3.3 (Laplace's Integral Representation)

$$P_l(x) = \frac{1}{\pi}\int_0^\pi \{x + \sqrt{(x^2-1)}\cos\theta\}^l\, d\theta.$$

PROOF

It may be shown by elementary methods (for example by means of the standard substitution $t = \tan(\theta/2)$) that

$$\int_0^\pi \frac{d\theta}{1+\lambda\cos\theta} = \frac{\pi}{\sqrt{(1-\lambda^2)}}. \tag{3.20}$$

If we now write $\lambda = -\{u\sqrt{(x^2-1)}\}/(1-ux)$, expand both sides of equation (3.20) in powers of u and equate the coefficients of corresponding powers of u, we shall obtain the desired result:

$$\frac{1}{1+\lambda\cos\theta} = \frac{1}{1 - \dfrac{u\sqrt{(x^2-1)}}{(1-ux)}\cos\theta}$$

$$= (1-ux)[1 - u\{x + \sqrt{(x^2-1)}\cos\theta\}]^{-1}$$

$$= (1-ux)\sum_{l=0}^{\infty} u^l\{x + \sqrt{(x^2-1)}\cos\theta\}^l$$

(since, by the binomial theorem $(1 - a)^{-1} = \sum\limits_{n=0}^{\infty} a^n$).

$$\frac{1}{\sqrt{(1 - \lambda^2)}} = \frac{1}{\sqrt{\left\{1 - \dfrac{u^2(x^2 - 1)}{(1 - ux)^2}\right\}}}$$

$$= \frac{(1 - ux)}{\sqrt{\{(1 - ux)^2 - u^2(x^2 - 1)\}}}$$

$$= \frac{(1 - ux)}{\sqrt{(1 - 2ux + u^2)}}.$$

Hence, substituting into equation (3.20) gives

$$\int_0^\pi \sum_{l=0}^{\infty} u^l \{x + \sqrt{(x^2 - 1)} \cos\theta\}^l \, d\theta = \frac{\pi}{\sqrt{(1 - 2ux + u^2)}}$$

i.e., $\displaystyle\sum_{l=0}^{\infty} u^l \int_0^\pi \{x + \sqrt{(x^2 - 1)} \cos\theta\}^l \, d\theta = \pi \sum_{l=0}^{\infty} u^l P_l(x)$

(by theorem 3.1).

Equating coefficients of u^l gives

$$\pi P_l(x) = \int_0^\pi \{x + \sqrt{(x^2 - 1)} \cos\theta\} \, d\theta$$

which is the required result.

3.4 EXPLICIT EXPRESSIONS FOR AND SPECIAL VALUES OF THE LEGENDRE POLYNOMIALS

From the definition (3.17) we may write down explicitly the Legendre polynomial of any given order. We give here the first few polynomials:

$$\begin{aligned}
P_0(x) &= 1, \\
P_1(x) &= x, \\
P_2(x) &= \tfrac{1}{2}(3x^2 - 1), \\
P_3(x) &= \tfrac{1}{2}(5x^3 - 3x), \\
P_4(x) &= \tfrac{1}{8}(35x^4 - 30x^2 + 3).
\end{aligned} \tag{3.21}$$

Theorem 3.4

(i) $P_l(1) = 1$.

(ii) $P_l(-1) = (-1)^l$.

(iii) $P_l'(1) = \tfrac{1}{2}l(l + 1)$.

(iv) $P_l'(-1) = (-1)^{l-1}\tfrac{1}{2}l(l + 1)$.

(v) $P_{2l}(0) = (-1)^l \dfrac{(2l)!}{2^{2l}(l!)^2}.$

(vi) $P_{2l+1}(0) = 0.$

(*By* $P_l'(1)$ *we mean* $[\{\mathrm{d}P_l(x)\}/\mathrm{d}x]_{x=1}$).

PROOF

(i) Set $x = 1$ in theorem 3.1 above and we obtain

$$\frac{1}{\sqrt{(1 - 2t + t^2)}} = \sum_{l=0}^{\infty} t^l P_l(1),$$

that is

$$\frac{1}{1 - t} = \sum_{l=0}^{\infty} t^l P_l(1).$$

But $1/(1 - t) = \sum_{l=0}^{\infty} t^l$ (by the binomial theorem or by considering the right-hand side as the sum to infinity of a geometric progression), so that we have $\sum_{l=0}^{\infty} t^l = \sum_{l=0}^{\infty} t^l P_l(1)$. For this to be true for all values of t in some range (in this case $|t| < 1$) we must have the coefficients of corresponding powers of t equal, i.e., $P_l(1) = 1$.

(ii) Exactly similar to (i) but setting $x = -1$ in theorem 3.1.

(iii) $P_l(x)$ satisfies Legendre's equation (3.2), so that we have

$$(1 - x^2)\frac{\mathrm{d}^2}{\mathrm{d}x^2}P_l(x) - 2x\frac{\mathrm{d}}{\mathrm{d}x}P_l(x) + l(l + 1)P_l(x) = 0 \qquad (3.22)$$

and setting $x = 1$ in this equation gives

$$-2P_l'(1) + l(l + 1)P_l(1) = 0,$$

which reduces on using part (i) above, to $P_l'(1) = \frac{1}{2}l(l + 1)$.

(iv) Exactly similar to (iii), but setting $x = -1$ in equation (3.22) and using part (ii) above.

(v, vi) Set $x = 0$ in theorem 3.1 above and we obtain

$$\frac{1}{\sqrt{(1 + t^2)}} = \sum_{l=0}^{\infty} t^l P_l(0).$$

Expanding the left-hand side by the binomial theorem gives us

$$\frac{1}{\sqrt{(1 + t^2)}} = (1 + t^2)^{-1/2}$$

$$= 1 + (-\tfrac{1}{2})t^2 + \frac{(-\tfrac{1}{2})(-\tfrac{3}{2})}{2!}(t^2)^2 + \cdots$$

$$+ \cdots + \frac{(-\frac{1}{2})(-\frac{3}{2}) \cdots \{-(2l-1)/2\}}{l!}(t^2)^l + \cdots$$

$$= \sum_{l=0}^{\infty} (-1)^l \frac{1.3.5 \cdots (2l-1)t^{2l}}{2^l . l!}$$

$$= \sum_{l=0}^{\infty} (-1)^l \frac{1.2.3.4.5 \cdots (2l-2)(2l-1)2l}{2^l l! . 2.4.6 \cdots (2l-2)2l} t^{2l}$$

$$= \sum_{l=0}^{\infty} (-1)^l \frac{(2l)!}{2^l l! . 2^l l!} t^{2l}$$

$$= \sum_{l=0}^{\infty} (-1)^l \frac{(2l)!}{2^{2l}(l!)^2} t^{2l}.$$

Thus we have

$$\sum_{l=0}^{\infty} (-1)^l \frac{(2l)!}{2^{2l}(l!)^2} t^{2l} = \sum_{l=0}^{\infty} t^l P_l(0)$$

and equating coefficients of corresponding powers of t on both sides gives

$$P_{2l}(0) = (-1)^l \frac{(2l)!}{2^{2l}(l!)^2}$$

$$P_{2l+1}(0) = 0.$$

3.5   ORTHOGONALITY PROPERTIES OF THE LEGENDRE POLYNO-MIALS

Theorem 3.5

$$\int_{-1}^{1} P_l(x)P_m(x) \, dx = \begin{cases} 0 & \text{if } l \neq m \\ \dfrac{2}{2l+1} & \text{if } l = m. \end{cases}$$

(*This result may be written more concisely if we introduce the Kronecker delta, defined by*

$$\delta_{lm} = \begin{cases} 0 \text{ if } l \neq m \\ 1 \text{ if } l = m. \end{cases}$$

Then the statement of the theorem is

$$\int_{-1}^{1} P_l(x)P_m(x) \, dx = \frac{2}{2l+1}\delta_{lm}.)$$

PROOF

$P_l(x)$ and $P_m(x)$ satisfy Legendre's equation (3.2), so that we have

$$(1 - x^2)\frac{d^2P_l}{dx^2} - 2x\frac{dP_l}{dx} + l(l + 1)P_l = 0$$

and
$$(1 - x^2)\frac{d^2P_m}{dx^2} - 2x\frac{dP_m}{dx} + m(m + 1)P_m = 0, \; †$$

which may be rewritten in the form

$$\frac{d}{dx}\left\{(1 - x^2)\frac{dP_l}{dx}\right\} + l(l + 1)P_l = 0 \tag{3.23}$$

and
$$\frac{d}{dx}\left\{(1 - x^2)\frac{dP_m}{dx}\right\} + m(m + 1)P_m = 0. \tag{3.24}$$

Multiplying equation (3.23) by $P_m(x)$, equation (3.24) by $P_l(x)$, subtracting equation (3.24) from equation (3.23) and integrating with respect to x from -1 to $+1$ gives

$$\int_{-1}^{1}\left[P_m\frac{d}{dx}\left\{(1 - x^2)\frac{dP_l}{dx}\right\} - P_l\frac{d}{dx}\left\{(1 - x^2)\frac{dP_m}{dx}\right\}\right] dx$$
$$+ \{l(l + 1) - m(m + 1)\}\int_{-1}^{1} P_lP_m \, dx = 0.$$

But since

$$\frac{d}{dx}\left\{P_m(1 - x^2)\frac{dP_l}{dx}\right\} = \frac{dP_m}{dx}\cdot(1 - x^2)\frac{dP_l}{dx} + P_m\frac{d}{dx}\left\{(1 - x^2)\frac{dP_l}{dx}\right\},$$

we shall have

$$\int_{-1}^{1}\left[\frac{d}{dx}\left\{P_m(1 - x^2)\frac{dP_l}{dx}\right\} - \frac{dP_m}{dx}(1 - x^2)\frac{dP_l}{dx} - \frac{d}{dx}\left\{P_l(1 - x^2)\frac{dP_m}{dx}\right\}\right.$$
$$\left. + \frac{dP_l}{dx}(1 - x^2)\frac{dP_m}{dx}\right] dx + (l^2 + l - m^2 - m)\int_{-1}^{1} P_lP_m \, dx = 0.$$

On integrating the first term we obtain

$$\left[P_m(1 - x^2)\frac{dP_l}{dx} - P_l(1 - x^2)\frac{dP_m}{dx}\right]_{-1}^{1}$$
$$+ (l - m)(l + m + 1)\int_{-1}^{1} P_lP_m \, dx = 0;$$

---

† Throughout this proof we denote $P_l(x)$ by P_l and $P_m(x)$ by P_m. The argument x is to be understood in every case.

but now the first term vanishes at both upper and lower limits, because of the $(1 - x^2)$ factor, so that we have

$$(l - m)(l + m + 1) \int_{-1}^{1} P_l P_m \, dx = 0, \text{ and when } l \neq m \text{ we can cancel}$$

the factor outside the integral to obtain

$$\int_{-1}^{1} P_l P_m \, dx = 0.$$

It remains to prove that $\int_{-1}^{1} \{P_l(x)\}^2 \, dx = 2/(2l + 1)$. For this we use the generating function of theorem 3.1:

$$\frac{1}{\sqrt{(1 - 2tx + t^2)}} = \sum_{l=0}^{\infty} t^l P_l(x)$$

so that
$$\frac{1}{(1 - 2tx + t^2)} = \left\{ \sum_{l=0}^{\infty} t^l P_l(x) \right\}^2$$

$$= \sum_{l=0}^{\infty} t^l P_l(x) . \sum_{m=0}^{\infty} t^m P_m(x)$$

$$= \sum_{l,\, m=0}^{\infty} t^{l+m} P_l(x) P_m(x).$$

We now integrate both sides with respect to x between -1 and $+1$:

$$\int_{-1}^{1} \frac{1}{(1 + t^2) - 2tx} \, dx = \sum_{l,m=0}^{\infty} t^{l+m} \int_{-1}^{1} P_l(x) P_m(x) \, dx.$$

But the left-hand side is a standard integral of the form

$$\int \{1/(a + bx)\} \, dx = (1/b) \ln (a + bx),$$

while the right-hand side contains only terms for which $l = m$, by the first part of this proof.

Hence

$$\left[-\frac{1}{2t} \ln (1 + t^2 - 2tx) \right]_{-1}^{1} = \sum_{l=0}^{\infty} t^{2l} \int_{-1}^{1} \{P_l(x)\}^2 \, dx$$

which gives

$$\sum_{l=0}^{\infty} t^{2l} \int_{-1}^{1} \{P_l(x)\}^2 \, dx = -\frac{1}{2t} \ln (1 + t^2 - 2t) + \frac{1}{2t} \ln (1 + t^2 + 2t)$$

$$= -\frac{1}{2t} \ln (1 - t)^2 + \frac{1}{2t} \ln (1 + t)^2$$

$$= \frac{1}{t}\left\{\ln\left(1+t\right) - \ln\left(1-t\right)\right\}$$

$$= \frac{1}{t}\left\{t - \frac{t^2}{2} + \frac{t^3}{3} \ldots + t + \frac{t^2}{2} + \frac{t^3}{3} \ldots\right\}$$

(using the series expansion of $\ln\left(1+t\right)$)

$$= \frac{1}{t}\left\{2t + 2\frac{t^3}{3} + 2\frac{t^5}{5} + \ldots\right\}$$

$$= 2\left\{1 + \frac{t^2}{3} + \frac{t^4}{5} + \ldots\right\}$$

$$= 2\sum_{l=0}^{\infty}\frac{t^{2l}}{2l+1}.$$

Equating coefficients of corresponding powers of t on both sides gives

$$\int_{-1}^{1}\{P_l(x)\}^2\,dx = \frac{2}{2l+1}$$

as required.

3.6   LEGENDRE SERIES

Theorem 3.6

If $f(x)$ is a polynomial of degree n, then

$$f(x) = \sum_{r=0}^{n} c_r P_r(x) \text{ with } c_r = (r + \tfrac{1}{2})\int_{-1}^{1} f(x)P_r(x)\,dx.$$

Also, if $f(x)$ is even (or odd), only those c_r with even (or odd) suffixes are non-zero.

PROOF

We have $f(x) = a_n x^n + a_{n-1}x^{n-1} + \ldots + a_1 x + a_0$, say, and we may write $P_n(x) = k_n x^n + k_{n-2}x^{n-2} + \ldots$ (since by equation (3.17) $P_n(x)$ is a polynomial of degree n, containing only odd or even powers of x according to whether n is odd or even), so that if we take $f(x) - (a_n/k_n)P_n(x)$ we obtain either zero (in which case the first part of the theorem is proved) or else a polynomial of degree $n - 1$. This means that

$$f(x) = c_n P_n(x) + g_{n-1}(x)$$

where $c_n = a_n/k_n$ and $g_{n-1}(x)$ is a polynomial of degree $n - 1$.
The same argument may be applied to $g_{n-1}(x)$ to give

$$g_{n-1}(x) = c_{n-1}P_{n-1}(x) + g_{n-2}(x)$$

and hence $\qquad f(x) = c_n P_n(x) + c_{n-1}P_{n-1}(x) + g_{n-2}(x).$

The same argument may now be applied to $g_{n-2}(x)$, etc., to yield eventually

$$f(x) = c_n P_n(x) + c_{n-1}P_{n-1}(x) + \ldots + c_1 P_1(x) + c_0 P_0(x)$$
$$= \sum_{r=0}^{n} c_r P_r(x).$$

If we now multiply both sides of this equation by $P_s(x)$ and integrate from -1 to $+1$, we obtain

$$\int_{-1}^{1} f(x)P_s(x)\,dx = \sum_{r=0}^{n} c_r \int_{-1}^{1} P_r(x)P_s(x)\,dx.$$

But, by theorem 3.6, the integral on the right-hand side is non-zero only for the value of r which equals s, in which case it is $2/(2s+1)$.

Therefore $\qquad \int_{-1}^{1} f(x)P_s(x)\,dx = c_s \dfrac{2}{2s+1},$

giving $c_r = (r + \frac{1}{2}) \int_{-1}^{1} f(x)P_r(x)$, as required.

Now suppose that $f(x)$ is even. Then, since $P_r(x)$ is even when r is even, and odd when r is odd, so the integrand $f(x)P_r(x)$ is also even when r is even and odd when r is odd. But an odd function integrated over the range -1 to $+1$ will give zero, since positive and negative values cancel one another. Hence c_r is zero when r is odd. Similarly when $f(x)$ is odd, c_r is zero when r is even.

COROLLARY

If $f(x)$ is a polynomial of degree less than l, then

$$\int_{-1}^{1} f(x)P_l(x)\,dx = 0.$$

PROOF

Suppose $f(x)$ is of degree n; then by the theorem we have

$$f(x) = \sum_{r=0}^{n} c_r P_r(x),$$

so that

$$\int_{-1}^{1} f(x)P_l(x)\,dx = \sum_{r=0}^{n} c_r \int_{-1}^{1} P_r(x)P_l(x)\,dx$$
$$= 0$$

by theorem 3.5, since $r \leqslant n < l$, so that r is never equal to l.

The results of the above theorem may be extended to functions which are not polynomials. We shall not prove this extension, but will merely quote the following result (the proof is not difficult, but is fairly lengthy).

Theorem 3.7

Suppose $f(x)$ satisfies the following conditions in the interval $-1 \leqslant x \leqslant 1$:
(i) $f(x)$ is continuous apart from a finite number of finite discontinuities (we then say that $f(x)$ is piecewise continuous); and
(ii) $f(x)$ has a finite number of maxima and minima.

Then the series $\displaystyle\sum_{r=0}^{\infty} c_r P_r(x)$, where

$$c_r = (r + \tfrac{1}{2}) \int_{-1}^{1} f(x) P_r(x) \, dx,$$

converges to $f(x)$ if x is not a point of discontinuity of $f(x)$ and to

$$\tfrac{1}{2}\{f(x+) + f(x-)\}$$

if x is a point of discontinuity.† Also, at the end points of the range, $x = \pm 1$, the series converges to $f(1-)$ and $f(-1+)$ respectively. This series is called the Legendre series for $f(x)$.

---

† By $f(x_0 +)$ we mean $\underset{\varepsilon \to 0}{\mathrm{Lim}}\ f(x_0 + \varepsilon)$ where $\varepsilon \to 0$ through positive values and by $f(x_0 -)$ we mean $\underset{\varepsilon \to 0}{\mathrm{Lim}}\ f(x_0 - \varepsilon)$ where again $\varepsilon \to 0$ through positive values. See, for example, Fig. 3.1.

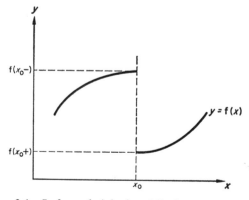

FIG. 3.1   Left- and right-hand limits at a point of discontinuity

3.7 RELATIONS BETWEEN THE LEGENDRE POLYNOMIALS AND THEIR DERIVATIVES; RECURRENCE RELATIONS

Theorem 3.8

(i) $P_l'(x) = \sum_{r=0}^{[\frac{1}{2}(l-1)]} (2l - 4r - 1)P_{l-2r-1}(x)$.

(ii) $xP_l(x) = \dfrac{l+1}{2l+1}P_{l+1}(x) + \dfrac{l}{2l+1}P_{l-1}(x)$.

(iii) $(l+1)P_{l+1}(x) - (2l+1)xP_l(x) + lP_{l-1}(x) = 0$.

(iv) $P_{l+1}'(x) - P_{l-1}'(x) = (2l+1)P_l(x)$.

(v) $xP_l'(x) - P_{l-1}'(x) = lP_l(x)$.

(vi) $P_l'(x) - xP_{l-1}'(x) = lP_{l-1}(x)$.

(vii) $(x^2 - 1)P_l'(x) = lxP_l(x) - lP_{l-1}(x)$.

(viii) $(x^2 - 1)P_l'(x) = (l+1)P_{l+1}(x) - (l+1)xP_l(x)$.

(ix) $\sum_{k=0}^{l} (2k+1)P_k(x)P_k(y) = \dfrac{l+1}{x-y} \{P_{l+1}(x)P_l(y) - P_l(x)P_{l+1}(y)\}$.

PROOF

(i) We know that $P_l(x)$ is a polynomial of degree l, containing only even powers of x if l is even, and only odd powers of x if l is odd. Hence $P_l'(x)$ is a polynomial of degree $l-1$ containing either odd or even powers of x according to whether l is even or odd. Hence by theorem 3.6 we have

$$P_l'(x) = c_{l-1}P_{l-1}(x) + c_{l-3}P_{l-3}(x)$$
$$+ \ldots + c_{l-2r-1}P_{l-2r-1}(x) + \ldots + \begin{cases} c_1P_1(x) \ (l \text{ even}) \\ c_0P_0(x) \ (l \text{ odd}) \end{cases}$$

with
$$c_s = (s + \tfrac{1}{2}) \int_{-1}^{1} P_l'(x)P_s(x) \, ds$$

$$= (s + \tfrac{1}{2}) \left\{ \Big[P_l(x)P_s(x) \Big]_{-1}^{1} - \int_{-1}^{1} P_l(x(P_s'(x) \, dx \right\}$$

(on integrating by parts)

$$= (s + \tfrac{1}{2})\{P_l(1)P_s(1) - P_l(-1)P_s(-1) - 0\}$$

(where the integral vanishes by the corollary to theorem 3.6, since $P_s(x)$ is a polynomial of degree $s-1$, and $s-1$ is always less than l)

$$= (s + \tfrac{1}{2})\{1 - (-1)^{s+l}\}$$

(by theorem 3.4 (i) and (ii)).

But s takes on the values $l - 1, l - 3, \ldots$, so that $s + l$ takes on the values $2l - 1, 2l - 3, \ldots$, which are always odd, irrespective of the values of l or s. Hence $(-1)^{s+l} = -1$ and we have

$$c_s = (s + \tfrac{1}{2})\{1 - (-1)\}$$
$$= (2s + 1).$$

Hence

$$c_{l-2r-1} = 2(l - 2r - 1) + 1$$
$$= 2l - 4r - 1$$

and so we have

$$P_l'(x) = (2l - 1)P_{l-1}(x) + (2l - 5)P_{l-3}(x) + \ldots$$
$$+ (2l - 4r - 1)P_{l-2r-1}(x) + \ldots + \begin{cases} 3P_1(x) \text{ if } l \text{ is even} \\ P_0(x) \text{ if } l \text{ is odd} \end{cases}$$
$$= \sum_{r=0}^{[\frac{1}{2}(l-1)]} (2l - 4r - 1)P_{l-2r-1}(x).$$

(ii) $xP_l(x)$ is a polynomial of degree $l + 1$, odd if l is even and even if l is odd. Hence by theorem 3.6 we have

$$xP_l(x) = c_{l+1}P_{l+1}(x) + c_{l-1}P_{l-1}(x) + \ldots + \begin{cases} c_1 P_1(x) \; (l \text{ even}) \\ c_0 P_0(x) \; (l \text{ odd}), \end{cases}$$

where

$$c_r = (r + \tfrac{1}{2}) \int_{-1}^{1} xP_l(x)P_r(x) \, dx$$
$$= (r + \tfrac{1}{2}) \int_{-1}^{1} P_l(x) . \{xP_r(x)\} \, dx.$$

But this integral is zero by the corollary to theorem 3.6 if $r + 1 < l$ (since then $xP_r(x)$ is a polynomial of degree less than l), i.e., if $r < l - 1$. Hence we have

$$xP_l(x) = c_{l+1}P_{l+1}(x) + c_{l-1}P_{l-1}(x). \tag{3.25}$$

To determine c_{l+1} and c_{l-1} we set $x = 1$ in equation (3.25) and in the same equation differentiated with respect to x, viz.

$$P_l(x) + xP_l'(x) = c_{l+1}P_{l+1}'(x) + c_{l-1}P_{l-1}'(x). \tag{3.26}$$

Setting $x = 1$ in equations (3.25) and (3.26) and using theorem 3.4 (i) and (iii) gives

$$1 = c_{l+1} + c_{l-1} \tag{3.27}$$

and $1 + \tfrac{1}{2}l(l + 1) = c_{l+1}\{\tfrac{1}{2}(l + 1)(l + 2)\} + c_{l-1}\{\tfrac{1}{2}(l - 1)l\}. \tag{3.28}$

Solving equations (3.27) and (3.28) for c_{l+1} and c_{l-1} gives

$$c_{l+1} = \frac{l+1}{2l+1}, \quad c_{l-1} = \frac{l}{2l+1}$$

so that on insertion of these values in equation (3.25) we obtain

$$xP_l(x) = \frac{l+1}{2l+1}P_{l+1}(x) + \frac{l}{2l+1}P_{l-1}(x).$$

(iii) Multiply both sides of equation (ii) above by $(2l+1)$ to obtain

$$(2l+1)xP_l(x) = (l+1)P_{l+1}(x) + lP_{l-1}(x).$$

On rearrangement, this equation becomes

$$(l+1)P_{l+1}(x) - (2l+1)xP_l(x) + lP_{l-1}(x) = 0,$$

which is the required result.

(iv) We may use result (i) for both $P'_{l+1}(x)$ and $P'_{l-1}(x)$:

$$P'_{l+1}(x) = (2l+1)P_l(x) + (2l-3)P_{l-2}(x) + (2l-7)P_{l-4}(x) + \ldots$$
$$P'_{l-1}(x) = \qquad\qquad (2l-3)P_{l-2}(x) + (2l-7)P_{l-4}(x) + \ldots$$

Subtracting these two equations gives

$$P'_{l+1}(x) - P'_{l-1}(x) = (2l+1)P_l(x).$$

(v) If we differentiate result (iii) with respect to x we obtain

$$(l+1)P'_{l+1}(x) - (2l+1)\{P_l(x) + xP'_l(x)\} + lP'_{l-1}(x) = 0$$

and if we now use (iv) to substitute for $P'_{l+1}(x)$ we shall have

$$(l+1)\{P'_{l-1}(x) + (2l+1)P_l(x)\} - (2l+1)\{P_l(x) + xP'_l(x)\} + lP'_{l-1}(x) = 0.$$

Collecting terms in P'_{l-1}, P_l and P'_l gives

$$(2l+1)P'_{l-1}(x) + (2l+1)(l+1-1)P_l(x) - (2l+1)xP'_l(x) = 0,$$

which reduces to $\qquad P'_{l-1}(x) + lP_l(x) - xP'_l(x) = 0,$

and on rearrangement this equation becomes

$$xP'_l(x) - P'_{l-1}(x) = P_l(x).$$

(vi) If we multiply (iv) by x we obtain

$$xP'_{l+1}(x) - xP'_{l-1}(x) = (2l+1)xP_l(x)$$

and substituting this expression for $(2l+1)xP_l(x)$ in (iii) gives

$$(l+1)P_{l+1}(x) + lP_{l-1}(x) = xP'_{l+1}(x) - xP'_{l-1}(x). \qquad (3.29)$$

If we now rewrite (v) with l replaced by $l+1$, we have

$$xP'_{l+1}(x) - P'_l(x) = (l+1)P_{l+1}(x),$$

and substituting this value of $(l+1)P_{l+1}(x)$ into equation (3.29) gives

$$xP'_{l+1}(x) - P'_l(x) + lP_{l-1}(x) = xP'_{l+1}(x) - xP'_{l-1}(x).$$

When rearranged, this equation gives

$$P_l'(x) - xP_{l-1}'(x) = lP_{l-1}(x),$$

which is the required result.

(vii) If we multiply (v) by x we obtain

$$x^2 P_l'(x) - xP_{l-1}'(x) = lxP_l(x)$$

and on subtracting (vi) from this we obtain

$$x^2 P_l'(x) - P_l'(x) = lxP_l(x) - lP_{l-1}(x)$$

which may be rewritten in the form

$$(x^2 - 1)P_l'(x) = lxP_l(x) - lP_{l-1}(x).$$

(viii) If we replace l by $l + 1$ in results (v) and (vi) we obtain

$$xP_{l+1}'(x) - P_l'(x) = (l + 1)P_{l+1}(x)$$

and

$$P_{l+1}'(x) - xP_l'(x) = (l + 1)P_l(x).$$

Eliminating $P_{l+1}'(x)$ between these (by multiplying the second equation by x and subtracting from the first) gives

$$-P_l'(x) + x^2 P_l'(x) = (l + 1)P_{l+1}(x) - (l + 1)xP_l(x),$$

which reduces to

$$(x^2 - 1)P_l'(x) = (l + 1)P_{l+1}(x) - (l + 1)xP_l(x).$$

(ix) Using (iii) we have

$$\begin{aligned}
P_{k+1}(x)P_k(y) - P_k(x)P_{k+1}(y) &= \frac{1}{k+1}\Big[\{(2k + 1)xP_k(x) - kP_{k-1}(x)\}P_k(y) \\
&\qquad - P_k(x)\{(2k + 1)yP_k(y) - kP_{k-1}(y)\}\Big] \\
&= \frac{2k + 1}{k + 1}(x - y)P_k(x)P_k(y) \\
&\qquad + \frac{k}{k + 1}\{P_k(x)P_{k-1}(y) - P_{k-1}(x)P_k(y)\};
\end{aligned}$$

multiplying both sides of this equation by $k + 1$, we obtain
$$(k + 1)\{P_{k+1}(x)P_k(y) - P_k(x)P_{k+1}(y)\}$$
$$= (2k+1)(x-y)P_k(x)P_k(y) + k\{P_k(x)P_{k-1}(y) - P_{k-1}(x)P_k(y)\}. \qquad (3.30)$$

If $(k + 1)\{P_{k+1}(x)P_k(y) - P_k(x)P_{k+1}(y)\}$ is denoted by f_k, equation (3.30) may be written in the form

$$f_k = (2k + 1)(x - y)P_k(x)P_k(y) + f_{k-1}. \qquad (3.31)$$

(Strictly, this equation is true for $k \geqslant 1$, since it is for this range of values of k that all quantities involved are well defined; but we may also make it true for $k = 0$ provided we *define* $f_{-1} = 0$, for then

$$f_0 = P_1(x)P_0(y) - P_0(x)P_1(y)$$
$$= x - y$$

$$\text{(by equations (3.21))}$$

and $x - y$ is also equal to

$$(2k + 1)(x - y)P_k(x)P_k(y) + f_{k-1} \text{ with } k = 0.)$$

If we now sum the set of equations (3.31) from $k=0$ to $k=l$, we obtain

$$\sum_{k=0}^{l} f_k = \sum_{k=0}^{l} (2k + 1)(x - y)P_k(x)P_k(y) + \sum_{k=0}^{l} f_{k-1}$$

$$= \sum_{k=0}^{l} (2k + 1)(x - y)P_k(x)P_k(y) + \sum_{k=1}^{l} f_{k-1}$$

$$= \sum_{k=0}^{l} (2k + 1)(x - y)P_k(x)P_k(y) + \sum_{k=0}^{l-1} f_k.$$

Hence

$$\sum_{k=0}^{l} f_k - \sum_{k=0}^{l-1} f_k = \sum_{k=0}^{l} (2k + 1)(x - y)P_k(x)P_k(y)$$

so that

$$f_l = (x - y) \sum_{k=0}^{l} (2k + 1)P_k(x)P_k(y)$$

and if we remember the definition of f_l we obtain

$$\frac{(l + 1)}{(x - y)} \{P_{l+1}(x)P_l(y) - P_l(x)P_{l+1}(y)\} = \sum_{k=0}^{l} (2k + 1)P_k(x)P_k(y).$$

3.8 ASSOCIATED LEGENDRE FUNCTIONS

Theorem 3.9

If z is a solution of Legendre's equation

$$(1 - x^2)\frac{d^2y}{dx^2} - 2x\frac{dy}{dx} + l(l + 1)y = 0$$

then $(1 - x^2)^{m/2} (d^m z/dx^m)$ is a solution of the equation

$$(1 - x^2)\frac{d^2y}{dx^2} - 2x\frac{dy}{dx} + \left\{l(l + 1) - \frac{m^2}{1 - x^2}\right\}y = 0$$

(known as the associated Legendre equation).

PROOF

Since z is a solution of Legendre's equation, we must have

$$(1 - x^2)\frac{\mathrm{d}^2 z}{\mathrm{d}x^2} - 2x\frac{\mathrm{d}z}{\mathrm{d}x} + l(l + 1)z = 0. \tag{3.32}$$

Now let us differentiate equation (3.32) m times with respect to x:

$$\frac{\mathrm{d}^m}{\mathrm{d}x^m}\left\{(1 - x^2)\frac{\mathrm{d}^2 z}{\mathrm{d}x^2}\right\} - 2\frac{\mathrm{d}^m}{\mathrm{d}x^m}\left\{x\frac{\mathrm{d}z}{\mathrm{d}x}\right\} + l(l + 1)\frac{\mathrm{d}^m z}{\mathrm{d}x^m} = 0$$

which, when we use Leibniz's theorem for the mth derivative of a product,† becomes

$$(1 - x^2)\frac{\mathrm{d}^{m+2} z}{\mathrm{d}x^{m+2}} + m\frac{\mathrm{d}}{\mathrm{d}x}(1 - x^2) \cdot \frac{\mathrm{d}^{m+1} z}{\mathrm{d}x^{m+1}} + \frac{m(m - 1)}{2}\frac{\mathrm{d}^2}{\mathrm{d}x^2}(1 - x^2) \cdot \frac{\mathrm{d}^m z}{\mathrm{d}x^m}$$

$$- 2\left\{x\frac{\mathrm{d}^{m+1} z}{\mathrm{d}x^{m+1}} + m\frac{\mathrm{d}}{\mathrm{d}x}x \cdot \frac{\mathrm{d}^m z}{\mathrm{d}x^m}\right\} + l(l + 1)\frac{\mathrm{d}^m z}{\mathrm{d}x^m} = 0$$

(since higher derivatives of $1 - x^2$ and x vanish).

Collecting terms in $\mathrm{d}^{m+2}z/\mathrm{d}x^{m+2}$, $\mathrm{d}^{m+1}z/\mathrm{d}x^{m+1}$ and $\mathrm{d}^m z/\mathrm{d}x^m$, we obtain

$$(1 - x^2)\frac{\mathrm{d}^{m+2} z}{\mathrm{d}x^{m+2}} - 2x(m + 1)\frac{\mathrm{d}^{m+1} z}{\mathrm{d}x^{m+1}} + \{l(l+1) - m(m-1) - 2m\}\frac{\mathrm{d}^m z}{\mathrm{d}x^m} = 0,$$

which, on denoting $\mathrm{d}^m z/\mathrm{d}x^m$ by z_1, becomes

$$(1 - x^2)\frac{\mathrm{d}^2 z_1}{\mathrm{d}x^2} - 2(m + 1)x\frac{\mathrm{d}z_1}{\mathrm{d}x} + \{l(l + 1) - m(m + 1)\}z_1 = 0. \tag{3.33}$$

If we now write

$$z_2 = (1 - x^2)^{m/2}z_1 = (1 - x^2)^{m/2}\frac{\mathrm{d}^m z}{\mathrm{d}x^m}$$

equation (3.33) becomes

$$(1 - x^2)\frac{\mathrm{d}^2}{\mathrm{d}x^2}\{z_2(1 - x^2)^{-m/2}\} - 2(m + 1)x\frac{\mathrm{d}}{\mathrm{d}x}\{z_2(1 - x^2)^{-m/2}\}$$

$$+ \{l(l + 1) - m(m + 1)\}z_2(1 - x^2)^{-m/2} = 0. \tag{3.34}$$

But

$$\frac{\mathrm{d}}{\mathrm{d}x}\{z_2(1 - x^2)^{-m/2}\} = \frac{\mathrm{d}z_2}{\mathrm{d}x}(1 - x^2)^{-m/2} + z_2 \cdot -\frac{m}{2}(1 - x^2)^{-(m/2)-1} \cdot -2x$$

$$= \frac{\mathrm{d}z_2}{\mathrm{d}x}(1 - x^2)^{-m/2} + mz_2 x(1 - x^2)^{-(m/2)-1}$$

$\dagger\ \dfrac{\mathrm{d}^m}{\mathrm{d}x^m}(uv) = \displaystyle\sum_{r=0}^{m} {}^m C_r \frac{\mathrm{d}^r u}{\mathrm{d}x^r}\frac{\mathrm{d}^{m-r} v}{\mathrm{d}x^{m-r}}.$

so that

$$\frac{d^2}{dx^2}\{z_2(1 - x^2)^{-m/2}\}$$

$$= \frac{d^2 z_2}{dx^2}(1 - x^2)^{-m/2} + \frac{dz_2}{dx} \cdot -\frac{m}{2}(1 - x^2)^{-(m/2)-1} \cdot (-2x)$$

$$+ m\left\{\frac{dz_2}{dx}x(1 - x^2)^{-(m/2)-1} + z_2(1 - x^2)^{-(m/2)-1}\right.$$

$$\left. + z_2 x\left(-\frac{m}{2} - 1\right)(1 - x^2)^{-(m/2)-2} \cdot -2x\right\}$$

$$= \frac{d^2 z_2}{dx^2}(1 - x^2)^{-m/2} + \frac{dz_2}{dx}mx(1 - x^2)^{-(m/2)-1} + m\frac{dz_2}{dx}x(1 - x^2)^{-(m/2)-1}$$

$$+ mz_2(1 - x^2)^{-(m/2)-1} + mz_2 x^2(m + 2)(1 - x^2)^{-(m/2)-2}.$$

Hence equation (3.34) becomes

$$\frac{d^2 z_2}{dx^2}(1 - x^2)^{-(m/2)+1} + 2mx(1 - x^2)^{-m/2}\frac{dz_2}{dx} + mz_2(1 - x^2)^{-m/2}$$

$$+ m(m + 2)(1 - x^2)^{-(m/2)-1}x^2 z_2$$

$$- 2(m + 1)x\left\{(1 - x^2)^{-m/2}\frac{dz_2}{dx} + mx(1 - x^2)^{-(m/2)-1}z_2\right\}$$

$$+ \{l(l + 1) - m(m + 1)\}z_2(1 - x^2)^{-m/2} = 0$$

which, on cancelling a common factor of $(1 - x^2)^{-m/2}$ and collecting like terms, becomes

$$(1 - x^2)\frac{d^2 z_2}{dx^2} + \{2mx - 2(m + 1)x\}\frac{dz_2}{dx}$$

$$+ \left\{m + \frac{m(m+2)}{1-x^2}x^2 - \frac{2(m+1)mx^2}{1-x^2} + l(l+1) - m(m+1)\right\}z_2 = 0. \quad (3.35)$$

The coefficient of dz_2/dx is just $-2x$, while the coefficient of z_2 is

$$l(l + 1) + \frac{(m^2 + 2m - 2m^2 - 2m)x^2}{1 - x^2} + m - m^2 - m$$

$$= l(l + 1) - \frac{m^2 x^2}{1 - x^2} - m^2$$

$$= l(l + 1) - \frac{m^2}{1 - x^2}.$$

Thus equation (3.35) reduces to

$$(1 - x^2)\frac{d^2 z_2}{dx^2} - 2x\frac{dz_2}{dx} + \left\{l(l + 1) - \frac{m^2}{1 - x^2}\right\}z_2 = 0$$

so that z_2 satisfies the associated Legendre equation which, by the definition of z_2, proves the theorem.

COROLLARY

The associated Legendre functions $P_l^m(x)$ defined by

$$P_l^m(x) = (1 - x^2)^{m/2} \frac{d^m}{dx^m} P_l(x) \qquad (3.36)$$

satisfy the associated Legendre equation.

PROOF

This result follows immediately from the theorem, since $P_l(x)$ satisfies Legendre's equation.

Using Rodrigues' formula (theorem 3.2), it is possible to rewrite definition (3.36) in the form

$$P_l^m(x) = \frac{1}{2^l l!}(1 - x^2)^{m/2} \frac{d^{l+m}}{dx^{l+m}}(x^2 - 1)^l.$$

The right-hand side of this expression is well defined for negative values of m such that $l + m \geqslant 0$, i.e., $m \geqslant -l$, whereas the original definition (3.36) of $P_l^m(x)$ was only valid for $m \geqslant 0$. Thus we may use this new form to define $P_l^m(x)$ for values of m such that $m \geqslant -l$.

It is easy to verify that if we consider m positive, the function $P_l^{-m}(x)$ defined in such a way is a solution of Legendre's associated equation as well as $P_l^m(x)$. In fact, it is not an independent solution; it may be proved that

$$P_l^{-m}(x) = (-1)^m \frac{(l - m)!}{(l + m)!} P_l^m(x) \qquad (3.37)$$

(see problem 3 at the end of this chapter).

3.9 PROPERTIES OF THE ASSOCIATED LEGENDRE FUNCTIONS

Theorem 3.10

(i) $P_l^0(x) = P_l(x)$.

(ii) $P_l^m(x) = 0$ if $m > l$.

PROOF

(i) This result is immediately obvious from definition (3.36).

(ii) Since $P_l(x)$ is a polynomial of degree l, it will reduce to zero when differentiated more than l times. Thus $\frac{d^m}{dx^m} P_l(x) = 0$ for $m > l$, and the required result then follows from definition (3.36).

Theorem 3.11 (Orthogonality Relation)

$$\int_{-1}^{1} P_l^m(x)P_{l'}^m(x)\,dx = \frac{2(l+m)!}{(2l+1)(l-m)!}\,\delta_{ll'}.$$

PROOF

We first prove that if $l \neq l'$

$$\int_{-1}^{1} P_l^m(x)P_{l'}^m(x)\,dx = 0.$$

This proof follows exactly the same lines as that of the first part of theorem 3.5, so we shall not repeat it here.

All that now remains to be proved is that

$$\int_{-1}^{1} \{P_l^m(x)\}^2\,dx = \frac{2(l+m)!}{(2l+1)(l-m)!}.$$

Assume first that $m > 0$; then from definition (3.36) we have

$$\int_{-1}^{1} \{P_l^m(x)\}^2\,dx$$

$$= \int_{-1}^{1} (1-x^2)^m \left\{\frac{d^m}{dx^m}P_l(x)\right\} \left\{\frac{d^m}{dx^m}P_l(x)\right\}\,dx$$

$$= \left[\left\{\frac{d^{m-1}}{dx^{m-1}}P_l(x)\right\} \left\{(1-x^2)^m \frac{d^m}{dx^m}P_l(x)\right\}\right]_{-1}^{+1}$$

$$- \int_{-1}^{1} \left\{\frac{d^{m-1}}{dx^{m-1}}P_l(x)\right\} \frac{d}{dx}\left\{(1-x^2)^m \frac{d^m}{dx^m}P_l(x)\right\}\,dx$$

(on integrating by parts)

$$= -\int_{-1}^{1} \left\{\frac{d^{m-1}}{dx^{m-1}}P_l(x)\right\} \frac{d}{dx}\left\{(1-x^2)^m \frac{d^m}{dx^m}P_l(x)\right\}\,dx \qquad (3.38)$$

(the first term vanishing at upper and lower limits because of the $(1-x^2)$ factor).

Now, from equation (3.33) with m replaced by $m-1$ we have that

$$(1-x^2)\frac{d^{m+1}}{dx^{m+1}}P_l(x) - 2mx\frac{d^m}{dx^m}P_l(x) + \{l(l+1)-(m-1)m\}\frac{d^{m-1}}{dx^{m-1}}P_l(x) = 0$$

which, when multiplied by $(1-x^2)^{m-1}$, becomes

$$(1-x^2)^m \frac{d^{m+1}}{dx^{m+1}}P_l(x) - 2mx(1-x^2)^{m-1}\frac{d^m}{dx^m}P_l(x)$$

$$+ (l+m)(l-m+1)(1-x^2)^{m-1}\frac{d^{m-1}}{dx^{m-1}}P_l(x) = 0$$

and this equation may be rewritten in the form

$$\frac{d}{dx}\left\{(1-x^2)^m \frac{d^m}{dx^m}P_l(x)\right\} = -(l+m)(l-m+1)(1-x^2)^{m-1}\frac{d^{m-1}}{dx^{m-1}}P_l(x).$$

Substituting this result in equation (3.38) gives

$$\int_{-1}^{1}\{P_l^m(x)\}^2\,dx$$

$$= \int_{-1}^{1}\left\{\frac{d^{m-1}}{dx^{m-1}}P_l(x)\right\}(l+m)(l-m+1)(1-x^2)^{m-1}\left\{\frac{d^{m-1}}{dx^{m-1}}P_l(x)\right\}\,dx$$

$$= (l+m)(l-m+1)\int_{-1}^{1}(1-x^2)^{m-1}\left\{\frac{d^{m-1}}{dx^{m-1}}P_l(x)\right\}^2\,dx$$

$$= (l+m)(l-m+1)\int_{-1}^{1}\{P_l^{m-1}(x)\}^2\,dx.$$

Applying this result again gives

$$\int_{-1}^{1}\{P_l^m(x)\}^2\,dx = (l+m)(l-m+1)(l+m-1)(l-m+2)\int_{-1}^{1}\{P_l^{m-2}(x)\}^2\,dx$$

$$= (l+m)(l+m-1)(l-m+1)(l-m+2)\int_{-1}^{1}\{P_l^{m-2}(x)\}^2\,dx,$$

and repeating the process m times in all we obtain

$$\int_{-1}^{1}\{P_l^m(x)\}^2\,dx$$

$$= (l+m)(l+m-1)\ldots(l+1).(l-m+1)(l-m+2)\ldots l.\int_{-1}^{1}\{P_l^0(x)\}^2\,dx$$

$$= (l+m)(l+m-1)\ldots(l+1).l(l-1)\ldots(l-m+2)(l-m+1).\frac{2}{2l+1}$$

(using theorem 3.5)

$$= \frac{(l+m)!}{(l-m)!}.\frac{2}{2l+1}$$

which is the required result.

Suppose now that $m < 0$, say $m = -n$ with $n > 0$.

Then $\quad \displaystyle\int_{-1}^{1}\{P_l^m(x)\}^2\,dx = \int_{-1}^{1}\{P_l^{-n}(x)\}^2\,dx$

$$= \int_{-1}^{1}\left\{(-1)^n\frac{(l-n)!}{(l+n)!}\right\}^2\{P_l^n(x)\}^2\,dx$$

(by equation (3.37))

$$= \left\{ \frac{(l-n)!}{(l+n)!} \right\}^2 \int_{-1}^{1} \{P_l^n(x)\}^2 \, dx$$

$$= \left\{ \frac{(l-n)!}{(l+n)!} \right\}^2 \frac{(l+n)!}{(l-n)!} \frac{2}{2l+1}$$

(by the result just proved, since $n > 0$)

$$= \frac{(l-n)!}{(l+n)!} \frac{2}{2l+1}$$

$$= \frac{(l+m)!}{(l-m)!} \frac{2}{2l+1}$$

which is the required result.

Theorem 3.12 (Recurrence relations)

(i) $P_l^{m+1}(x) - \dfrac{2mx}{\surd(1-x^2)} P_l^m(x) + \{l(l+1) - m(m-1)\} P_l^{m-1}(x) = 0.$

(ii) $(2l+1)x P_l^m(x) = (l+m) P_{l-1}^m(x) + (l-m+1) P_{l+1}^m(x).$

(iii) $\surd(1-x^2) P_l^m(x) = \dfrac{1}{2l+1} \{P_{l+1}^{m+1}(x) - P_{l-1}^{m+1}(x)\}.$

(iv) $\surd(1-x^2) P_l^m(x) = \dfrac{1}{2l+1} \{(l+m)(l+m-1) P_{l-1}^{m-1}(x)$

$$- (l-m+1)(l-m+2) P_{l+1}^{m-1}(x)\}.$$

Proof

(i) This is the fundamental relationship linking three associated Legendre functions with the same l values and consecutive m values.

Let us denote $(d^m/dx^m) P_l(x)$ by $P_l^{(m)}(x)$ so that definition (3.36) may be written in the form

$$P_l^m(x) = (1-x^2)^{m/2} P_l^{(m)}(x). \tag{3.39}$$

Now, in equation (3.33) we know that we may take $z = P_l(x)$ and hence $z_1 = P_l^{(m)}(x)$, so that we obtain

$$(1-x^2)\frac{d^2}{dx^2} P_l^{(m)}(x) - 2(m+1)x\frac{d}{dx} P_l^{(m)}(x)$$

$$+ \{l(l+1) - m(m+1)\} P_l^{(m)}(x) = 0.$$

Using the definition of $P_l^{(m)}(x)$, this equation becomes

$$(1-x^2) P_l^{(m+2)}(x) - 2(m+1)x P_l^{(m+1)}(x)$$

$$+ \{l(l+1) - m(m+1)\} P_l^{(m)}(x) = 0$$

which, on multiplying throughout by $(1 - x^2)^{m/2}$, gives

$$(1 - x^2)^{(m/2)+1}P_l^{(m+2)}(x) - 2(m + 1)x(1 - x^2)^{m/2}P_l^{(m+1)}(x)$$
$$+ \{l(l + 1) - m(m + 1)\}(1 - x^2)^{m/2}P_l^{(m)}(x) = 0.$$

Hence, using equation (3.39), we have

$$P_l^{m+2}(x) - 2(m + 1)x\frac{1}{\sqrt{(1 - x^2)}} \cdot P_l^{m+1}(x)$$
$$+ \{l(l + 1) - m(m + 1)\}P_l^m(x) = 0$$

which, when m is replaced by $m - 1$, becomes

$$P_l^{m+1}(x) - \frac{2mx}{\sqrt{(1 - x^2)}}P_l^m(x) + \{l(l + 1) - (m - 1)m\}P_l^{m-1}(x) = 0;$$

this is the required result.

(ii) This is the fundamental relationship between associated Legendre functions with equal m values but consecutive l values.

By theorem 3.8 (iii) we have

$$(l + 1)P_{l+1}(x) - (2l + 1)xP_l(x) + lP_{l-1}(x) = 0$$

which, when differentiated m times (making use of Leibniz's theorem for the second term), gives

$$(l + 1)P_{l+1}^{(m)}(x) - (2l + 1)\{xP_l^{(m)}(x) + mP_l^{(m-1)}(x)\}$$
$$+ lP_{l-1}^{(m)}(x) = 0. \quad (3.40)$$

Similarly by theorem 3.8 (iv) we have

$$P_{l+1}^{(1)}(x) - P_{l-1}^{(1)}(x) = (2l + 1)P_l(x)$$

which when differentiated $m - 1$ times gives

$$P_{l+1}^{(m)}(x) - P_{l-1}^{(m)}(x) = (2l + 1)P_l^{(m-1)}(x). \quad (3.41)$$

Using equation (3.41) to substitute for $P_l^{(m-1)}(x)$ in equation (3.40) gives

$$(l + 1)P_{l+1}^{(m)}(x) - (2l + 1)xP_l^{(m)}(x) - m\{P_{l+1}^{(m)}(x) - P_{l-1}^{(m)}(x)\} + lP_{l-1}^{(m)}(x) = 0.$$

Multiplying this equation throughout by $(1 - x^2)^{m/2}$ and using equation (3.39) gives

$$(l+1)P_{l+1}^m(x) - (2l+1)xP_l^m(x) - mP_{l+1}^m(x) + mP_{l-1}^m(x) + lP_{l-1}^m(x) = 0.$$

Collecting like terms gives

$$(l + 1 - m)P_{l+1}^m(x) - (2l + 1)xP_l^m(x) + (l + m)P_{l-1}^m(x) = 0$$

which, when rearranged, is the required result.

(iii) Multiply equation (3.41) throughout by $(1 - x^2)^{m/2}$ and we obtain

$$(1 - x^2)^{m/2}P_{l+1}^{(m)}(x) - (1 - x^2)^{m/2}P_{l-1}^{(m)}(x) = (2l + 1)(1 - x^2)^{m/2}P_l^{(m-1)}(x)$$

which, on using equation (3.39), becomes

$$P_{l+1}^m(x) - P_{l-1}^m(x) = (2l+1)\sqrt{(1-x^2)}P_l^{m-1}(x). \qquad (3.42)$$

Replacing m by $m+1$ gives

$$P_{l+1}^{m+1}(x) - P_{l-1}^{m+1}(x) = (2l+1)\sqrt{(1-x^2)}P_l^m(x)$$

which, when divided by $2l+1$, is just the required result.

(iv) We use (ii) to replace $xP_l^m(x)$ in (i) by

$$\frac{1}{2l+1}\{(l+m)P_{l-1}^m(x) + (l-m+1)P_{l+1}^m(x)\}$$

so that we obtain

$$P_l^{m+1}(x) - \frac{2m}{\sqrt{(1-x^2)}}\frac{1}{2l+1}\{(l+m)P_{l-1}^m(x) + (l-m+1)P_{l+1}^m(x)\}$$
$$+ \{l(l+1) - m(m-1)\}P_l^{m-1}(x) = 0.$$

If we now use equation (3.42) for $P_l^{m-1}(x)$, we obtain

$$P_l^{m+1}(x) - \frac{1}{\sqrt{(1-x^2)}}\frac{2m}{(2l+1)}\{(l+m)P_{l-1}^m(x) + (l-m+1)P_{l+1}^m(x)\}$$

$$+ \{l(l+1) - m(m-1)\}\frac{1}{\sqrt{(1-x^2)}}\frac{1}{2l+1}\{P_{l+1}^m(x) - P_{l-1}^m(x)\}$$

$$= 0.$$

By straightforward algebraic manipulation this reduces to

$$\sqrt{(1-x^2)}P_l^{m+1}(x)$$

$$= \frac{1}{2l+1}\{(l+m)(l+m+1)P_{l-1}^m(x) - (l-m)(l-m+1)P_{l+1}^m(x)\}$$

which, when m is replaced by $m-1$, is just the required result.

3.10 LEGENDRE FUNCTIONS OF THE SECOND KIND

In the first section of this chapter we obtained two independent series solutions $y_1(x)$ and $y_2(x)$ of Legendre's equation. We obtained solutions finite for $-1 \leqslant x \leqslant 1$ (indeed, finite for all finite values of x) by taking l integral; then for l even $y_1(x)$ reduced to a polynomial, while for l odd $y_2(x)$ reduced to a polynomial. In both these cases the other series remains infinite; it may be shown to be convergent for $|x| < 1$ and divergent for $|x| \geqslant 1$. In some physical situations we wish two independent solutions valid for the region $|x| > 1$; one of these is, of course given by $P_l(x)$, while a second solution is given by the following theorem (note that it is still infinite for $x = \pm 1$).

Theorem 3.13

A second independent solution of Legendre's equation is given by

$$Q_l(x) = \tfrac{1}{2}P_l(x) \ln \frac{1+x}{1-x} - \sum_{r=0}^{\left[\frac{l-1}{2}\right]} \frac{(2l-4r-1)}{(2r+1)(l-r)} P_{l-2r-1}(x)$$

$$(l \geqslant 1)$$

$$Q_0(x) = \tfrac{1}{2} \ln \frac{1+x}{1-x}$$

$$\text{where} \quad \left[\frac{l-1}{2}\right] = \begin{cases} \dfrac{l-1}{2} & \text{if } l \text{ is odd} \\[2mm] \dfrac{l-2}{2} & \text{if } l \text{ is even.} \end{cases}$$

$Q_l(x)$ *is called the Legendre function of the second kind.*

Proof†

In Legendre's equation, set $y = zP_l(x)$ so that z is a new dependent variable. We have

$$\frac{dy}{dx} = P_l(x)\frac{dz}{dx} + z\frac{dP_l}{dx},$$

$$\frac{d^2y}{dx^2} = P_l(x)\frac{d^2z}{dx^2} + 2\frac{dz}{dx}\frac{dP_l}{dx} + z\frac{d^2P_l}{dx^2}$$

and hence the equation becomes

$$(1-x^2)P_l(x)\frac{d^2z}{dx^2} + 2(1-x^2)\frac{dz}{dx}\frac{dP_l}{dx} + (1-x^2)z\frac{d^2P_l}{dx^2} - 2xP_l(x)\frac{dz}{dx}$$

$$- 2xz\frac{dP_l}{dx} + l(l+1)zP_l(x) = 0.$$

Collecting terms in z, dz/dx and d^2z/dx^2, we have

$$z\left\{(1-x^2)\frac{d^2P_l}{dx^2} - 2x\frac{dP_l}{dx} + l(l+1)P_l(x)\right\}$$

$$+ \frac{dz}{dx}\left\{2(1-x^2)\frac{dP_l}{dx} - 2xP_l(x)\right\} + (1-x^2)P_l(x)\frac{d^2z}{dx^2} = 0,$$

which, on using the fact that P_l satisfies Legendre's equation, becomes

$$(1-x^2)P_l(x)\frac{d^2z}{dx^2} + \frac{dz}{dx}\left\{2(1-x^2)\frac{dP_l}{dx} - 2xP_l(x)\right\} = 0.$$

---

† The proof of this theorem may be omitted on a first reading. The proof ends on page 77.

Hence
$$\frac{d^2z/dx^2}{dz/dx} + 2\frac{dP_l/dx}{P_l(x)} - \frac{2x}{1-x^2} = 0,$$

and this is equivalent to

$$\frac{d}{dx}\ln\left(\frac{dz}{dx}\right) + 2\frac{d}{dx}\ln P_l(x) + \frac{d}{dx}\ln(1-x^2) = 0,$$

which when integrated gives

$$\ln\frac{dz}{dx} + \ln\{P_l(x)\}^2 + \ln(1-x^2) = \text{constant}.$$

Therefore $\dfrac{dz}{dx}\{P_l(x)\}^2(1-x^2) = \text{constant} = A$, say,

so that
$$\frac{dz}{dx} = \frac{A}{\{P_l(x)\}^2(1-x^2)}$$

and hence
$$z = A\int\frac{dx}{\{P_l(x)\}^2(1-x^2)}.$$

This means that we have a solution of Legendre's equation given by

$$Q_l(x) = P_l(x)\int\frac{dx}{\{P_l(x)\}^2(1-x^2)}. \tag{3.43}$$

We must now show that this is of the form stated in the theorem. We first dispose of the case $l = 0$:

$$Q_0(x) = P_0(x)\int\frac{dx}{\{P_0(x)\}^2(1-x^2)}$$

$$= \int\frac{dx}{1-x^2}$$

$$= \int\frac{1}{2}\left(\frac{1}{1-x} + \frac{1}{1+x}\right)dx$$

$$= \tfrac{1}{2}\{-\ln(1-x) + \ln(1+x)\}$$

$$= \tfrac{1}{2}\ln\frac{1+x}{1-x}.$$

If now $l \neq 0$, we remember that $P_l(x)$ is a polynomial of degree l, so that it may be written in the form

$$P_l(x) = k_l(x-\alpha_1)(x-\alpha_2)\ldots(x-\alpha_l).$$

Thus

$$\frac{1}{(1-x^2)\{P_l(x)\}^2} = \frac{1}{(1-x)(1+x)k_l^2(x-\alpha_1)^2(x-\alpha_2)^2\ldots(x-\alpha_l)^2}$$

$$= \frac{a_0}{1 - x} + \frac{b_0}{1 + x} + \sum_{r=1}^{l} \left\{ \frac{c_r}{(x - \alpha_r)} + \frac{d_r}{(x - \alpha_r)^2} \right\}$$
(3.44)

on splitting into partial fractions.

We may determine a_0, b_0 and c_r fairly simply. Multiplying both sides of equation (3.44) by $(1 - x^2)\{P_l(x)\}^2$ gives

$$1 = a_0(1 + x)\{P_l(x)\}^2 + b_0(1 - x)\{P_l(x)\}^2$$

$$+ (1 - x^2)\{P_l(x)\}^2 \left\{ \sum_{r=1}^{l} \frac{c_r}{(x - \alpha_r)} + \frac{d_r}{(x - \alpha_r)^2} \right\}.$$

Setting $x = 1$ in this equation and remembering that $P_l(1) = 1$ gives $a_0 = \frac{1}{2}$, while setting $x = -1$ and remembering that $P_l(-1) = (-1)^l$ gives $b_0 = \frac{1}{2}$.

We now show that

$$c_i = \left[\frac{d}{dx} \left\{ (x - \alpha_i)^2 \frac{1}{(1 - x^2)\{P_l(x)\}^2} \right\} \right]_{x=\alpha_i}.$$

To prove this we note that

$$\frac{d}{dx} \{(x - \alpha_i)^2 f(x)\} = 2(x - \alpha_i)f(x) + (x - \alpha_i)^2 \frac{df}{dx}$$

$$= 0 \text{ when } x = \alpha_i, \text{ provided that}$$
$$f(x) \text{ is finite at } x = \alpha_i.$$

The only terms on the right-hand side of equation (3.44) which are not finite at $x = \alpha_i$ are $c_i/(x - \alpha_i)$ and $d_i/\{(x - \alpha_i)^2\}$. Hence we have

$$\left[\frac{d}{dx}(x - \alpha_i)^2 \frac{1}{(1 - x^2)\{P_l(x)\}^2} \right]_{x=\alpha_i}$$

$$- \left[\frac{d}{dx}(x - \alpha_i)^2 \left\{ \frac{c_i}{(x - \alpha_i)} + \frac{d_i}{(x - \alpha_i)^2} \right\} \right]_{x=\alpha_i}$$

$$= \left[\frac{d}{dx} \{c_i(x - \alpha_i) + d_i\} \right]_{x=\alpha_i}$$

$$= [c_i]_{x=\alpha_1}$$

$$= c_i.$$

Thus, if we write $P_l(x) = (x - \alpha_i)L(x)$ we have

$$c_i = \left[\frac{d}{dx} \frac{1}{(1 - x^2)\{L(x)\}^2} \right]_{x=\alpha_i}$$

$$= \left[\frac{2x}{(1 - x^2)\{L(x)\}^2} - \frac{2L'(x)}{(1 - x^2)\{L(x)\}^3} \right]_{x=\alpha_i}$$

$$= \left[\frac{2xL(x) - 2(1 - x^2)L'(x)}{(1 - x^2)\{L(x)\}^3} \right]_{x=\alpha_i}$$

$$= \frac{2\{\alpha_i L(\alpha_i) - (1 - \alpha_i^2)L'(\alpha_i)\}}{(1 - \alpha_i^2)^2\{L(\alpha_i)\}^3}. \tag{3.45}$$

But we know by setting $P_l(x) = (x - \alpha_i)L(x)$ in Legendre's equation that

$$(1 - x^2)\frac{d^2}{dx^2}\{(x - \alpha_i)L(x)\} - 2x\frac{d}{dx}\{(x - \alpha_i)L(x)\}$$
$$+ l(l + 1)(x - \alpha_i)L(x) = 0,$$

which, on performing the differentiations, becomes

$$(1 - x^2)\{(x - \alpha_i)L''(x) + 2L'(x)\} - 2x\{(x - \alpha_i)L'(x) + L(x)\}$$
$$+ l(l + 1)(x - \alpha_i)L(x) = 0,$$

and setting $x = \alpha_i$ in this equation gives

$$(1 - \alpha_i^2)2L'(\alpha_i) - 2\alpha_i L(\alpha_i) = 0$$

so that by substituting back into equation (3.45) we obtain $c_i = 0$.

Thus from equation (3.44) we have

$$\frac{1}{(1 - x^2)\{P_l(x)\}^2} = \frac{1}{2(1 - x)} + \frac{1}{2(1 + x)} + \sum_{r=1}^{l} \frac{d_r}{(x - \alpha_r)^2}$$

where the d_r are constants whose values will not concern us.

Thus

$$\int \frac{1}{(1 - x^2)\{P_l(x)\}^2}dx = -\tfrac{1}{2}\ln(1 - x) + \tfrac{1}{2}\ln(1 + x) - \sum_{r=1}^{l} \frac{d_r}{(x - \alpha_r)}$$

$$= \tfrac{1}{2}\ln\frac{1 + x}{1 - x} - \sum_{r=1}^{l} \frac{d_r}{(x - \alpha_r)},$$

so that from equation (3.43) we have

$$Q_l(x) = \tfrac{1}{2}P_l(x)\ln\frac{1 + x}{1 - x} - \sum_{r=1}^{l} d_r \frac{P_l(x)}{x - \alpha_r}.$$

But $(x - \alpha_r)$ is, for all α_r, a factor of $P_l(x)$, so that $P_l(x)/(x - \alpha_r)$ is a

polynomial in x of degree $l - 1$. Thus $\sum_{r=1}^{l} d_r \{P_l(x)\}/(x - \alpha_r)$ is a polynomial of degree $l - 1$; let us denote it by $W_{l-1}(x)$. Then we have

$$Q_l(x) = \tfrac{1}{2}P_l(x) \ln \frac{1+x}{1-x} - W_{l-1}(x). \qquad (3.46)$$

To determine $W_{l-1}(x)$ we remember that $Q_l(x)$ is a solution of Legendre's equation so that

$$\frac{d}{dx}\left\{(1 - x^2)\frac{dQ_l}{dx}\right\} + l(l + 1)Q_l = 0,$$

which, on use of equation (3.46), gives

$$\frac{1}{2}\frac{d}{dx}\left\{(1 - x^2)\frac{d}{dx}P_l(x) \ln \frac{1+x}{1-x}\right\} + l(l + 1).\tfrac{1}{2}P_l(x) \ln \frac{1+x}{1-x}$$

$$- \frac{d}{dx}\left\{(1 - x^2)\frac{dW_{l-1}}{dx}\right\} - l(l + 1)W_{l-1} = 0. \quad (3.47)$$

But

$$\frac{d}{dx}P_l(x) \ln \frac{1+x}{1-x} = P_l'(x) \ln \frac{1+x}{1-x} + P_l(x)\left\{\frac{1}{1+x} + \frac{1}{1-x}\right\}$$

$$= P_l'(x) \ln \frac{1+x}{1-x} + P_l(x)\frac{2}{1-x^2}$$

so that

$$\frac{d}{dx}\left\{(1 - x^2)\frac{d}{dx}P_l(x) \ln \frac{1+x}{1-x}\right\}$$

$$= \frac{d}{dx}\left\{(1 - x^2)P_l'(x) \ln \frac{1+x}{1-x} + 2P_l(x)\right\}$$

$$= \ln \frac{1+x}{1-x}\frac{d}{dx}\{(1 - x^2)P_l'(x)\} + (1 - x^2)P_l'(x)\frac{2}{1-x^2} + 2P_l'(x).$$

Hence equation (3.47) becomes

$$\tfrac{1}{2}\ln \frac{1+x}{1-x}\left[\frac{d}{dx}\{(1 - x^2)P_l'(x)\} + l(l + 1)P_l(x)\right] + 2P_l'(x)$$

$$- \frac{d}{dx}\left\{(1 - x^2)\frac{dW_{l-1}}{dx}\right\} - l(l + 1)W_{l-1} = 0$$

which, on remembering that $P_l(x)$ satisfies Legendre's equation, reduces to

$$\frac{d}{dx}\left\{(1 - x^2)\frac{dW_{l-1}}{dx}\right\} + l(l + 1)W_{l-1} = 2\frac{dP_l}{dx}. \qquad (3.48)$$

Now, by theorem 3.8 (i) we have

$$\frac{dP_l}{dx} = (2l - 1)P_{l-1}(x) + (2l - 5)P_{l-3}(x) + \ldots$$

$$+(2l - 4r - 1)P_{l-2r-1}(x) + \ldots$$

$$= \sum_{r=0}^{[\frac{1}{2}(l-1)]}(2l - 4r - 1)P_{l-2r-1}(x) \tag{3.49}$$

so that if we assume for $W_{l-1}(x)$ (which we know to be a polynomial of degree $l - 1$) an expression of the form

$$W_{l-1}(x) = a_0 P_{l-1}(x) + a_1 P_{l-3}(x) + \ldots$$

$$= \sum_{r=0}^{[\frac{1}{2}(l-1)]} a_r P_{l-2r-1}(x) \tag{3.50}$$

and substitute equations (3.49) and (3.50) into equation (3.48), we shall obtain

$$\sum_{r=0}^{[\frac{1}{2}(l-1)]} a_r \frac{d}{dx}\left\{(1 - x^2)P'_{l-2r-1}(x)\right\} + l(l + 1) \sum_{r=0}^{[\frac{1}{2}(l-1)]} a_r P_{l-2r-1}(x)$$

$$= 2\sum_{r=0}^{[\frac{1}{2}(l-1)]}(2l - 4r - 1)P_{l-2r-1}(x). \tag{3.51}$$

But by Legendre's equation we have

$$\frac{d}{dx}\left\{(1 - x^2)P'_{l-2r-1}(x)\right\} + (l - 2r - 1)(l - 2r)P_{l-2r-1}(x) = 0,$$

so that equation (3.51) becomes

$$\sum_{r=0}^{[\frac{1}{2}(l-1)]} a_r\{-(l - 2r - 1)(l - 2r) + l(l + 1)\}P_{l-2r-1}(x)$$

$$= \sum_{r=0}^{[\frac{1}{2}(l-1)]}2(2l - 4r - 1)P_{l-2r-1}(x).$$

The coefficient of each polynomial must be the same on both sides, so that we obtain

$$\{-(l - 2r - 1)(l - 2r) + l(l + 1)\}a_r = 2(2l - 4r - 1). \tag{3.52}$$

But $-(l - 2r - 1)(l - 2r) + l(l + 1)$

$$
\begin{aligned}
&= -(l - 2r)^2 + (l - 2r) + l(l + 1) \\
&= -l^2 + 4rl - 4r^2 + l - 2r + l^2 + l \\
&= 4r(l - r) + 2(l - r) \\
&= 2(l - r)(2r + 1).
\end{aligned}
$$

Hence equation (3.52) reduces to

$$2(l - r)(2r + 1)a_r = 2(2l - 4r - 1)$$

which gives

$$a_r = \frac{2l - 4r - 1}{(l - r)(2r + 1)} \tag{3.53}$$

and now, by combining equations (3.53), (3.50) and (3.46), we obtain immediately the result of the theorem.

That the solution of Legendre's equation $Q_l(x)$ which we have obtained is independent of $P_l(x)$ is readily seen: because of the factor $\ln \frac{1 + x}{1 - x}$, $Q_l(x)$ is infinite at both $x = \pm 1$, whereas we know that $P_l(x)$ is finite for these values of x.

We may use this theorem to write down explicitly the first few Legendre functions of the second kind:

$$Q_0(x) = \tfrac{1}{2} \ln \frac{1 + x}{1 - x}$$

$$Q_1(x) = \frac{x}{2} \ln \frac{1 + x}{1 - x} - 1$$

$$Q_2(x) = \tfrac{1}{4}(3x^2 - 1) \ln \frac{1 + x}{1 - x} - \frac{3}{2}x$$

$$Q_3(x) = \tfrac{1}{4}(5x^3 - 3x) \ln \frac{1 + x}{1 - x} - \frac{5}{2}x^2 + \frac{2}{3}.$$

We now state without proof several theorems concerning Legendre functions of the second kind.

Theorem 3.14

$$\frac{1}{x - y} = \sum_{l=0}^{\infty} (2l + 1)P_l(x)Q_l(y)$$

if $x > 1$ and $|y| < 1$.

Theorem 3.15 (Neumann's Formula)

$$Q_l(x) = \frac{1}{2} \int_{-1}^{1} \frac{P_l(y)}{x - y}\, dy.$$

Theorem 3.16

The results contained in theorem 3.8 (ii — ix) remain true when $P_l(x)$ is replaced by $Q_l(x)$.

Theorem 3.17

The associated Legendre functions of the second kind defined by

$$Q_l^m(x) = (1 - x^2)^{m/2} \frac{d^m}{dx^m} Q_l(x)$$

satisfy Legendre's associated equation.

3.11 SPHERICAL HARMONICS

In many branches of physics and engineering there is interest in the equation

$$\frac{1}{\sin\theta}\left(\frac{\partial}{\partial\theta}\sin\theta\frac{\partial\Psi}{\partial\theta}\right) + \frac{1}{\sin^2\theta}\frac{\partial^2\Psi}{\partial\phi^2} + l(l+1)\Psi = 0, \qquad (3.54)$$

solutions of which we shall call spherical harmonics. (This equation usually arises in the solution of a differential equation such as Laplace's or Schrödinger's in terms of spherical polar co-ordinates r, θ, ϕ, so that the range of the variables involved is $0 \leqslant \theta \leqslant \pi$, $0 \leqslant \phi \leqslant 2\pi$ and we often require a solution which is finite and continuous for these values—the continuity implying that the value of Ψ at $\phi = 2\pi$ is the same as at $\phi = 0$.)

One method of finding a solution of equation (3.54) is the so-called method of separation of variables—we look for a solution of the form $\Psi(\theta, \phi) = \Theta(\theta)\Phi(\phi)$. Inserting this expression into the given equation gives

$$\frac{\Phi(\phi)}{\sin\theta}\left\{\frac{d}{d\theta}\left(\sin\theta\frac{d\Theta}{d\theta}\right)\right\} + \frac{\Theta(\theta)}{\sin^2\theta}\frac{d^2\Phi}{d\phi^2} + l(l+1)\Theta(\theta)\Phi(\phi) = 0$$

or, dividing throughout by $\Theta(\theta)\Phi(\phi)$ and multiplying by $\sin^2\theta$,

$$\frac{\sin\theta}{\Theta}\frac{d}{d\theta}\left(\sin\theta\frac{d\Theta}{d\theta}\right) + \frac{1}{\Phi}\frac{d^2\Phi}{d\phi^2} + l(l+1)\sin^2\theta = 0$$

which, when rearranged, becomes

$$\frac{\sin\theta}{\Theta}\frac{d}{d\theta}\left(\sin\theta\frac{d\Theta}{d\theta}\right) + l(l+1)\sin^2\theta = -\frac{1}{\Phi}\frac{d^2\Phi}{d\phi^2}.$$

Now the left-hand side of this equation is a function only of the variable θ, while the right-hand side is a function only of the variable ϕ. Since these two variables are independent, it follows that left-hand side and right-hand side must separately be a constant which we shall denote by m^2.

Thus we have

$$\frac{\sin\theta}{\Theta}\frac{d}{d\theta}\left(\sin\theta\frac{d\Theta}{d\theta}\right) + l(l+1)\sin^2\theta = m^2 \tag{3.55}$$

and

$$-\frac{1}{\Phi}\frac{d^2\Phi}{d\phi^2} = m^2. \tag{3.56}$$

Equation (3.56) is just

$$\frac{d^2\Phi}{d\phi^2} = -m^2\Phi \tag{3.57}$$

while equation (3.55) simplifies to

$$\frac{1}{\sin\theta}\frac{d}{d\theta}\left(\sin\theta\frac{d\Theta}{d\theta}\right) + \left\{l(l+1) - \frac{m^2}{\sin^2\theta}\right\}\Theta = 0. \tag{3.58}$$

Equation (3.57) has the general solution

$$\Phi = Ae^{im\phi} + Be^{-im\phi}$$

where, if the solution is to be continuous, we require $\Phi(2\pi) = \Phi(0)$, so that m must be an integer (which we may take conventionally to be positive).

In equation (3.58) we make the change of variable $\cos\theta = x$. Then we have $-\sin\theta\, d\theta = dx$

and hence

$$\frac{1}{\sin\theta}\frac{d}{d\theta} = -\frac{d}{dx}$$

and

$$\sin\theta\frac{d}{d\theta} = \sin^2\theta\,.\,-\frac{d}{dx} = -(1-x^2)\frac{d}{dx}.$$

Accordingly, equation (3.58) becomes

$$\frac{d}{dx}\left\{(1-x^2)\frac{d\Theta}{dx}\right\} + \left\{l(l+1) - \frac{m^2}{1-x^2}\right\}\Theta = 0$$

which we recognise as Legendre's associated equation; it will have a solution finite at $\theta = 0$ and π ($x = +1$ and -1) only if l is integral. In that case the finite solution is given by $\Theta = P_l^m(x) = P_l^m(\cos\theta)$.

Thus the general solution which is finite at both $\theta = 0$ and π and is continuous must be

$$\Psi(\theta, \phi) = (Ae^{im\phi} + Be^{-im\phi})P_l^m(\cos\theta)$$

which, because of equation (3.37), we may write in the form

$$\Psi = A_1 e^{im\phi}P_l^m(\cos\theta) + A_2 e^{-im\phi}P_l^{-m}(\cos\theta)$$

where
$$A_1 = A$$
and
$$A_2 = (-1)^m \frac{(l+m)!}{(l-m)!} B.$$

If now we denote
$$y_l^m(\theta, \phi) \equiv e^{im\phi} P_l^m(\cos \theta) \tag{3.59}$$
we may write the general solution in the form
$$\Psi = A_1 y_l^m(\theta, \phi) + A_2 y_l^{-m}(\theta, \phi).$$

Of course, this is a solution of the original equation (3.54) for any value of m, and since (3.54) is homogeneous we have the solution
$$\Psi = \sum_{m=0}^{l} \{A_1^{(m)} y_l^m(\theta, \phi) + A_2^{(m)} y_l^{-m}(\theta, \phi)\}.$$

For many purposes it is more useful to consider a multiple of y_l^m (which we shall denote by Y_l^m) as the basic solution; a multiple chosen so that the solutions are orthogonal and normalised in the sense that
$$\int_0^{2\pi} d\phi \int_0^\pi d\theta \sin\theta \{Y_l^m(\theta, \phi)\}^* Y_{l'}^{m'}(\theta, \phi) = \delta_{ll'} \delta_{mm'} \tag{3.60}$$
(where the * denotes complex conjugation).

We may readily prove that this is accomplished by taking
$$Y_l^m(\theta, \phi) = (-1)^m \frac{1}{\sqrt{(2\pi)}} \sqrt{\left\{\frac{(2l+1)(l-m)!}{2(l+m)!}\right\}} y_l^m(\theta, \phi)$$
$$= (-1)^m \frac{1}{\sqrt{(2\pi)}} \sqrt{\left\{\frac{(2l+1)(l-m)!}{2(l+m)!}\right\}} e^{im\phi} P_l^m(\cos \theta). \tag{3.61}$$

For then we have
$$\int_0^{2\pi} d\phi \int_0^\pi d\theta \sin\theta \{Y_l^m(\theta, \phi)\}^* Y_{l'}^{m'}(\theta, \phi)$$
$$= (-1)^{m+m'} \frac{1}{2\pi} \sqrt{\left\{\frac{(2l+1)(2l'+1)(l-m)!\,(l'-m')!}{4(l+m)!\,(l'+m')!}\right\}}$$
$$\int_0^{2\pi} e^{i(m'-m)\phi} d\phi \int_0^\pi P_l^m(\cos\theta) P_{l'}^{m'}(\cos\theta) \sin\theta \, d\theta$$

(using the fact that $P_l^m(x)$ is real),
$$= (-1)^{m+m'} \frac{1}{2\pi} \sqrt{\left\{\frac{(2l+1)(2l'+1)(l-m)!\,(l'-m')!}{4(l+m)!\,(l'+m')!}\right\}} 2\pi \, \delta_{m'm}$$
$$\int_{-1}^1 P_l^m(x) P_{l'}^{m'}(x) \, dx$$

(since the first integral vanishes unless $m' = m$, in which case it is equal to 2π; and in the second integral we have made the substitution $x = \cos\theta$)

$$= (-1)^{2m} \sqrt{\left\{ \frac{(2l+1)(2l'+1)(l-m)!\,(l'-m)!}{4(l+m)!\,(l'+m)!} \right\}} \delta_{m'm}$$

$$\int_{-1}^{1} P_l^m(x) P_{l'}^m(x)\,dx$$

$$= \sqrt{\left\{ \frac{(2l+1)(2l'+1)(l-m)!\,(l'-m)!}{4(l+m)!\,(l'+m)!} \right\}} \delta_{m'm} \frac{2(l+m)!}{(2l+1)(l-m)!} \delta_{ll'}$$

(by theorem 3.11)

$$= \delta_{ll'}\delta_{mm'}.$$

The factor $(-1)^m$ in definition (3.61) of $Y_l^m(\theta, \phi)$, which we shall take as the basic spherical harmonic, was not necessary for the orthonormality property; however, its introduction is conventional (although the reader is warned that in the topic of spherical harmonics different authors may employ different conventions).

Theorem 3.18

$$\{Y_l^m(\theta, \phi)\}^* = (-1)^m Y_l^{-m}(\theta, \phi).$$

PROOF

$$\{Y_l^m(\theta, \phi)\}^*$$

$$= (-1)^m \frac{1}{\sqrt{(2\pi)}} \sqrt{\left\{ \frac{2l+1}{2} \frac{(l-m)!}{(l+m)!} \right\}} e^{-im\phi} P_l^m(\cos\theta)$$

(by equation (3.61))

$$= (-1)^m \frac{1}{\sqrt{(2\pi)}} \sqrt{\left\{ \frac{2l+1}{2} \frac{(l-m)!}{(l+m)!} \right\}} e^{-im\phi} (-1)^{-m}$$

$$\frac{(l+m)!}{(l-m)!} P_l^{-m}(\cos\theta)$$

(by equation (3.37))

$$= (-1)^m . (-1)^{-m} \frac{1}{\sqrt{(2\pi)}} \sqrt{\left\{ \frac{2l+1}{2} \frac{(l+m)!}{(l-m)!} \right\}} e^{-im\phi} P_l^{-m}(\cos\theta)$$

$$= (-1)^m Y_l^{-m}(\theta, \phi)$$

(by equation (3.61)).

We may use the definitions of $Y_l^m(\theta, \phi)$ and $P_l^m(\cos \theta)$ to obtain the following explicit expressions for the first few spherical harmonics:

$$Y_0^0 = \sqrt{\left(\frac{1}{4\pi}\right)};$$

$$Y_1^{\pm 1} = \pm \sqrt{\left(\frac{3}{8\pi}\right)} \sin \theta \, e^{\pm i\phi}, \quad Y_1^0 = \sqrt{\left(\frac{3}{4\pi}\right)} \cos \theta;$$

$$Y_2^{\pm 2} = \sqrt{\left(\frac{15}{32\pi}\right)} \sin^2 \theta \, e^{\pm 2i\phi}, \quad Y_2^{\pm 1} = -\sqrt{\left(\frac{15}{8\pi}\right)} \sin \theta \cos \theta \, e^{\pm i\phi},$$

$$Y_2^0 = \sqrt{\left(\frac{5}{16\pi}\right)}(3 \cos^2 \theta - 1). \tag{3.62}$$

3.12 GRAPHS OF THE LEGENDRE FUNCTIONS

In this section we give graphs of some of the functions encountered in this chapter.

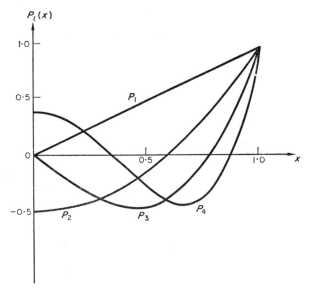

FIG. 3.2 $P_l(x)$, $0 \leqslant x \leqslant 1$, $l = 1, 2, 3, 4$

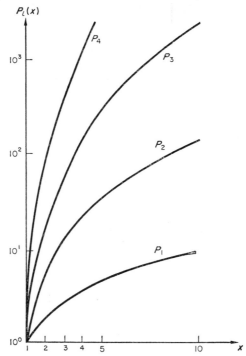

FIG. 3.3 $P_l(x)$, $x \geqslant 1$, $l = 1, 2, 3, 4$ (Note that the scale on the vertical axis is logarithmic.)

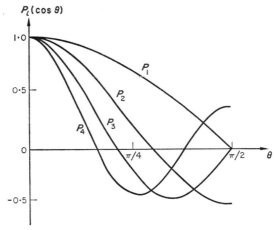

FIG. 3.4 $P_l(\cos\theta)$, $0 \leqslant \theta \leqslant \pi/2$, $l = 1, 2, 3, 4$

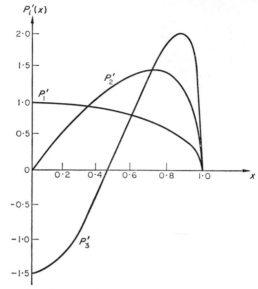

FIG. 3.5 $P_l'(x)$, $0 \leqslant x \leqslant 1$, $l = 1, 2, 3$

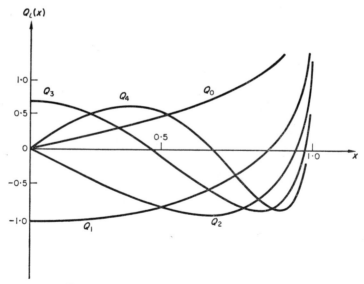

FIG. 3.6 $Q_l(x)$, $0 \leqslant x \leqslant 1$, $l = 0, 1, 2, 3, 4$

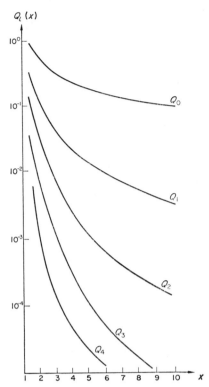

FIG. 3.7 $Q_l(x)$, $x \geqslant 1$, $l = 0, 1, 2, 3, 4$ (Note that the scale
on the vertical axis is logarithmic.)

3.13   EXAMPLES

Example 1

Show that $\displaystyle\int_{-1}^{1} x^2 P_{l+1}(x) P_{l-1}(x) \, dx = \frac{2l(l+1)}{(4l^2 - 1)(2l + 3)}.$

Deduce the value of $\displaystyle\int_{0}^{1} x^2 P_{l+1}(x) P_{l-1}(x) \, dx.$

We use theorem 3.8(ii) to dispose of the x^2 appearing in the integrand,
and we may then use the orthonormality property of theorem 3.5.
Thus,

$$\int_{-1}^{1} x^2 P_{l+1}(x) P_{l-1}(x) \, dx = \int_{-1}^{1} \{x P_{l+1}(x)\}\{x P_{l-1}(x)\} \, dx$$

$$= \int_{-1}^{1} \left\{ \frac{l+2}{2l+3} P_{l+2}(x) + \frac{l+1}{2l+3} P_l(x) \right\}$$

$$\left\{ \frac{l}{2l-1} P_l(x) + \frac{l-1}{2l-1} P_{l-2}(x) \right\} dx$$

$$= \int_{-1}^{1} \frac{l+1}{2l+3} P_l(x) \cdot \frac{l}{2l-1} P_l(x) \, dx$$

(the other terms vanishing by theorem 3.5, since they are of the form $\int_{-1}^{1} P_l(x) P_m(x) \, dx$ with $l \neq m$)

$$= \frac{l(l+1)}{(2l+3)(2l-1)} \int_{-1}^{1} \{P_l(x)\}^2 \, dx$$

$$= \frac{l(l+1)}{(2l+3)(2l-1)} \frac{2}{2l+1}$$

(by theorem 3.5)

$$= \frac{2l(l+1)}{(4l^2-1)(2l+3)}.$$

We know that $P_l(x)$ is a polynomial of degree l, so that the above integrand is a polynomial of degree $2 + (l+1) + (l-1) = 2(l+1)$, i.e., of even degree. Thus the integrand is even, so that

$$\int_{-1}^{1} x^2 P_{l+1}(x) P_{l-1}(x) \, dx = 2 \int_{0}^{1} x^2 P_{l+1}(x) P_{l-1}(x) \, dx$$

and hence

$$\int_{0}^{1} x^2 P_{l-1}(x) P_{l-1}(x) \, dx = \frac{l(l+1)}{(4l^2-1)(2l+3)}.$$

Example 2

Evaluate $\int_{0}^{1} P_l(x) \, dx$ *when l is odd.*

By theorem 3.8 (iv) we have

$$\int_{0}^{1} P_l(x) \, dx = \frac{1}{2l+1} \int_{0}^{1} \{P'_{l+1}(x) - P'_{l-1}(x)\} \, dx$$

$$= \frac{1}{2l+1} \left[P_{l+1}(x) - P_{l-1}(x) \right]_{0}^{1}$$

$$= \frac{1}{2l+1} \{P_{l+1}(1) - P_{l-1}(1) - P_{l+1}(0) + P_{l-1}(0)\}$$

$$= \frac{1}{2l+1} \left\{ 1 - 1 - \frac{(-1)^{(l+1)/2}}{2^{l+1}} \frac{(l+1)!}{[\{(l+1)/2\}!]^2} \right.$$

$$\left. + \frac{(-1)^{(l-1)/2}}{2^{l-1}} \frac{(l-1)!}{[\{(l-1)/2\}!]^2} \right\}$$

(by theorem 3.4(i) and (v), remembering that $l+1$ and $l-1$
are both even)

$$= \frac{1}{2l+1} \frac{(-1)^{(l-1)/2}}{2^{l-1}} \frac{(l-1)!}{[\{(l-1)/2\}!]^2} \left[1 - \frac{(-1)(l+1)l}{2^2\{(l+1)/2\}^2} \right]$$

$$= \frac{1}{2l+1} \frac{(-1)^{(l-1)/2}}{2^{l-1}} \frac{(l-1)!}{[\{(l-1)/2\}!]^2} \left[1 + \frac{l}{l+1} \right]$$

$$= \frac{(-1)^{(l-1)/2}(l-1)!}{2^l (\frac{1}{2}l + \frac{1}{2})(\frac{1}{2}l - \frac{1}{2})! (\frac{1}{2}l - \frac{1}{2})!}$$

$$= \frac{(-1)^{(l-1)/2}(l-1)!}{2^l (\frac{1}{2}l + \frac{1}{2})! (\frac{1}{2}l - \frac{1}{2})!}.$$

Example 3

If $f(x) = |x|$ *for* $-1 \leqslant x \leqslant 1$, *expand* $f(x)$ *in the form* $\sum\limits_{r=0}^{\infty} c_r P_r(x)$.

By theorem 3.7 we know that such an expansion is possible and that
c_r is given by

$$c_r = (r + \tfrac{1}{2}) \int_{-1}^{1} |x| P_r(x) \, dx.$$

Now, $|x|$ is an even function and $P_r(x)$ is even if r is even and odd if r
is odd. Hence if r is odd $|x| P_r(x)$ is odd, so that $\int_{-1}^{1} |x| P_r(x) \, dx = 0$
and hence $c_r = 0$. On the other hand, if r is even, $|x| P_r(x)$ is even, and
hence

$$\int_{-1}^{1} |x| P_r(x) \, dx = 2 \int_{0}^{1} |x| P_r(x) \, dx$$

$$= 2 \int_{0}^{1} x P_r(x) \, dx$$

so that now

$$c_r = (2r + 1) \int_{0}^{1} x P_r(x) \, dx. \tag{3.63}$$

To evaluate this integral we use theorem 3.8(ii):

$$c_r = (2r+1) \int_0^1 \left\{ \frac{r+1}{2r+1} P_{r+1}(x) + \frac{r}{2r+1} P_{r-1}(x) \right\} dx$$

$$= \int_0^1 \{(r+1)P_{r+1}(x) + rP_{r-1}(x)\} dx.$$

Now, r is even, so that both $r+1$ and $r-1$ are odd, and we may use the result of example 2 to obtain

$$c_r = (r+1)\frac{(-1)^{r/2}r!}{2^{r+1}(\frac{1}{2}r+1)!(\frac{1}{2}r)!} + r\frac{(-1)^{(r/2)-1}(r-2)!}{2^{r-1}(\frac{1}{2}r)!(\frac{1}{2}r-1)!}$$

$$= \frac{(-1)^{r/2}(r-2)!}{2^{r-1}(\frac{1}{2}r)!(\frac{1}{2}r-1)!} \left\{ \frac{(r+1)r(r-1)}{2^2(\frac{1}{2}r+1)\frac{1}{2}r} - r \right\}$$

$$= \frac{(-1)^{r/2}(r-2)!}{2^{r-1}(\frac{1}{2}r)!(\frac{1}{2}r-1)!} \left\{ \frac{(r+1)(r-1)}{r+2} - r \right\}$$

$$= \frac{(-1)^{r/2}(r-2)!}{2^{r-1}(\frac{1}{2}r)!(\frac{1}{2}r-1)!} \left\{ \frac{r^2-1-r^2-2r}{2(\frac{1}{2}r+1)} \right\}$$

$$= \frac{(-1)^{(r/2)+1}(2r+1)(r-2)!}{2^r(\frac{1}{2}r+1)!(\frac{1}{2}r-1)!}. \tag{3.64}$$

Thus we have

$$f(x) = \sum_{n=0}^{\infty} \frac{(-1)^{n+1}(4n+1)(2n-2)!}{2^{2n}(n+1)!(n-1)!} P_{2n}(x).$$

Example 4

If $x > 1$, show that $P_l(x) < P_{l+1}(x)$.

We prove this by the method of induction: assume first that $P_{l-1}(x) < P_l(x)$ and use this to prove that $P_l(x) < P_{l+1}(x)$. Then since the result is trivially true for $l = 0$ ($P_0(x) = 1$ and $P_1(x) = x$) it will be true for all l.

We may assume throughout this proof that $P_l(x) > 0$. For, from Rodrigues' formula (theorem 3.2), it is readily seen that if $x > 1$ (which it is in this example) then $P_l(x) > 0$ for all values of l.

Now, by theorem 3.8(iii) we have

$$(l+1)\frac{P_{l+1}}{P_l} - (2l+1)x + \frac{lP_{l-1}}{P_l} = 0.$$

Thus

$$\frac{P_{l+1}}{P_l} = \frac{(2l+1)x}{l+1} - \frac{l}{l+1}\frac{P_{l-1}}{P_l}$$

$$> \frac{(2l+1)}{l+1} - \frac{l}{l+1}$$

(since $x > 1$ and we have
assumed that $P_{l-1}/P_l < 1$)

$$= \frac{l+1}{l+1}$$

$$= 1.$$

Since P_l is positive for all l, this implies that $P_{l+1} > P_l$ and hence the method of induction guarantees the result to be true for all values of l.

Example 5

Prove that $l\{Q_l(x)P_{l-1}(x) - Q_{l-1}(x)P_l(x)\}$
$$= (l-1)\{Q_{l-1}(x)P_{l-2}(x) - Q_{l-2}(x)P_{l-1}(x)\}$$
and deduce that $l\{Q_l(x)P_{l-1}(x) - Q_{l-1}(x)P_l(x)\} = -1.$

From theorem 3.8(iii) with l replaced by $l-1$ we have

$$lP_l(x) - (2l-1)xP_{l-1}(x) + (l-1)P_{l-2}(x) = 0 \qquad (3.65)$$

and by theorem 3.16 we have also

$$lQ_l(x) - (2l-1)xQ_{l-1}(x) + (l-1)Q_{l-2}(x) = 0. \qquad (3.66)$$

Multiplying equation (3.65) by $Q_{l-1}(x)$, equation (3.66) by $P_{l-1}(x)$ and subtracting gives

$$l\{P_l(x)Q_{l-1}(x) - Q_l(x)P_{l-1}(x)\}$$
$$+ (l-1)\{P_{l-2}(x)Q_{l-1}(x) - Q_{l-2}(x)P_{l-1}(x)\} = 0,$$

which is equivalent to

$$l\{Q_l(x)P_{l-1}(x) - Q_{l-1}(x)P_l(x)\}$$
$$= (l-1)\{Q_{l-1}(x)P_{l-2}(x) - Q_{l-2}(x)_lP_{-1}(x)\}$$

as required.

If we now define

$$F(l) = l\{Q_l(x)P_{l-1}(x) - Q_{l-1}(x)P_l(x)\}$$

this result may be written in the form

$$F(l) = F(l-1),$$

and hence we have

$$F(l) = F(l-1) = F(l-2) = \ldots = F(1).$$

Thus $F(l) = F(1)$

so that $l\{Q_l(x)P_{l-1}(x) - Q_{l-1}(x)P_l(x)\} = Q_1(x)P_0(x) - Q_0(x)P_1(x)$.

But we know that $\qquad P_0(x) = 1$,
$$P_1(x) = x,$$

$$Q_0(x) = \tfrac{1}{2}\ln\frac{1+x}{1-x},$$

$$Q_1(x) = \tfrac{1}{2}x\ln\frac{1+x}{1-x} - 1$$

so that we obtain

$$l\{Q_l(x)P_{l-1}(x) - Q_{l-1}(x)P_l(x)\} = \tfrac{1}{2}x\ln\frac{1+x}{1-x} - 1 - \tfrac{1}{2}x\ln\frac{1+x}{1-x}$$

$$= -1,$$

which is the required result.

PROBLEMS

(1) Show that $\displaystyle\int_{-1}^{1} xP_l(x)P_{l-1}(x)\,dx = \frac{2l}{4l^2-1}$.

(2) Show that $\displaystyle\int_{-1}^{1} (1-x^2)P_l'(x)P_m'(x)\,dx = \frac{2l(l+1)}{2l+1}\delta_{lm}$.

(3) If $D \equiv \dfrac{d}{dx}$, use Leibniz's theorem to prove that

$$(1-x^2)^m D^{l+m}(x^2-1)^l = (-1)^m \frac{(l+m)!}{(l-m)!} D^{l-m}(x^2-1)$$

$$(0 \leqslant m \leqslant l)$$

and hence deduce that $P_l^{-m}(x) = (-1)^m \dfrac{(l-m)!}{(l+m)!} P_l^m(x)$.

(4) If $f(x) = \begin{cases} \tfrac{1}{2} & (0 < x < 1) \\ -\tfrac{1}{2} & (-1 < x < 0) \end{cases}$

expand $f(x)$ in the form $\displaystyle\sum_{r=0}^{\infty} c_r P_r(x)$.

(5) Show that $\displaystyle\sum_{n=0}^{\infty} P_{n+m}^m(x)t^n = \frac{(2m)!(1-x^2)^{m/2}}{2^m m!(1-2tx+t^2)^{m+\frac{1}{2}}}$.

(6) If $u_n = \int_{-1}^{1} x^{-1} P_n(x) P_{n-1}(x) \, dx$, show that $n u_n + (n-1) u_{n-1} = 2$, and hence evaluate u_n.

(7) Show that $\displaystyle\sum_{r=0}^{n} (2r+1) P_r(x) = P'_{n+1}(x) + P'_n(x)$.

(8) Show that $(1-x) \displaystyle\sum_{r=0}^{n} (2r+1) P_r(x) = (n+1)\{P_n(x) - P_{n+1}(x)\}$.

(9) Assuming the result of theorem 3.14, prove theorem 3.15.

(10) Show that $P_l(x) Q'_l(x) - P'_l(x) Q_l(x) = \dfrac{1}{1-x^2}$.

(11) Show that $Y_l^m(0, \phi) = \sqrt{\left(\dfrac{2l+1}{4\pi}\right)} \delta_{m0}$.

(12) If $x > 1$, prove that

$$Q_l(x) = \frac{1}{2^{l+1}} \int_{-1}^{1} \frac{(1-t^2)^l}{(x-t)^{l+1}} \, dt$$

and deduce that

(i) by making the substitution $t = \dfrac{e^\theta \sqrt{(x+1)} - \sqrt{(x-1)}}{e^\theta \sqrt{(x+1)} + \sqrt{(x-1)}}$

we obtain

$$Q_l(x) = \int_0^\infty \frac{d\theta}{\{x + \sqrt{(x^2-1)} \cosh \theta\}^{l+1}};$$

(ii) $Q_l(x) = \dfrac{2^l}{x^{l+1}} \displaystyle\sum_{r=0}^{\infty} \frac{(l+r)!(l+2r)!}{r!(2l+2r+1)!} \frac{1}{x^{2r}}$.

4

BESSEL FUNCTIONS

4.1 BESSEL'S EQUATION AND ITS SOLUTIONS; BESSEL FUNCTIONS OF THE FIRST AND SECOND KIND

Bessel's equation of order n is

$$x^2 \frac{d^2y}{dx^2} + x\frac{dy}{dx} + (x^2 - n^2)y = 0 \tag{4.1}$$

(where, since it is only n^2 that enters the equation, we may always take n to be non-negative).

Since this is of the form of equation (1.2) with $q(x) = 1$ and $r(x) = x^2 - n^2$, we may apply the methods of Chapter 1 and be assured that any series solution obtained will be convergent for all values of x.

Setting $z(x, s) = \sum_{r=0}^{\infty} a_r x^{s+r}$ and requiring z to be a solution of equation (4.1) leads, by the same method as in previous cases, to the system of equations

$$\{s(s - 1) + s - n^2\}a_0 = 0, \tag{4.2}$$

$$\{(s + 1)s + (s + 1) - n^2\}a_1 = 0 \tag{4.3}$$

and

$$\{(s + r)(s + r - 1) + (s + r) - n^2\}a_r + a_{r-2} = 0$$
$$(r \geqslant 2). \tag{4.4}$$

Equation (4.2) gives the indicial equation $s^2 - n^2 = 0$ with roots $s = \pm n$. We shall obtain two solutions from these which will be independent, apart, possibly, from the case when the two roots differ by an integer, i.e., when $2n$ is integral.

Equation (4.3) is

$$\{(s + 1)^2 - n^2\}a_1 = 0$$

and, since $s^2 = n^2$, we cannot also have $(s + 1)^2 = n^2$†, so that $(s + 1)^2 - n^2 \neq 0$ and hence $a_1 = 0$.

Equation (4.4) is just

$$\{(s + r)^2 - n^2\}a_r + a_{r-2} = 0$$

which gives

$$a_r = -\frac{a_{r-2}}{(s + r)^2 - n^2}.$$

Taking $s = n$, this becomes

$$a_r = -\frac{a_{r-2}}{(n + r)^2 - n^2}$$

$$= -\frac{a_{r-2}}{(n + r - n)(n + r + n)}$$

$$= -\frac{a_{r-2}}{r(2n + r)} \qquad (r \geqslant 2). \qquad (4.5)$$

Thus we have

$$a_2 = -\frac{a_0}{2(2n + 2)} = -\frac{a_0}{2^2.1(n + 1)},$$

$$a_4 = -\frac{a_2}{4(2n + 4)} = -\frac{a_2}{2^2.2(n + 2)} = \frac{a_0}{2^4.2!(n + 1)(n + 2)},$$

$$a_6 = -\frac{a_4}{6(2n + 6)} = -\frac{a_4}{2^2.3(n + 3)}$$

$$= -\frac{a_0}{2^6.3!(n + 1)(n + 2)(n + 3)}$$

and in general

$$a_{2r} = (-1)^r \frac{a_0}{2^{2r}r!(n + 1)(n + 2) \dots (n + r)}.$$

---

† The only situation in which we can have $s^2 = (s + 1)^2 = n^2$ is $n = \frac{1}{2}, s = -\frac{1}{2}$. For this case it is true that $s = -\frac{1}{2}$ makes a_1 indeterminate and leads to two independent solutions, but the results of the text still hold good, since zero is a possible choice for a_1 and we obtain the second independent solution from $s = \frac{1}{2}$.

We simplify the appearance of this expression somewhat by noting that $(n + 1)(n + 2) \ldots (n + r)$

$$= (n + r)(n + r - 1) \ldots (n + 2)(n + 1)\frac{\Gamma(n + 1)}{\Gamma(n + 1)}$$

$$= \frac{\Gamma(n + r + 1)}{\Gamma(n + 1)}$$

on using repeatedly the fact that $x\Gamma(x) = \Gamma(x + 1)$ (theorem 2.2). Thus we now have

$$a_{2r} = (-1)^r \frac{a_0\Gamma(n + 1)}{2^{2r}r!\Gamma(n + r + 1)}.$$

Also, if we use the fact that $a_1 = 0$ together with equation (4.5), we obtain

$$a_1 = a_3 = a_5 = \ldots = a_{2r+1} = \ldots = 0.$$

Hence, substituting these values for the a_r into the series for $z(x, s)$, we obtain as a solution of Bessel's equation

$$\sum_{r=0}^{\infty} a_0(-1)^r \frac{\Gamma(n + 1)}{2^{2r}r!\Gamma(n + r + 1)}x^{2r+n}.$$

This is a solution for any value of a_0; let us choose $a_0 = 1/\{2^n\Gamma(n + 1)\}$ and we obtain the solution which we shall denote by $J_n(x)$ and shall call the Bessel function of the first kind of order n:

$$J_n(x) = \sum_{r=0}^{\infty} (-1)^r \frac{1}{r!\Gamma(n + r + 1)}\left(\frac{x}{2}\right)^{2r+n}. \qquad (4.6)$$

From the remarks at the beginning of this section it is clear that the infinite series in equation (4.6) will be convergent for all values of x.

So far we have dealt with the root of the indicial equation $s = n$. The other root $s = -n$ will also give a solution of Bessel's equation, and the form of this solution is obtained just by replacing n in all the equations above by $-n$, so that we obtain the solution to Bessel's equation

$$J_{-n}(x) = \sum_{r=0}^{\infty} (-1)^r \frac{1}{r!\Gamma(-n + r + 1)}\left(\frac{x}{2}\right)^{2r-n}. \qquad (4.7)$$

Suppose now that n is non-integral. Then, since r is always integral, the factor $\Gamma(-n + r + 1)$ in equation (4.7) cannot have its argument equal to a negative integer or zero, and hence must always be finite and non-zero. Thus equation (4.7) shows that $J_{-n}(x)$ contains negative powers of x (they arise for those values of r such that $2r < n$), whereas equation (4.6) shows that $J_n(x)$ does not contain any negative powers. Hence, at $x = 0$, $J_n(x)$ is finite while $J_{-n}(x)$ is infinite, so that one cannot be a constant multiple of the other, and we have shown that $J_n(x)$ and $J_{-n}(x)$ are independent solutions of Bessel's equation for n non-integral (which is a stronger condition than $2n$ non-integral, obtained from the general theory). The explicit relationship between $J_n(x)$ and $J_{-n}(x)$ for integral n is shown in the following theorem.

Theorem 4.1

When n is an integer (positive or negative),
$$J_{-n}(x) = (-1)^n J_n(x).$$

PROOF

First consider $n > 0$.
Then
$$J_{-n}(x) = \sum_{r=0}^{\infty} (-1)^r \frac{1}{r!\Gamma(-n+r+1)} \left(\frac{x}{2}\right)^{2r-n}$$

from equation (4.7).

But $\Gamma(-n+r+1)$ is infinite (and hence $1/\{\Gamma(-n+r+1)\}$ is zero) for those values of r which make the argument a negative integer or zero, i.e., for $r = 0, 1, 2, \ldots (n-1)$ (remembering that this is possible because n is integral).

Hence the sum over r in the above expression for $J_{-n}(x)$ can equally well be taken from n to infinity, and then
$$J_{-n}(x) = \sum_{r=n}^{\infty} (-1)^r \frac{1}{r!\Gamma(-n+r+1)} \left(\frac{x}{2}\right)^{2r-n}$$
$$= \sum_{m=0}^{\infty} (-1)^{m+n} \frac{1}{(m+n)!\Gamma(m+1)} \left(\frac{x}{2}\right)^{2(m+n)-n}$$

(where we have changed the variable of summation to $m = r - n$)
$$= (-1)^n \sum_{m=0}^{\infty} (-1)^m \frac{1}{(m+n)!\Gamma(m+1)} \left(\frac{x}{2}\right)^{2m+n}.$$

But
$$J_n(x) = \sum_{m=0}^{\infty} (-1)^m \frac{1}{m!\Gamma(n+m+1)} \left(\frac{x}{2}\right)^{2m+n}$$
$$\text{(by equation (4.6))}$$

so all that remains in order to complete the proof is to show that

$$(m + n)!\Gamma(m + 1) = m!\Gamma(n + m + 1)$$

for n and m integral.
But

$$(m + n)!\Gamma(m + 1) = (m + n)(m + n - 1)\ldots(m + 1)m!\Gamma(m + 1)$$
$$= m!\Gamma(m + n + 1)$$

(on using repeatedly the result that $\Gamma(x + 1) = x\Gamma(x)$), and thus the result is proved.

Now consider $n < 0$; in this case we may write $n = -p$ with $p > 0$. Then what we require to prove is that

$$J_p(x) = (-1)^{-p}J_{-p}(x)$$

or

$$(-1)^p J_p(x) = J_{-p}(x)$$

which, of course, since p is positive, is just the result we have proved above.

Let us summarise what we have proved so far: we have shown that if n is not an integer then $J_n(x)$ and $J_{-n}(x)$ (defined by equations (4.6) and (4.7), respectively) are independent solutions of Bessel's equation (so that the general solution is given by $AJ_n(x) + BJ_{-n}(x)$) while if n is an integer they are still solutions of Bessel's equation but are related by

$$J_{-n}(x) = (-1)^n J_n(x).$$

Theorem 4.2

The two independent solutions of Bessel's equation may be taken to be

$$J_n(x)$$

and

$$Y_n(x) = \frac{\cos n\pi\, J_n(x) - J_{-n}(x)}{\sin n\pi}$$

for all values of n.

PROOF

We consider separately the cases n non-integral and n integral.

(i) n non-integral.

Here $\sin n\pi \neq 0$, so that $Y_n(x)$ is just a linear combination of $J_n(x)$ and $J_{-n}(x)$. But from the above discussion we know that in this case $J_n(x)$ and $J_{-n}(x)$ are independent solutions, so that $J_n(x)$ and a linear combination of $J_n(x)$ and $J_{-n}(x)$ must also be independent solutions. Hence $J_n(x)$ and $Y_n(x)$ must be independent solutions.

(ii) n integral.

In this case $\sin n\pi = 0$ and $\cos n\pi = (-1)^n$, so that by theorem 4.1 we have

$$\cos n\pi J_n(x) - J_{-n}(x) = (-1)^n J_n(x) - (-1)^n J_n(x) = 0.$$

Hence $Y_n(x)$ has the form $0/0$ and so is undefined. However, we may give it a meaning by defining it as

$$Y_n(x) = \lim_{\nu \to n} Y_\nu(x)$$

$$= \lim_{\nu \to n} \frac{\cos \pi J_\nu(x) - J_{-\nu}(x)}{\sin \nu\pi} \tag{4.8}$$

$$= \frac{[(\partial/\partial\nu)\{\cos \nu\pi J_\nu(x) - J_{-\nu}(x)\}]_{\nu=n}}{[(\partial/\partial\nu) \sin \nu\pi]_{\nu=n}}$$

$$\text{(by L'Hôpital's rule)}\dagger$$

$$= \frac{[-\pi \sin \nu\pi J_\nu(x) + \cos \nu\pi (\partial/\partial\nu)J_\nu(x) - (\partial/\partial\nu) J_{-\nu}(x)]_{\nu=n}}{[\pi \cos \nu\pi]_{\nu=n}}$$

$$= \frac{\cos n\pi[(\partial/\partial\nu)J_\nu(x)]_{\nu=n} - [(\partial/\partial\nu)J_{-\nu}(x)]_{\nu=n}}{\pi \cos n\pi}$$

$$= \frac{1}{\pi}[(\partial/\partial\nu)J_\nu(x) - (-1)^n(\partial/\partial\nu)J_{-\nu}(x)]_{\nu=n}. \tag{4.9}$$

We must now prove two things; firstly that $Y_n(x)$ as defined by equation (4.9) is in fact a solution of Bessel's equation and, secondly, that it is a solution independent from $J_n(x)$. To accomplish the first of these we note that $J_\nu(x)$ obeys Bessel's equation of order ν:

$$x^2\frac{d^2 J_\nu}{dx^2} + x\frac{dJ_\nu}{dx} + (x^2 - \nu^2)J_\nu = 0$$

which, when differentiated with respect to ν, gives

$$x^2\frac{d^2}{dx^2}\frac{\partial J_\nu}{\partial\nu} + x\frac{d}{dx}\frac{\partial J_\nu}{\partial\nu} + (x^2 - \nu^2)\frac{\partial J_\nu}{\partial\nu} - 2\nu J_\nu = 0. \tag{4.10}$$

Also, of course, $J_{-\nu}(x)$ satisfies Bessel's equation of order ν. so that we have in exactly the same way

$$x^2\frac{d^2}{dx^2}\frac{\partial J_{-\nu}}{\partial\nu} + x\frac{d}{dx}\frac{\partial J_{-\nu}}{\partial\nu} + (x^2 - \nu^2)\frac{\partial J_{-\nu}}{\partial\nu} - 2\nu J_{-\nu} = 0. \tag{4.11}$$

---

† L'Hôpital's rule states that if $f(a) = g(a) = 0$, then

$$\lim_{x \to a} \frac{f(x)}{g(x)} = \frac{f^{(r)}(a)}{g^{(r)}(a)}$$

where $f^{(r)}(a)$ and $g^{(r)}(a)$ are the lowest-order derivatives of $f(x)$ and $g(x)$, respectively, which are not both zero at $x = a$.

Multiplying equation (4.11) by $(-1)^\nu$ and subtracting from equation (4.10) gives

$$x^2 \frac{d^2}{dx^2}\left\{\frac{\partial J_\nu}{\partial \nu} - (-1)^\nu \frac{\partial J_{-\nu}}{\partial \nu}\right\} + x\frac{d}{dx}\left\{\frac{\partial J_\nu}{\partial \nu} - (-1)^\nu \frac{\partial J_{-\nu}}{\partial \nu}\right\}$$

$$+ (x^2 - \nu^2)\left\{\frac{\partial J_\nu}{\partial \nu} - (-1)^\nu \frac{\partial J_{-\nu}}{\partial \nu}\right\} - 2\nu\{J_\nu - (-1)^\nu J_{-\nu}\} = 0.$$

Setting $\nu = n$ in this last equation and using equation (4.9) gives

$$x^2 \frac{d^2}{dx^2} Y_n(x) + x\frac{d}{dx}Y_n(x) + (x^2 - n^2)Y_n(x)$$

$$- \frac{2n}{\pi}\{J_n(x) - (-1)^n J_{-n}(x)\} = 0.$$

But now n is an integer, so that we may use the result of theorem 4.1 that $J_{-n}(x) = (-1)^n J_n(x)$ to obtain

$$x^2 \frac{d^2}{dx^2} Y_n(x) + x\frac{d}{dx}Y_n(x) + (x^2 - n^2)Y_n(x) = 0$$

which just states that $Y_n(x)$ satisfies Bessel's equation of order n.

That $Y_n(x)$ is independent from $J_n(x)$ may be seen from the result of the next theorem, which implies that at $x = 0$ $Y_n(x)$ is infinite, while we know that $J_n(x)$ is finite.

Theorem 4.3 (Explicit expression for $Y_n(x)$ for n integral)

$$Y_n(x) = \frac{2}{\pi}\left\{\ln\frac{x}{2} + \gamma - \frac{1}{2}\sum_{r=1}^{n}\frac{1}{r}\right\}J_n(x)$$

$$- \frac{1}{\pi}\sum_{s=0}^{\infty}(-1)^s \frac{1}{s!(n+s)!}\left(\frac{x}{2}\right)^{n+2s}\sum_{r=1}^{s}\left\{\frac{1}{r} + \frac{1}{r+n}\right\}$$

$$- \frac{1}{\pi}\sum_{s=0}^{n-1}\frac{(n-s-1)!}{s!}\left(\frac{x}{2}\right)^{-n+2s}$$

where γ is Euler's constant (see Appendix 2).

PROOF

We shall omit the proof of this theorem, merely noting that the method to follow is to use the series expansions (4.6) and (4.7) in equation (4.9). Euler's constant appears because of properties of the derivative of the gamma function.

Theorem 4.4

When n is integral, $Y_{-n}(x) = (-1)^n \, Y_n(x)$.

PROOF

From equation (4.9) we have

$$Y_{-n}(x) = \frac{1}{\pi} \left[\frac{\partial}{\partial \nu} J_\nu(x) - (-1)^{-n} \frac{\partial}{\partial \nu} J_{-\nu}(x) \right]_{\nu = -n}$$

$$= \frac{1}{\pi} \left[\frac{\partial}{\partial(-\nu)} J_{-\nu}(x) - (-1)^{-n} \frac{\partial}{\partial(-\nu)} J_\nu(x) \right]_{\nu = n}$$

$$= \frac{1}{\pi} \left[-\frac{\partial}{\partial \nu} J_{-\nu}(x) + (-1)^{+n} \frac{\partial}{\partial \nu} J_\nu(x) \right]_{\nu = n}$$

$$= (-1)^n \frac{1}{\pi} \left[\frac{\partial}{\partial \nu} J_\nu(x) - (-1)^n \frac{\partial}{\partial \nu} J_{-\nu}(x) \right]_{\nu = n}$$

$$= (-1)^n Y_n(x).$$

We shall call $J_n(x)$ and $Y_n(x)$ Bessel functions of order n of the first and second kinds respectively. ($Y_n(x)$ is sometimes called the Neumann function of order n and denoted by $N_n(x)$.) As we have seen, $J_n(x)$ and $Y_n(x)$ (with n considered positive) provide us with two independent solutions of Bessel's equation, $J_n(x)$ always being finite at $x = 0$ and $Y_n(x)$ always infinite at $x = 0$.

4.2 GENERATING FUNCTION FOR THE BESSEL FUNCTIONS

Theorem 4.5

$$\exp\left\{ \frac{1}{2}x\left(t - \frac{1}{t} \right) \right\} = \sum_{n=-\infty}^{\infty} t^n J_n(x).$$

PROOF

We expand $\exp\left\{ \frac{1}{2}x\left(t - \frac{1}{t} \right) \right\}$ in powers of t and show that the coefficient of t^n is $J_n(x)$:

$$\exp\left\{ \frac{1}{2}x\left(t - \frac{1}{t} \right) \right\} = \exp\left(\frac{1}{2}xt \right) \cdot \exp\left(-\frac{1}{2}\frac{x}{t} \right)$$

$$= \sum_{r=0}^{\infty} \frac{\left(\frac{1}{2}xt \right)^r}{r!} \sum_{s=0}^{\infty} \frac{\left(-\frac{1}{2}x/t \right)^s}{s!}$$

S F—H

$$= \sum_{r,\,s=0}^{\infty} \frac{(\frac{1}{2})^r x^r t^r (-1)^s (\frac{1}{2})^s x^s t^{-s}}{r!\,s!}$$

$$= \sum_{r,\,s=0}^{\infty} (-1)^s \left(\frac{1}{2}\right)^{r+s} \frac{x^{r+s} t^{r-s}}{r!\,s!}. \qquad (4.12)$$

We now pick out the coefficient of t^n, where first we consider $n \geqslant 0$. For a fixed value of r, to obtain the power of t as t^n we must have $s = r - n$. Thus for this particular value of r the coefficient of t^n is

$$(-1)^{r-n} \left(\frac{1}{2}\right)^{2r-n} \frac{x^{2r-n}}{r!(r-n)!}.$$

We get the total coefficient of t^n by summing over all allowed values of r. Since $s = r - n$ and we require $s \geqslant 0$, we must have $r \geqslant n$. Hence the total coefficient of t^n is

$$\sum_{r=n}^{\infty} (-1)^{r-n} \left(\frac{1}{2}\right)^{2r-n} \frac{x^{2r-n}}{r!(r-n)!} = \sum_{p=0}^{\infty} (-1)^p \frac{(x/2)^{2p+n}}{(p+n)!\,p!}$$

(where we have set $p = r - n$)

$$= \sum_{p=0}^{\infty} (-1)^p \frac{(x/2)^{2p+n}}{\Gamma(p+n+1)\,p!}$$

(remembering that both p and n are integral, so that we may use the result of theorem 2.3 that $\Gamma(p+n+1) = (p+n)!$)

$$= J_n(x)$$

(by equation (4.6)).

If now $n < 0$, we still have the coefficient of t^n for a fixed value of r given by

$$(-1)^{r-n} \left(\frac{1}{2}\right)^{2r-n} \frac{x^{2r-n}}{r!(r-n)!}$$

but now the requirement that $s \geqslant 0$ with $s = r - n$ is satisfied for *all* values of r. Thus the coefficient of t^n is just

$$\sum_{r=0}^{\infty} (-1)^{r-n} \left(\frac{1}{2}\right)^{2r-n} \frac{x^{2r-n}}{r!(r-n)!} = (-1)^{-n} \sum_{r=0}^{\infty} (-1)^r \frac{(x/2)^{2r-n}}{r!\,\Gamma(r-n+1)}$$

$$= (-1)^n J_{-n}(x)$$

(by equation (4.7))

$$= J_n(x)$$

(by theorem 4.1).

4.3 INTEGRAL REPRESENTATIONS FOR BESSEL FUNCTIONS

Theorem 4.6

$$J_n(x) = \frac{1}{\pi} \int_0^\pi \cos(n\phi - x \sin \phi) \, d\phi$$

$$(n \text{ integral}).$$

PROOF

Since $J_{-n}(x) = (-1)^n J_n(x)$ for n integral, the result of theorem 4.5 may be written in the form

$$\exp\left\{\frac{1}{2}x\left(t - \frac{1}{t}\right)\right\} = J_0(x) + \sum_{n=1}^{\infty} \{t^n + (-1)^n t^{-n}\} J_n(x).$$

If we now write $t = e^{i\phi}$ so that

$$t - \frac{1}{t} = e^{i\phi} - e^{-i\phi} = 2i \sin \phi$$

this equation becomes

$$e^{ix \sin \phi} = J_0(x) + \sum_{n=1}^{\infty} \{e^{in\phi} + (-1)^n e^{-in\phi}\} J_n(x).$$

But when n is even

$$e^{in\phi} + (-1)^n e^{-in\phi} = e^{in\phi} + e^{-in\phi} = 2 \cos n\phi,$$

while when n is odd we have

$$e^{in\phi} + (-1)^n e^{-in\phi} = e^{in\phi} - e^{-in\phi} = 2i \sin n\phi.$$

Thus we have

$$e^{ix \sin \phi} = J_0(x) + \sum_{n \text{ even}} 2 \cos n\phi \, J_n(x) + \sum_{n \text{ odd}} 2i \sin n\phi \, J_n(x)$$

$$= J_0(x) + \sum_{k=1}^{\infty} 2 \cos 2k\phi \, J_{2k}(x) + i \sum_{k=1}^{\infty} 2 \sin(2k - 1)\phi \, J_{2k-1}(x).$$

Equating real and imaginary parts of this equation gives

$$\cos(x \sin \phi) = J_0(x) + \sum_{k=1}^{\infty} 2 \cos 2k\phi \, J_{2k}(x) \tag{4.13}$$

$$\sin(x \sin \phi) = \sum_{k=1}^{\infty} 2 \sin(2k - 1)\phi \, J_{2k-1}(x). \tag{4.14}$$

If we multiply both sides of equation (4.13) by $\cos n\phi$ $(n \geqslant 0)$, both sides of equation (4.14) by $\sin n\phi$ $(n \geqslant 1)$, integrate from 0 to π and use the identities

$$\int_0^\pi \cos m\phi \cos n\phi \, d\phi = \begin{cases} 0 & (m \neq n) \\ \pi/2 & (m = n \neq 0) \\ \pi & (m = n = 0) \end{cases}$$

and

$$\int_0^\pi \sin m\phi \sin n\phi \, d\phi = \begin{cases} 0 & (m \neq n) \\ \pi/2 & (m = n \neq 0), \end{cases}$$

we obtain the results

$$\int_0^\pi \cos n\phi \cos (x \sin \phi) \, d\phi = \begin{cases} \pi J_n(x) & (n \text{ even}) \\ 0 & (n \text{ odd}) \end{cases}$$

and

$$\int_0^\pi \sin n\phi \sin (x \sin \phi) \, d\phi = \begin{cases} 0 & (n \text{ even}) \\ \pi J_n(x) & (n \text{ odd}). \end{cases}$$

Adding these last two equations gives

$$\int_0^\pi \{\cos n\phi \cos (x \sin \phi) + \sin n\phi \sin (x \sin \phi)\} \, d\phi = \pi J_n(x)$$

for all positive integral n.

Hence

$$\int_0^\pi \cos (n\phi - x \sin \phi) \, d\phi = \pi J_n(x)$$

which is the required result for positive n.

If n is negative, we may set $n = -m$ where m is positive, so that the required result is

$$\int_0^\pi \cos (-m\phi - x \sin \phi) \, d\phi = \pi J_{-m}(x)$$

(where m is positive).

But $\displaystyle\int_0^\pi \cos (-m\phi - x \sin \phi) \, d\phi$

$$= \int_\pi^0 \cos \{-m(\pi - \theta) - x \sin (\pi - \theta)\}. \, -d\theta$$

(where we have changed the variable by setting $\theta = \pi - \phi$)

$$= \int_0^\pi \cos \{-m\pi + m\theta - x \sin \theta\} \, d\theta$$

$$= \int_0^\pi \{\cos (m\theta - x \sin \theta) \cos m\pi$$

$$+ \sin (m\theta - x \sin \theta) \sin m\pi\} \, d\theta$$

$$= (-1)^m \int_0^\pi \cos(m\theta - x \sin \theta) \, d\theta$$

$$= (-1)^m \pi J_m(x)$$

(since we know the result to be true for positive m)

$$= \pi J_{-m}(x)$$

$$= \pi J_n(x).$$

Theorem 4.7

$$J_n(x) = \frac{(\tfrac{1}{2}x)^n}{\sqrt{(\pi)}\Gamma(n + \tfrac{1}{2})} \int_{-1}^1 (1 - t^2)^{n-\frac{1}{2}} e^{ixt} \, dt \quad (n > -\tfrac{1}{2}).$$

PROOF

Consider the integral I defined by

$$I = \int_{-1}^1 (1 - t^2)^{n-\frac{1}{2}} e^{ixt} \, dt$$

$$= \int_{-1}^1 (1 - t^2)^{n-\frac{1}{2}} \sum_{r=0}^\infty \frac{(ixt)^r}{r!} \, dt$$

$$= \sum_{r=0}^\infty \frac{(ix)^r}{r!} \int_{-1}^1 (1 - t^2)^{n-\frac{1}{2}} t^r \, dt.$$

Now, if r is odd, the integrand in $\int_{-1}^1 (1 - t^2)^{n-\frac{1}{2}} t^r \, dt$ is an odd function of t, so that the integral is zero; while if r is even (say, equal to $2s$), the integrand is even, so that we have

$$\int_{-1}^1 (1 - t^2)^{n-\frac{1}{2}} t^r \, dt = \int_{-1}^1 (1 - t^2)^{n-\frac{1}{2}} t^{2s} \, dt$$

$$= 2 \int_0^1 (1 - t^2)^{n-\frac{1}{2}} t^{2s} \, dt$$

$$= \int_0^1 (1 - u)^{n-\frac{1}{2}} u^{s-\frac{1}{2}} \, du$$

(where we have made the change of variable $u = t^2$, $du = 2t \, dt$)

$$= B(n + \tfrac{1}{2}, s + \tfrac{1}{2})$$

(by the definition of the beta function; we must have $n > -\tfrac{1}{2}$ to ensure the convergence of the integral (see Section 2.1))

$$= \frac{\Gamma(n + \frac{1}{2})\Gamma(s + \frac{1}{2})}{\Gamma(n + s + 1)}$$

(by theorem 2.7).

Thus $\quad I = \sum_{s=0}^{\infty} \frac{(ix)^{2s}}{(2s)!} \frac{\Gamma(n + \frac{1}{2})\Gamma(s + \frac{1}{2})}{\Gamma(n + s + 1)}$

$$= \Gamma(n + \tfrac{1}{2}) \sum_{s=0}^{\infty} (-1)^s \frac{x^{2s}}{(2s)!} \frac{1}{\Gamma(n + s + 1)} \frac{(2s)!}{2^{2s}s!} \sqrt{\pi}$$

(using the corollary to theorem 2.10)

$$= \Gamma(n + \tfrac{1}{2})(\sqrt{\pi})\left(\frac{x}{2}\right)^{-n} \sum_{s=0}^{\infty} \frac{(-1)^s (x/2)^{2s+n}}{\Gamma(n + s + 1)s!}$$

$$= \Gamma(n + \tfrac{1}{2})(\sqrt{\pi})\left(\frac{x}{2}\right)^{-n} J_n(x)$$

(by equation (4.6)).

Thus $\quad J_n(x) = \frac{1}{(\sqrt{\pi})\Gamma(n + \frac{1}{2})}\left(\frac{x}{2}\right)^n I$

$$= \frac{1}{(\sqrt{\pi})\Gamma(n + \frac{1}{2})}\left(\frac{x}{2}\right)^n \int_{-1}^{1} (1 - t^2)^{n-\frac{1}{2}} e^{ixt} \, dt.$$

4.4 RECURRENCE RELATIONS

Theorem 4.8

(i) $\dfrac{d}{dx}\{x^n J_n(x)\} = x^n J_{n-1}(x).$

(ii) $\dfrac{d}{dx}\{x^{-n} J_n(x)\} = -x^{-n} J_{n+1}(x).$

(iii) $J_n'(x) = J_{n-1}(x) - \dfrac{n}{x}J_n(x).$

(iv) $J_n'(x) = \dfrac{n}{x}J_n(x) - J_{n+1}(x).$

(v) $J_n'(x) = \tfrac{1}{2}\{J_{n-1}(x) - J_{n+1}(x)\}.$

(vi) $J_{n-1}(x) + J_{n+1}(x) = \dfrac{2n}{x}J_n(x).$

PROOF

(i) From equation (4.6) we have

$$J_n(x) = \sum_{r=0}^{\infty} (-1)^r \frac{1}{r!\Gamma(n+r+1)} \left(\frac{x}{2}\right)^{2r+n}$$

so that

$$\frac{d}{dx}\{x^n J_n(x)\} = \frac{d}{dx} \sum_{r=0}^{\infty} (-1)^r \frac{1}{r!\Gamma(n+r+1)} \frac{1}{2^{2r+n}} x^{2r+2n}$$

$$= \sum_{r=0}^{\infty} (-1)^r \frac{1}{r!\Gamma(n+r+1)2^{2r+n}} (2r+2n)x^{2r+2n-1}$$

$$= x^n \sum_{r=0}^{\infty} (-1)^r \frac{1}{r!(n+r)\Gamma(n+r)2^{2r+n}} 2(n+r)x^{2r+(n-1)}$$

(using the result of theorem 2.2 that $\Gamma(x+1) = x\Gamma(x)$)

$$= x^n \sum_{r=0}^{\infty} (-1)^r \frac{1}{r!\Gamma(n+r)} \left(\frac{x}{2}\right)^{2r+(n-1)}$$

$$= x^n J_{n-1}(x)$$

(by equation (4.6)).

(Note that in this theorem no restriction is placed on n: it may be integral or non-integral, positive or negative.)

(ii) We have

$$\frac{d}{dx}\{x^{-n} J_n(x)\} = \frac{d}{dx} \sum_{r=0}^{\infty} (-1)^r \frac{1}{r!\Gamma(n+r+1)} \frac{1}{2^{2r+n}} x^{2r}$$

$$= \sum_{r=0}^{\infty} (-1)^r \frac{1}{r!\Gamma(n+r+1)} \frac{1}{2^{2r+n}} 2rx^{2r-1}$$

$$= \sum_{r=1}^{\infty} (-1)^r \frac{1}{r!\Gamma(n+r+1)} \frac{1}{2^{2r+(n-1)}} rx^{2r-1}$$

(since the factor r in the numerator makes the term with $r = 0$ vanish; we remember that $0! = 1$)

$$= \sum_{s=0}^{\infty} (-1)^{s+1} \frac{1}{(s+1)!\Gamma(n+s+2)} \frac{1}{2^{2(s+1)+n-1}} (s+1)x^{2(s+1)-1}$$

(where we have set $s = r - 1$)

$$= \sum_{s=0}^{\infty} (-1)^{s+1} \frac{1}{s!\Gamma(n+s+2)} \frac{1}{2^{2s+n+1}} x^{2s+1}$$

$$= -x^{-n} \sum_{s=0}^{\infty} (-1)^s \frac{1}{s!\Gamma(n+s+2)} \left(\frac{x}{2}\right)^{2s+n+1}$$

$$= -x^{-n} J_{n+1}(x)$$

(on use of equation (4.6)).

(iii) From result (i) above, by carrying out the differentiation of the product on the left-hand side, we have

$$nx^{n-1} J_n(x) + x^n J_n'(x) = x^n J_{n-1}(x)$$

which, on dividing throughout by x^n, gives

$$\frac{n}{x} J_n(x) + J_n'(x) = J_{n-1}(x),$$

and hence

$$J_n'(x) = J_{n-1}(x) - \frac{n}{x} J_n(x).$$

(iv) We carry out the differentiation in result (ii) above to obtain

$$-nx^{(-n-1)} J_n(x) + x^{-n} J_n'(x) = -x^{-n} J_{n+1}(x)$$

which, on multiplying throughout by x^n, gives

$$-\frac{n}{x} J_n(x) + J_n'(x) = -J_{n+1}(x).$$

Thus

$$J_n'(x) = \frac{n}{x} J_n(x) - J_{n+1}(x).$$

(v) Add results (iii) and (iv) and the result follows immediately.

(vi) Similarly, if we subtract result (iv) from result (iii) we obtain the required relationship.

Theorem 4.9

All the results of theorem 4.8 remain true when the Bessel functions of the first kind are replaced by the corresponding Bessel functions of the second kind.

PROOF

We shall prove that result (i) remains true for $Y_n(x)$; a similar method will prove result (ii), and then results (iii–vi) follow in the same way as they did in theorem 4.8.

Thus what we have to prove here is that $(d/dx)\{x^n Y_n(x)\} = x^n Y_{n-1}(x)$. We must consider separately the cases of integral and non-integral n.

(a) Non-integral n.

Here we may write

$$Y_n(x) = \frac{\cos n\pi J_n(x) - J_{-n}(x)}{\sin n\pi}$$

so that

$$\frac{d}{dx}\{x^n Y_n(x)\}$$

$$= \frac{1}{\sin n\pi}[\cos n\pi \frac{d}{dx}\{x^n J_n(x)\} - \frac{d}{dx}\{x^n J_{-n}(x)\}]$$

$$= \frac{1}{\sin n\pi}[\cos n\pi . x^n J_{n-1}(x) - \{-x^n J_{-n+1}(x)\}]$$

(where we have used theorem 4.8 (i) for the first derivative and theorem 4.8 (ii) for the second)

$$= \frac{1}{\sin n\pi} x^n[\cos n\pi J_{n-1}(x) + J_{-(n-1)}(x)]$$

$$= \frac{1}{\sin \{(n-1)\pi + \pi\}} x^n[\cos \{(n-1)\pi + \pi\} J_{n-1}(x) + J_{-(n-1)}(x)]$$

$$= \frac{1}{-\sin (n-1)\pi} x^n[-\cos (n-1)\pi J_{n-1}(x) + J_{-(n-1)}(x)]$$

$$= x^n . \frac{\cos (n-1)\pi J_{n-1}(x) - J_{-(n-1)}(x)}{\sin (n-1)\pi}$$

$$= x^n Y_{n-1}(x).$$

(b) Integral n.

Here we note that $Y_n(x) = \lim_{\nu \to n} Y_\nu(x)$ and that by part (a)

$$(d/dx)\{x^\nu Y_\nu(x)\} = x^\nu Y_{\nu-1}(x).$$

Taking the limit of this result as $\nu \to n$ gives the required result.

4.5 HANKEL FUNCTIONS

We define the Hankel functions (sometimes called Bessel functions of the third kind) by

$$H_n^{(1)}(x) = J_n(x) + i Y_n(x)$$
$$H_n^{(2)}(x) = J_n(x) - i Y_n(x).$$

These are obviously independent solutions of Bessel's equation. Both are, of course, infinite at $x = 0$; their usefulness is connected with their behaviour for large values of x, which we shall investigate in a later section.

Theorem 4.10

All the recurrence relations of theorem 4.8 remain true when $J_n(x)$ is replaced by either $H_n^{(1)}(x)$ or $H_n^{(2)}(x)$.

PROOF

Again we prove relation (i) only, the remainder following as before. But we know relation (i) to hold for both $J_n(x)$ and $Y_n(x)$, so that we have

$$\frac{d}{dx}\{x^n J_n(x)\} = x^n J_{n-1}(x)$$

and

$$\frac{d}{dx}\{x^n Y_n(x)\} = x^n Y_{n-1}(x).$$

Hence

$$\frac{d}{dx}\{x^n J_n(x)\} \pm i\frac{d}{dx}\{x^n Y_n(x)\} = x^n J_{n-1}(x) \pm i x^n Y_{n-1}(x),$$

so that

$$\frac{d}{dx}[x^n\{J_n(x) \pm i Y_n(x)\}] = x^n\{J_{n-1}(x) \pm i Y_{n-1}(x)\},$$

which, on remembering the definitions of $H_n^{(1)}(x)$ and $H_n^{(2)}(x)$, gives

$$\frac{d}{dx}\{x^n H_n^{(1)}(x)\} = x^n H_{n-1}^{(1)}(x)$$

(taking the plus sign)

and

$$\frac{d}{dx}\{x^n H_n^{(2)}(x)\} = x^n H_{n-1}^{(2)}(x)$$

(taking the minus sign).

4.6   EQUATIONS REDUCIBLE TO BESSEL'S EQUATION

Theorem 4.11

The general solution of

$$x^2 \frac{d^2y}{dx^2} + x\frac{dy}{dx} + (\lambda^2 x^2 - n^2)y = 0$$

is

$$A J_n(\lambda x) + B Y_n(\lambda x).$$

PROOF

Make the substitution $t = \lambda x$

so that
$$\frac{dy}{dx} = \lambda \frac{dy}{dt}$$

and
$$\frac{d^2y}{dx^2} = \lambda^2 \frac{d^2y}{dt^2}.$$

Then the given equation becomes
$$t^2 \frac{d^2y}{dt^2} + t \frac{dy}{dt} + (t^2 - n^2)y = 0$$

which is Bessel's equation of order n, so that the general solution is
$$y = A J_n(t) + B Y_n(t)$$

and hence, replacing t by λx, the general solution of the original equation is
$$y = A J_n(\lambda x) + B Y_n(\lambda x).$$

Theorem 4.12

The general solution of
$$x^2 \frac{d^2y}{dx^2} + (1 - 2\alpha)x\frac{dy}{dx} + \{\beta^2\gamma^2x^{2\gamma} + (\alpha^2 - n^2\gamma^2)\}y = 0$$

is
$$A x^\alpha J_n(\beta x^\gamma) + B x^\alpha Y_n(\beta x^\gamma).$$

PROOF

We first make the change of variable $y = x^\alpha z$.

Then
$$\frac{dy}{dx} = x^\alpha \frac{dz}{dx} + \alpha x^{\alpha-1}z$$

and
$$\frac{d^2y}{dx^2} = x^\alpha \frac{d^2z}{dx^2} + 2\alpha x^{\alpha-1}\frac{dz}{dx} + \alpha(\alpha - 1)x^{\alpha-2}z$$

so that the given equation becomes
$$x^{\alpha+2}\frac{d^2z}{dx^2} + 2\alpha x^{\alpha+1}\frac{dz}{dx} + \alpha(\alpha - 1)x^\alpha z + (1 - 2\alpha)\left\{x^{\alpha-1}\frac{dz}{dx} + \alpha x^\alpha z\right\}$$
$$+ \{\beta^2\gamma^2x^{2\gamma} + (\alpha^2 - n^2\gamma^2)\}x^\alpha z = 0$$

which, on collecting terms in d^2z/dx^2, dz/dx and z becomes
$$x^2\frac{d^2z}{dx^2} + \{2\alpha x + (1 - 2\alpha)x\}\frac{dz}{dx}$$
$$+ \{\alpha(\alpha - 1) + (1 - 2\alpha)\alpha + \beta^2\gamma^2x^{2\gamma} + (\alpha^2 - n^2\gamma^2)\}z = 0$$

which simplifies to

$$x^2 \frac{d^2z}{dx^2} + x\frac{dz}{dx} + \{\beta^2\gamma^2x^{2\gamma} - n^2\gamma^2\}z = 0. \qquad (4.15)$$

Now change the independent variable x by setting $t = x^\gamma$.

Then
$$\frac{dz}{dx} = \frac{dz}{dt}\frac{dt}{dx} = \gamma x^{\gamma-1}\frac{dz}{dt}$$

and
$$\frac{d^2z}{dx^2} = \gamma(\gamma - 1)x^{\gamma-2}\frac{dz}{dt} + \gamma x^{\gamma-1}\frac{d}{dx}\frac{dz}{dt}$$

$$= \gamma(\gamma - 1)x^{\gamma-2}\frac{dz}{dt} + \gamma x^{\gamma-1}.\gamma x^{\gamma-1}\frac{d^2z}{dt^2}$$

$$= \gamma^2 x^{2\gamma-2}\frac{d^2z}{dt^2} + \gamma(\gamma - 1)x^{\gamma-2}\frac{dz}{dt}$$

so that equation (4.15) becomes

$$\gamma^2 x^{2\gamma}\frac{d^2z}{dt^2} + \gamma(\gamma - 1)x^\gamma\frac{dz}{dt} + \gamma x^\gamma\frac{dz}{dt} + \{\beta^2\gamma^2x^{2\gamma} - n^2\gamma^2\}z = 0,$$

which, on collecting like terms and cancelling a common factor of γ^2, gives

$$t^2\frac{d^2z}{dt^2} + t\frac{dz}{dt} + \{\beta^2t^2 - n^2\}z = 0.$$

But this is just the equation of theorem 4.11 with solution

$$z = AJ_n(\beta t) + BY_n(\beta t).$$

Hence the solution of the original equation is obtained by substituting back the relationships $y = x^\alpha z$ and $t = x^\gamma$:

$$y = Ax^\alpha J_n(\beta x^\gamma) + Bx^\alpha Y_n(\beta x^\gamma).$$

4.7   MODIFIED BESSEL FUNCTIONS

Consider the differential equation

$$x^2\frac{d^2y}{dx^2} + x\frac{dy}{dx} - (x^2 + n^2)y = 0. \qquad (4.16)$$

This has the form of the equation in theorem 4.11 with $\lambda^2 = -1$. Thus it has the general solution

$$y = AJ_n(ix) + BY_n(ix).$$

Now, the solutions $J_n(ix)$ and $Y_n(ix)$ have the disadvantage of not necessarily being real when x is real. However, we may take the constant multiple of $J_n(ix)$ defined by

$$I_n(x) = i^{-n}J_n(ix)$$

and use it as one of the independent solutions of equation (4.16). It is easy to show that it is a real function of x:

$$I_n(x) = i^{-n}J_n(ix)$$

$$= i^{-n}\sum_{r=0}^{\infty}(-1)^r\frac{1}{r!\Gamma(n+r+1)}\left(\frac{ix}{2}\right)^{2r+n}$$

$$= i^{-n}\sum_{r=0}^{\infty}(-1)^r\frac{1}{r!\Gamma(n+r+1)}i^{2r}i^n\left(\frac{x}{2}\right)^{2r+n}$$

$$= \sum_{r=0}^{\infty}\frac{1}{r!\Gamma(n+r+1)}\left(\frac{x}{2}\right)^{2r+n}. \tag{4.17}$$

$I_n(x)$ so defined is called the modified Bessel function of the first kind, and equation (4.16) is called Bessel's modified equation.

Theorem 4.13

If n is integral, $I_{-n}(x) = I_n(x)$.

PROOF

$$I_{-n}(x) = i^n J_{-n}(ix)$$
$$= i^n(-1)^n J_n(ix)$$
$$\text{(by theorem 4.1)}$$
$$= i^n(-1)^n i^n I_n(x)$$
$$= (-1)^{2n}I_n(x)$$
$$= I_n(x).$$

We may obtain the second independent solution to Bessel's modified equation by considering $Y_n(ix)$; or alternatively we may employ a method similar to that used for the definition of $Y_n(x)$.

$I_n(x)$ and $I_{-n}(x)$ are both solutions of equation (4.16). When n is non-integral they are independent solutions (since $J_n(ix)$ and $J_{-n}(ix)$ are independent solutions). However, when n is integral $I_{-n}(x) = I_n(x)$. Define now

$$K_n(x) = \frac{\pi}{2}\frac{I_{-n}(x) - I_n(x)}{\sin n\pi}. \tag{4.18}$$

When n is non-integral, this is well defined, and $I_n(x)$ and $K_n(x)$ together provide independent solutions of equation (4.16). When n is integral, $K_n(x)$ is indeterminate as it stands and has to be defined by

$$K_n(x) = \lim_{\nu \to n} \frac{\pi}{2} \frac{I_{-\nu}(x) - I_\nu(x)}{\sin \nu \pi}$$

$$= \frac{\pi}{2} \frac{[(\partial/\partial\nu)I_{-\nu}(x) - (\partial/\partial\nu)I_\nu(x)]_{\nu=n}}{\pi[\cos \nu\pi]_{\nu=n}}$$

(by L'Hôpital's rule)

$$= \frac{(-1)^n}{2} \left[\frac{\partial}{\partial\nu}I_{-\nu}(x) - \frac{\partial}{\partial\nu}I_\nu(x) \right]_{\nu=n}.$$

As in theorem 4.2, it may be shown that this provides a second independent solution of Bessel's modified equation for integral values of n. The explicit series for $K_n(x)$ may be obtained from those for $J_n(x)$ and $Y_n(x)$ by use of the following theorem.

Theorem 4.14

$$K_n(x) = \frac{\pi}{2}i^{n+1}\{J_n(ix) + iY_n(ix)\} = \frac{\pi}{2}i^{n+1}H_n^{(1)}(ix).$$

PROOF

$$K_n(x) = \frac{\pi}{2} \frac{I_{-n}(x) - I_n(x)}{\sin n\pi}$$

(by definition (4.18))

$$= \frac{\pi}{2} \frac{i^n J_{-n}(ix) - i^{-n}J_n(ix)}{\sin n\pi}.$$

But from the definition of $Y_n(x)$ in theorem 4.2 we have that

$$J_{-n}(ix) = \cos n\pi \, J_n(ix) - \sin n\pi \, Y_n(ix).$$

Hence

$$K_n(x) = \frac{\pi}{2} \frac{i^n \cos n\pi \, J_n(ix) - i^{-n}J_n(ix) - i^n \sin n\pi \, Y_n(ix)}{\sin n\pi}$$

$$= \frac{\pi}{2}i^{n+1}\left\{ iY_n(ix) + \frac{-i\cos n\pi - i^{-2n-1}}{\sin n\pi}J_n(ix) \right\}. \qquad (4.19)$$

But

$$-i\cos n\pi - i^{-2n-1} = -i\cos n\pi + i.i^{-2n}$$

$$= -i\cos n\pi + i(e^{i\pi/2})^{-2n}$$

(writing $i = e^{i\pi/2}$)

$$= -i \cos n\pi + i\, e^{-in\pi}$$
$$= -i \cos n\pi + i(\cos n\pi - i \sin n\pi)$$
$$= \sin n\pi.$$

Thus, using equation (4.19) we have

$$K_n(x) = \frac{\pi}{2}i^{n+1}\{iY_n(ix) + J_n(ix)\}.$$

4.8 RECURRENCE RELATIONS FOR THE MODIFIED BESSEL FUNCTIONS

The modified Bessel functions satisfy recurrence relations similar to, but not identical with, those of theorem 4.8. Also, in contrast to the functions $J_n(x)$ and $Y_n(x)$, which satisfy the same relations as one another, $I_n(x)$ and $K_n(x)$ satisfy different relations from one another.

Theorem 4.15

(i) $\dfrac{d}{dx}\{x^n I_n(x)\} = x^n I_{n-1}(x).$

(ii) $\dfrac{d}{dx}\{x^{-n} I_n(x)\} = x^{-n} I_{n+1}(x).$

(iii) $I_n'(x) = I_{n-1}(x) - \dfrac{n}{x}I_n(x).$

(iv) $I_n'(x) = \dfrac{n}{x}I_n(x) + I_{n+1}(x).$

(v) $I_n'(x) = \tfrac{1}{2}\{I_{n-1}(x) + I_{n+1}(x)\}.$

(vi) $I_{n-1}(x) - I_{n+1}(x) = \dfrac{2n}{x}I_n(x).$

PROOF

We shall prove results (i) and (ii). The remaining results follow from (i) and (ii) exactly as in theorem 4.8.

(i) From theorem 4.8 (i) we have

$$\frac{d}{dx}\{x^n J_n(x)\} = x^n J_{n-1}(x).$$

Replacing x by ix gives

$$\frac{d}{d(ix)}\{i^n x^n J_n(ix)\} = i^n x^n J_{n-1}(ix),$$

which, on using the fact that $I_n(x) = i^{-n}J_n(ix)$, becomes

$$\frac{1}{i}\frac{d}{dx}\{i^n x^n i^n I_n(x)\} = i^n x^n i^{n-1} I_{n-1}(x)$$

and this equation, on cancelling a factor of i^{2n-1} throughout, gives

$$\frac{d}{dx}\{x^n I_n(x)\} = x^n I_{n-1}(x).$$

(ii) From theorem 4.8 (ii) we have

$$\frac{d}{dx}\{x^{-n}J_n(x)\} = -x^{-n}J_{n+1}(x),$$

which, on replacing x by ix, becomes

$$\frac{d}{d(ix)}\{i^{-n}x^{-n}J_n(ix)\} = -i^{-n}x^{-n}J_{n+1}(ix).$$

Thus

$$\frac{1}{i}\frac{d}{dx}\{i^{-n}x^{-n}i^n I_n(x)\} = -i^{-n}x^{-n}i^{n+1}I_{n+1}(x)$$

and hence

$$\frac{1}{i}\frac{d}{dx}\{x^{-n}I_n(x)\} = -ix^{-n}I_{n+1}(x)$$

so that

$$\frac{d}{dx}\{x^{-n}I_n(x)\} = x^{-n}I_{n+1}(x).$$

Theorem 4.16

(i) $\dfrac{d}{dx}\{x^n K_n(x)\} = -x^n K_{n-1}(x).$

(ii) $\dfrac{d}{dx}\{x^{-n}K_n(x)\} = -x^{-n}K_{n+1}(x).$

(iii) $K_n'(x) = -K_{n-1}(x) - \dfrac{n}{x}K_n(x).$

(iv) $K_n'(x) = \dfrac{n}{x}K_n(x) - K_{n+1}(x).$

(v) $K_n'(x) = -\tfrac{1}{2}\{K_{n-1}(x) + K_{n+1}(x)\}.$

(vi) $K_{n-1}(x) - K_{n+1}(x) = -\dfrac{2n}{x}K_n(x).$

Proof

Again, we prove only results (i) and (ii). Also, in the same way as in theorem 4.9, we prove the results for non-integral n and appeal to continuity for a proof in the integral case.

(i) From theorem 4.14 we have

$$K_n(x) = \frac{\pi}{2} i^{n+1} H_n^{(1)}(ix)$$

and by theorem 4.10 we know that $H_n^{(1)}(x)$ satisfies the first recurrence relation of theorem 4.8.

Hence
$$\frac{d}{dx}\{x^n H_n^{(1)}(x)\} = x^n H_{n-1}^{(1)}(x),$$

which, on replacing x by ix, gives

$$\frac{d}{d(ix)}\{i^n x^n H_n^{(1)}(ix)\} = i^n x^n H_{n-1}^{(1)}(ix).$$

Thus
$$\frac{1}{i}\frac{d}{dx}\{i^n x^n \frac{2}{\pi} i^{-n-1} K_n(x)\} = i^n x^n \frac{2}{\pi} i^{-n} K_{n-1}(x)$$

so that
$$-\frac{d}{dx}\{x^n K_n(x)\} = x^n K_{n-1}(x)$$

and hence
$$\frac{d}{dx}\{x^n K_n(x)\} = - x^n K_{n-1}(x).$$

(ii) Similarly $H_n^{(1)}(x)$, by theorem 4.10, satisfies the second recurrence relation of theorem 4.8 so that

$$\frac{d}{dx}\{x^{-n} H_n^{(1)}(x)\} = -x^{-n} H_{n+1}^{(1)}(x)$$

which, on replacing x by ix, gives

$$\frac{d}{d(ix)}\{i^{-n} x^{-n} H_n^{(1)}(ix)\} = -i^{-n} x^{-n} H_{n+1}^{(1)}(ix),$$

and hence, using theorem 4.14,

$$\frac{1}{i}\frac{d}{dx}\{i^{-n} x^{-n} \frac{2}{\pi} i^{-n-1} K_n(x)\} = -i^{-n} x^{-n} \frac{2}{\pi} i^{-n-2} K_{n+1}(x).$$

S F—I

Therefore

$$i^{-2n-2}\frac{d}{dx}\{x^{-n}K_n(x)\} = -i^{-2n-2}K_{n+1}(x),$$

from which a common factor of i^{-2n-2} cancels to give

$$\frac{d}{dx}\{x^{-n}K_n(x)\} = -K_{n+1}(x).$$

4.9   INTEGRAL REPRESENTATIONS FOR THE MODIFIED BESSEL FUNCTIONS

Theorem 4.17

(i) $I_n(x) = \dfrac{1}{(\sqrt{\pi})\Gamma(n+\frac{1}{2})}\left(\dfrac{x}{2}\right)^n \displaystyle\int_{-1}^{1} e^{-xt}(1-t^2)^{(n-\frac{1}{2})}\,dt$

$$(n > -\tfrac{1}{2}).$$

(ii) $K_n(x) = \dfrac{\sqrt{\pi}}{\Gamma(n+\frac{1}{2})}\left(\dfrac{x}{2}\right)^n \displaystyle\int_{1}^{\infty} e^{-xt}(t^2-1)^{n-\frac{1}{2}}\,dt$

$$(n > -\tfrac{1}{2}, x > 0).$$

PROOF

(i) By equation (4.17) we have

$$I_n(x) = i^{-n}J_n(ix)$$

and by theorem 4.7 we have

$$J_n(x) = \frac{1}{(\sqrt{\pi})\Gamma(n+\frac{1}{2})}\left(\frac{x}{2}\right)^n \int_{-1}^{1}(1-t^2)^{n-\frac{1}{2}}e^{ixt}\,dt$$

$$(n > -\tfrac{1}{2})$$

so that

$$I_n(x) = i^{-n}\frac{1}{(\sqrt{\pi})\Gamma(n+\frac{1}{2})}i^n\left(\frac{x}{2}\right)^n \int_{-1}^{1}(1-t^2)^{n-\frac{1}{2}}e^{-xt}\,dt$$

$$= \frac{1}{(\sqrt{\pi})\Gamma(n+\frac{1}{2})}\left(\frac{x}{2}\right)^n \int_{-1}^{1}(1-t^2)^{n-\frac{1}{2}}e^{-xt}\,dt.$$

(ii) We first show that the integral

$$P = x^n \int_{1}^{\infty} e^{-xt}(t^2-1)^{n-\frac{1}{2}}\,dt \quad (n > -\tfrac{1}{2}, x > 0) \qquad (4.20)$$

satisfies Bessel's modified equation

$$x^2\frac{d^2y}{dx^2} + x\frac{dy}{dx} - (x^2+n^2)y = 0.$$

We have

$$\frac{dP}{dx} = nx^{n-1} \int_1^\infty e^{-xt}(t^2 - 1)^{n-\frac{1}{2}} \, dt + x^n \int_1^\infty -t e^{-xt}(t^2 - 1)^{n-\frac{1}{2}} \, dt$$

and

$$\frac{d^2P}{dx^2} = n(n-1)x^{n-2} \int_1^\infty e^{-xt}(t^2 - 1)^{n-\frac{1}{2}} \, dt$$

$$+ 2nx^{n-1} \int_1^\infty -t \, e^{-xt}(t^2 - 1)^{n-\frac{1}{2}} \, dt$$

$$+ x^n \int_1^\infty t^2 \, e^{-xt}(t^2 - 1)^{n-\frac{1}{2}} \, dt$$

so that

$$x^2 \frac{d^2P}{dx^2} + x\frac{dP}{dx} - (x^2 + n^2)P$$

$$= x^n \int_1^\infty \{n(n-1) - 2nxt + x^2t^2 + n - xt - x^2 - n^2\} e^{-xt}(t^2 - 1)^{n-\frac{1}{2}} \, dt$$

$$= x^{n+1} \int_1^\infty \{x(t^2 - 1) - 2(n + \tfrac{1}{2})t\} e^{-xt}(t^2 - 1)^{n-\frac{1}{2}} \, dt$$

$$= x^{n+1} \int_1^\infty \{xe^{-xt}(t^2 - 1)^{n+\frac{1}{2}} - (n + \tfrac{1}{2})(t^2 - 1)^{n-\frac{1}{2}}2t \, e^{-xt}\} \, dt$$

$$= -x^{n+1} \int_1^\infty \frac{d}{dt}\{e^{-xt}(t^2 - 1)^{n+\frac{1}{2}}\} \, dt$$

$$= -x^{n+1}[e^{-xt}(t^2 - 1)^{n+\frac{1}{2}}]_1^\infty$$

$$= 0,$$

since the integrated part vanishes at the upper limit, $t = \infty$, because of the factor e^{-xt} (remembering that we are considering here $x > 0$) and at the lower limit, $t = 1$, because of the factor $(t^2 - 1)^{n+\frac{1}{2}}$ (remembering that $n + \frac{1}{2} > 0$).

Thus P satisfies Bessel's modified equation and therefore must be of the form

$$P = AI_n(x) + BK_n(x).$$

We show now that $A = 0$. We do this by considering the limit as $x \to \infty$. From the series (4.18) for $I_n(x)$ we see that $I_n(x)$ consists of a power series with positive coefficients, and hence $I_n(x) \to \infty$ as $x \to \infty$. Consider now $P(x)$. We have, from the definition, $P(x) > 0$, and we shall show that $P(x)$ is less than some quantity which tends to zero as x tends to infinity so that $P(x)$ itself must tend to zero as x tends to infinity.

Since the asymptotic behaviour of an exponential dominates that of a power, we must have $(t^2 - 1)^{n-\frac{1}{2}} < e^{xt/2}$ for x large enough (say for $x > X$).

Then for $x > X$ we have

$$P(x) < x^n \int_1^\infty e^{-xt} e^{xt/2} \, dt$$

$$= x^n \int_1^\infty e^{-xt/2} \, dt$$

$$= x^n \left[-\frac{2}{x} e^{-xt/2} \right]_1^\infty$$

$$= 2x^{n-1} e^{-x/2}$$

which $\longrightarrow 0$ as $x \longrightarrow \infty$, again using the fact that the exponential dominates the power.

Thus we have shown that $P(x) \longrightarrow 0$ as $x \longrightarrow \infty$, whereas $I_n(x) \longrightarrow \infty$. Hence $P(x)$ cannot contain any multiple of $I_n(x)$ and we must have

$$P(x) = BK_n(x).$$

To determine the constant B we examine the behaviour of both $P(x)$ and $K_n(x)$ as $x \longrightarrow 0$.

For $K_n(x)$ only the lowest power of x is important in this limit, and we may use the definition

$$K_n(x) = \frac{\pi}{2} \frac{I_{-n}(x) - I_n(x)}{\sin n\pi}$$

together with

$$I_n(x) = \sum_{r=0}^\infty \frac{1}{r!\Gamma(n + r + 1)} \left(\frac{x}{2}\right)^{2r+n}$$

to see that the lowest power of x in $I_n(x)$ is

$$\frac{1}{\Gamma(n + 1)} \left(\frac{x}{2}\right)^n$$

and hence in $K_n(x)$ is

$$\frac{\pi}{2 \sin n\pi} \frac{1}{\Gamma(-n + 1)} \left(\frac{x}{2}\right)^{-n}.$$

Hence as $x \longrightarrow 0$, $K_n(x) \longrightarrow \dfrac{\pi}{2\Gamma(1 - n) \sin n\pi} \left(\dfrac{2}{x}\right)^n$ which, on making use of the result of theorem 2.12 that

$$\Gamma(x)\Gamma(1 - x) = \frac{\pi}{\sin \pi x},$$

may be written in the form

$$K_n(x) \rightarrow \frac{\Gamma(n)2^{n-1}}{x^n}.$$

To study the behaviour of $P(x)$ near $x = 0$ we make the change of variable

$$t = 1 + \frac{u}{x}$$

so that

$$dt = \frac{1}{x}\, du.$$

Also, when $t = 1$, $u = 0$ and when $t = \infty$, $u = \infty$.

Thus, using equation (4.20),

$$P(x) = x^n \int_0^\infty e^{-x-u} \left(\frac{2u}{x} + \frac{u^2}{x^2}\right)^{n-\frac{1}{2}} \frac{1}{x}\, du$$

$$= \frac{1}{x^n} e^{-x} \int_0^\infty e^{-u} \left(1 + \frac{2x}{u}\right)^{n-\frac{1}{2}} u^{2n-1}\, du.$$

For small values of x we may make the approximations $e^{-x} \simeq 1$ and $\left(1 + \dfrac{2x}{u}\right)^{n-\frac{1}{2}} \simeq 1$ to obtain

$$P(x) \rightarrow \frac{1}{x^n} \int_0^\infty e^{-u} u^{2n-1}\, du$$

$$= \frac{1}{x^n}\Gamma(2n)$$

(by the definition of the gamma function).

Thus for small values of x the result $P(x) = BK_n(x)$ reduces to

$$\frac{1}{x^n}\Gamma(2n) = B\frac{\Gamma(n)2^{n-1}}{x^n}$$

giving

$$B = \frac{\Gamma(2n)}{\Gamma(n)2^{n-1}}.$$

But by theorem 2.10 we have

$$\Gamma(2n) = \frac{2^{2n-1}}{\sqrt{\pi}}\Gamma(n)\Gamma(n + \tfrac{1}{2})$$

so that

$$B = \frac{2^{2n-1}\Gamma(n)\Gamma(n + \tfrac{1}{2})}{(\sqrt{\pi})\Gamma(n)2^{n-1}}$$

$$= \frac{2^n\Gamma(n + \tfrac{1}{2})}{\sqrt{\pi}}.$$

Hence

$$P(x) = \frac{2^n \Gamma(n + \tfrac{1}{2})}{\sqrt{\pi}} K_n(x),$$

giving

$$K_n(x) = \frac{\sqrt{\pi}}{2^n \Gamma(n + \tfrac{1}{2})} P(x)$$

and thus, using the definition of $P(x)$,

$$K_n(x) = \frac{\sqrt{\pi}}{\Gamma(n + \tfrac{1}{2})} \left(\frac{x}{2}\right)^n \int_1^\infty e^{-xt} (t^2 - 1)^{n-\frac{1}{2}} \, dt.$$

4.10 KELVIN'S FUNCTIONS

Consider the differential equation

$$x^2 \frac{d^2 y}{dx^2} + x \frac{dy}{dx} - (ik^2 x^2 + n^2) y = 0. \tag{4.21}$$

This is of the form of Bessel's modified equation

$$x^2 \frac{d^2 y}{dx^2} + x \frac{dy}{dx} - (\lambda^2 x^2 + n^2) y = 0$$

with $\lambda^2 = ik^2$. Hence, since the general solution of Bessel's modified equation is

$$y = AI_n(\lambda x) + BK_n(\lambda x),$$

the general solution of equation (4.21) must be

$$y = AI_n(i^{\frac{1}{2}} k x) + BK_n(i^{\frac{1}{2}} k x).\dagger$$

Also, since $I_n(x) = i^{-n} J_n(ix)$, we may take the independent solutions of equation (4.21) as $J_n(i^{3/2} k x)$ and $K_n(i^{1/2} k x)$.

Of course, when x is real $J_n(i^{3/2} x)$ and $K_n(i^{1/2} x)$ are not necessarily real; we obtain real functions by the following definitions:

$$\mathrm{ber}_n x = \mathrm{Re}\, J_n(i^{3/2} x)$$
$$\mathrm{bei}_n x = \mathrm{Im}\, J_n(i^{3/2} x)$$
$$J_n(i^{3/2} x) = \mathrm{ber}_n x + i\, \mathrm{bei}_n x. \tag{4.22}$$

$$\mathrm{ker}_n x = \mathrm{Re}\, i^{-n} K_n(i^{1/2} x)$$
$$\mathrm{kei}_n x = \mathrm{Im}\, i^{-n} K_n(i^{1/2} x)$$
$$i^{-n} K_n(i^{1/2} x) = \mathrm{ker}_n x + i\, \mathrm{kei}_n x. \tag{4.23}$$

---

† Strictly speaking, $i^{\frac{1}{2}}$ is a two-valued function with values $e^{i\pi/4}$ and $e^{i5\pi/4}$. We remove this ambiguity by taking the value $e^{i\pi/4}$.

(If $n = 0$ the notation used is often ber x, etc.)

Thus the general solution of equation (4.21) is given by

$$y = A_1(\text{ber}_n kx + i\, \text{bei}_n kx) + A_2(\text{ker}_n kx + i\, \text{kei}_n kx). \qquad (4.24)$$

4.11   SPHERICAL BESSEL FUNCTIONS

Consider the equation

$$x^2 \frac{d^2y}{dx^2} + 2x\frac{dy}{dx} + \{k^2x^2 - l(l+1)\}y = 0. \qquad (4.25)$$

This is of the form of the equation of theorem 4.12 with

$$1 - 2\alpha = 2$$
$$\gamma = 1$$
$$\beta^2\gamma^2 = k^2$$
$$\alpha^2 - n^2\gamma^2 = -l(l+1).$$

Solving these equations for α, β, γ, n gives

$$\alpha = -\tfrac{1}{2},\ \beta = k,\ \gamma = 1,\ n = l + \tfrac{1}{2}$$

and hence by theorem 4.12 the general solution of the above equation is given by

$$y = Ax^{-\frac{1}{2}}J_{l+\frac{1}{2}}(kx) + Bx^{-\frac{1}{2}}Y_{l+\frac{1}{2}}(kx)$$
$$= A_1 j_l(kx) + A_2 y_l(kx)$$

where we have defined the spherical Bessel functions $j_l(x)$ and $y_l(x)$ by

$$j_l(x) = \sqrt{\left(\frac{\pi}{2x}\right)} J_{l+\frac{1}{2}}(x) \qquad (4.26)$$

$$y_l(x) = \sqrt{\left(\frac{\pi}{2x}\right)} Y_{l+\frac{1}{2}}(x) \qquad (4.27)$$

and A_1, A_2 are new arbitrary constants related to A, B by $A_1 = \sqrt{(2k/\pi)}A$, $A_2 = \sqrt{(2k/\pi)}B$.

Spherical Hankel functions may also be defined in a way exactly analogous to the definition of Hankel functions:

$$h_l^{(1)}(x) = j_l(x) + iy_l(x) \qquad (4.28)$$
$$h_l^{(2)}(x) = j_l(x) - iy_l(x). \qquad (4.29)$$

In applications it turns out that the spherical Bessel functions of most interest are those of integral order. We shall show that such spherical

Bessel functions may in fact be written in closed form in terms of elementary functions. First, however, we prove recurrence relations analogous to those in theorems 4.8, 4.9 and 4.10 for the Bessel functions.

Theorem 4.18

If $f_n(x)$ is any of $j_n(x)$, $y_n(x)$, $h_n^{(1)}(x)$ or $h_n^{(2)}(x)$, then

(i) $\dfrac{d}{dx}\{x^{n+1}f_n(x)\} = x^{n+1}f_{n-1}(x).$

(ii) $\dfrac{d}{dx}\{x^{-n}f_n(x)\} = -x^{-n}f_{n+1}(x).$

(iii) $f_n'(x) = f_{n-1}(x) - \dfrac{n+1}{x}f_n(x).$

(iv) $f_n'(x) = \dfrac{n}{x}f_n(x) - f_{n+1}(x).$

(v) $(2n+1)f_n'(x) = nf_{n-1}(x) - (n+1)f_{n+1}(x).$

(vi) $f_{n-1}(x) + f_{n+1}(x) = \dfrac{2n+1}{x}f_n(x).$

PROOF

We first prove the results for $j_n(x)$.

(i) From theorem 4.8 (i) with n replaced by $n + \frac{1}{2}$ we have

$$\frac{d}{dx}\{x^{n+\frac{1}{2}}J_{n+\frac{1}{2}}(x)\} = x^{n+\frac{1}{2}}J_{n+\frac{1}{2}-1}(x)$$

which, on using definition (4.26), becomes

$$\frac{d}{dx}\left\{x^{n+\frac{1}{2}}\sqrt{(2/\pi)}x^{\frac{1}{2}}j_n(x)\right\} = x^{n+\frac{1}{2}}\sqrt{(2/\pi)}x^{\frac{1}{2}}j_{n-1}(x)$$

and this simplifies to

$$\frac{d}{dx}\{x^{n+1}j_n(x)\} = x^{n+1}j_{n-1}(x).$$

(ii) From theorem 4.8 (ii) with n replaced by $n + \frac{1}{2}$ we have

$$\frac{d}{dx}\{x^{-n-\frac{1}{2}}J_{n+\frac{1}{2}}(x)\} = -x^{-n-\frac{1}{2}}J_{n+\frac{1}{2}+1}(x).$$

Again, use of definition (4.26) gives

$$\frac{d}{dx}\left\{x^{-n-\frac{1}{2}}\sqrt{(2/\pi)}x^{\frac{1}{2}}j_n(x)\right\} = -x^{-n-\frac{1}{2}}\sqrt{(2/\pi)}x^{\frac{1}{2}}j_{n+1}(x)$$

and hence

$$\frac{d}{dx}\{x^{-n}j_n(x)\} = - x^{-n}j_{n+1}(x).$$

(iii) If we carry out the differentiation on the left-hand side of (i) above, we obtain

$$x^{n+1}j_n'(x) + (n+1)x^n j_n(x) = x^{n+1}j_{n-1}(x).$$

On dividing throughout by x^{n+1}, this gives

$$j_n'(x) + \frac{n+1}{x}j_n(x) = j_{n-1}(x)$$

and thus

$$j_n'(x) = j_{n-1}(x) - \frac{n+1}{x}j_n(x).$$

(iv) Carry out the differentiation on the left-hand side of (ii) above, and we obtain

$$x^{-n}j_n'(x) - nx^{-n-1}j_n(x) = - x^{-n}j_{n+1}(x).$$

Cancelling a common factor of x^{-n} then gives

$$j_n'(x) - \frac{n}{x}j_n(x) = -j_{n+1}(x)$$

and hence

$$j_n'(x) = \frac{n}{x}j_n(x) - j_{n+1}(x).$$

(v) Multiply result (iii) by n, result (iv) by $(n+1)$ and add, and we obtain the required result.

(vi) Subtract result (iv) from result (iii), and we obtain the required result.

The proofs for $y_n(x)$, $h_n^{(1)}(x)$, and $h_n^{(2)}(x)$ follow in the same way, since these functions bear the same relationship to $Y_{n+\frac{1}{2}}(x)$, $H_{n+\frac{1}{2}}^{(1)}(x)$ and $H_{n+\frac{1}{2}}^{(2)}(x)$ that $j_n(x)$ does to $J_{n+\frac{1}{2}}(x)$ and by theorems 4.9 and 4.10 the various Bessel functions all satisfy the same recurrence relations.

Theorem 4.19

(i) $j_0(x) = \dfrac{\sin x}{x}.$

(ii) $y_0(x) = -\dfrac{\cos x}{x}.$

(iii) $h_0^{(1)}(x) = -i\,\dfrac{e^{ix}}{x}.$

(iv) $h_0^{(2)}(x) = i\,\dfrac{e^{-ix}}{x}.$

PROOF

(i) We have, by equation (4.26),

$$j_0(x) = \sqrt{(\pi/2x)}J_{\frac{1}{2}}(x) = \sqrt{\left(\frac{\pi}{2x}\right)}\sum_{r=0}^{\infty}(-1)^r\frac{1}{r!\,\Gamma(\frac{1}{2}+r+1)}\left(\frac{x}{2}\right)^{2r+\frac{1}{2}}$$

(from equation (4.6));

but, by the corollary to theorem 2.10, we have

$$\Gamma(r+1+\tfrac{1}{2}) = \frac{(2r+2)!}{2^{2r+2}(r+1)!}\sqrt{\pi}$$

so that we now have

$$j_0(x) = \frac{\sqrt{\pi}}{2^{\frac{1}{2}}x^{\frac{1}{2}}}\sum_{r=0}^{\infty}(-1)^r\frac{2^{2r+2}(r+1)!}{r!(2r+2)!\sqrt{\pi}}\frac{x^{2r+\frac{1}{2}}}{2^{2r+\frac{1}{2}}}$$

$$= \sum_{r=0}^{\infty}(-1)^r\frac{2(r+1)}{(2r+2)!}x^{2r}$$

$$= \sum_{r=0}^{\infty}(-1)^r\frac{x^{2r}}{(2r+1)!}$$

$$= \frac{1}{x}\sum_{r=0}^{\infty}(-1)^r\frac{x^{2r+1}}{(2r+1)!} = \frac{1}{x}\sin x$$

(on recognising the infinite series for $\sin x$).

(ii) We have

$$y_0(x) = \sqrt{\left(\frac{\pi}{2x}\right)}Y_{\frac{1}{2}}(x)$$

(by definition (4.27))

$$= \sqrt{\left(\frac{\pi}{2x}\right)}\frac{\cos\frac{1}{2}\pi\,J_{\frac{1}{2}}(x) - J_{-\frac{1}{2}}(x)}{\sin\frac{1}{2}\pi}$$

(by the definition of $Y_n(x)$ in theorem 4.2)

$$= -\sqrt{\left(\frac{\pi}{2x}\right)}J_{-\frac{1}{2}}(x)$$

$$= -\sqrt{\left(\frac{\pi}{2x}\right)} \sum_{r=0}^{\infty} (-1)^r \frac{1}{r!\,\Gamma(-\frac{1}{2}+r+1)} \left(\frac{x}{2}\right)^{2r-\frac{1}{2}}$$

(by the series (4.7)).

But again, by the corollary of theorem 2.10, we have

$$\Gamma(-\tfrac{1}{2}+r+1) = \Gamma(r+\tfrac{1}{2})$$
$$= \frac{(2r)!}{2^{2r}r!}\sqrt{\pi}$$

so that

$$y_0(x) = -\frac{\sqrt{\pi}}{2^{\frac{1}{2}}x^{\frac{1}{2}}} \sum_{r=0}^{\infty} (-1)^r \frac{2^{2r}r!}{r!\,(2r)!\sqrt{\pi}} \frac{x^{2r-\frac{1}{2}}}{2^{2r-\frac{1}{2}}}$$

$$= -\sum_{r=0}^{\infty} (-1)^r \frac{x^{2r-1}}{(2r)!}$$

$$= -\frac{1}{x} \sum_{r=0}^{\infty} (-1)^r \frac{x^{2r}}{(2r)!}$$

$$= -\frac{1}{x}\cos x,$$

(on recognising the infinite series for $\cos x$).

(iii)
$$h_0^{(1)}(x) = j_0(x) + iy_0(x)$$

(by definition (4.28))

$$= \frac{1}{x}\sin x - i\frac{1}{x}\cos x$$

$$= -\frac{i}{x}(\cos x + i\sin x)$$

$$= -i\frac{e^{ix}}{x}.$$

(iv)
$$h_0^{(2)}(x) = j_0(x) - iy_0(x)$$

$$= \frac{1}{x}\sin x + i\frac{1}{x}\cos x$$

$$= \frac{i}{x}(\cos x - i\sin x)$$

$$= i\frac{e^{-ix}}{x}.$$

Theorem 4.20 (Rayleigh's Formulae)

If n is a non-negative integer, then

(i) $j_n(x) = (-1)^n x^n \left(\frac{1}{x}\frac{d}{dx}\right)^n \left(\frac{\sin x}{x}\right);$

(ii) $y_n(x) = -(-1)^n x^n \left(\frac{1}{x}\frac{d}{dx}\right)^n \left(\frac{\cos x}{x}\right)$

(iii) $h_n^{(1)}(x) = -i(-1)^n x^n \left(\frac{1}{x}\frac{d}{dx}\right)^n \left(\frac{e^{ix}}{x}\right);$

(iv) $h_n^{(2)}(x) = i(-1)^n x^n \left(\frac{1}{x}\frac{d}{dx}\right)^n \left(\frac{e^{-ix}}{x}\right).$

PROOF

We give the proof for (i) only, the proofs for the other three results being similar.

We shall use the method of induction; i.e., we shall assume the result true for $n = N$, say, and then prove it true for $n = N + 1$. Then since theorem 4.19 guarantees the result true for $n = 0$, it follows that it must be true for all positive integral n.

Assuming the result true for $n = N$ implies that

$$j_N(x) = (-1)^N x^N \left(\frac{1}{x}\frac{d}{dx}\right)^N \left(\frac{\sin x}{x}\right).$$

From theorem 4.18 (ii) we have

$$j_{N+1}(x) = -x^N \frac{d}{dx}\{x^{-N} j_N(x)\}$$

$$= -x^N \frac{d}{dx}\left\{x^{-N}(-1)^N x^N \left(\frac{1}{x}\frac{d}{dx}\right)^N \left(\frac{\sin x}{x}\right)\right\}$$

(using the fact that we are assuming the result to be true for $n = N$)

$$= -(-1)^N x^N \frac{d}{dx}\left(\frac{1}{x}\frac{d}{dx}\right)^N \left(\frac{\sin x}{x}\right)$$

$$= (-1)^{N+1} x^{N+1} \left(\frac{1}{x}\frac{d}{dx}\right)\left(\frac{1}{x}\frac{d}{dx}\right)^N \left(\frac{\sin x}{x}\right)$$

$$= (-1)^{N+1} x^{N+1} \left(\frac{1}{x}\frac{d}{dx}\right)^{N+1} \left(\frac{\sin x}{x}\right)$$

which thus proves the result true for $n = N + 1$.

Hence, by the remarks above, the result must be true for all positive integral n.

We may use the results of this theorem to write down explicitly the first few spherical Bessel functions of integral order. We obtain in this way:

$$j_1(x) = \frac{\sin x}{x^2} - \frac{\cos x}{x},$$

$$j_2(x) = \left(\frac{3}{x^3} - \frac{1}{x}\right) \sin x - \frac{3}{x^2} \cos x,$$

$$j_3(x) = \left(\frac{15}{x^4} - \frac{6}{x^2}\right) \sin x - \left(\frac{15}{x^3} - \frac{1}{x}\right) \cos x; \qquad (4.30)$$

$$y_1(x) = -\frac{\cos x}{x^2} - \frac{\sin x}{x},$$

$$y_2(x) = -\left(\frac{3}{x^3} - \frac{1}{x}\right) \cos x - \frac{3}{x^2} \sin x,$$

$$y_3(x) = -\left(\frac{15}{x^4} - \frac{6}{x^2}\right) \cos x - \left(\frac{15}{x^3} - \frac{1}{x}\right) \sin x. \qquad (4.31)$$

It is to be noted that because of the relationships (4.26) and (4.27) all the above information concerning spherical Bessel functions of integral order provides an equal amount of information concerning Bessel functions of half-odd integral order.

4.12 BEHAVIOUR OF THE BESSEL FUNCTIONS FOR LARGE AND SMALL VALUES OF THE ARGUMENT

Theorem 4.21

As $x \longrightarrow \infty$ we have†

(i) $J_n(x) \sim \left(\frac{2}{\pi x}\right)^{\frac{1}{2}} \cos\left\{x - (n + \tfrac{1}{2})\frac{\pi}{2}\right\};$

(ii) $Y_n(x) \sim \left(\frac{2}{\pi x}\right)^{\frac{1}{2}} \sin\left\{x - (n + \tfrac{1}{2})\frac{\pi}{2}\right\};$

(iii) $H_1^{(n)}(x) \sim \left(\frac{2}{\pi x}\right)^{\frac{1}{2}} \exp\left[i\left\{x - (n + \tfrac{1}{2})\frac{\pi}{2}\right\}\right];$

(iv) $H_n^{(2)}(x) \sim \left(\frac{2}{\pi x}\right)^{\frac{1}{2}} \exp\left[-i\left\{x - (n + \tfrac{1}{2})\frac{\pi}{2}\right\}\right];$

---

† Here we use the symbol $\sim$ rather loosely to mean 'behaves like'. A more precise definition is: $f(x) \sim g(x)$ as $x \to a$ if $\lim_{x \to a} (f(x)/g(x)) = 1$.

(v) $I_n(x) \sim \dfrac{1}{\sqrt{(2\pi x)}} e^x$;

(vi) $K_n(x) \sim \left(\dfrac{\pi}{2x}\right)^{\frac{1}{2}} e^{-x}$;

(vii) $j_n(x) \sim \dfrac{1}{x} \sin\left(x - \dfrac{n\pi}{2}\right)$;

(viii) $y_n(x) \sim -\dfrac{1}{x} \cos\left(x - \dfrac{n\pi}{2}\right)$;

(ix) $h_n^{(1)}(x) \sim -\dfrac{i}{x} \exp\left[i\{x - (n\pi/2)\}\right]$;

(x) $h_n^{(2)}(x) \sim \dfrac{i}{x} \exp\left[-i\{x - (n\pi/2)\}\right]$.

PROOF

We shall first prove result (vi) and then deduce the remainder of the results from it.

(vi) By theorem 4.17 (ii) we have

$$K_n(x) = \frac{\sqrt{\pi}}{\Gamma(n + \frac{1}{2})} \left(\frac{x}{2}\right)^n \int_1^\infty e^{-xt}(t^2 - 1)^{n-\frac{1}{2}} \, dt.$$

We now make the change of variable

$$t = 1 + \frac{u}{x}$$

so that

$$dt = \frac{1}{x} \, du.$$

Also, when $t = 1$, $u = 0$ and when $t = \infty$, $u = \infty$.

Thus

$$K_n(x) = \frac{\sqrt{\pi}}{\Gamma(n + \frac{1}{2})} \left(\frac{x}{2}\right)^n \int_0^\infty e^{-(x+u)} \left(\frac{u^2}{x^2} + \frac{2u}{x}\right)^{n-\frac{1}{2}} \frac{1}{x} \, du$$

$$= \frac{\sqrt{\pi}}{\Gamma(n + \frac{1}{2})} \left(\frac{x}{2}\right)^n e^{-x} \left(\frac{2}{x}\right)^{n-\frac{1}{2}} \frac{1}{x} \int_0^\infty e^{-u} \left(\frac{u}{2x} + 1\right)^{n-\frac{1}{2}} u^{n-\frac{1}{2}} \, du$$

$$= \frac{\sqrt{\pi}}{\Gamma(n + \frac{1}{2})} \left(\frac{2}{x}\right)^{-\frac{1}{2}} \frac{1}{x} e^{-x} \int_0^\infty e^{-u} u^{n-\frac{1}{2}} \left(1 + \frac{u}{2x}\right)^{n-\frac{1}{2}} \, du.$$

For large values of x we have $u/2x$ small, so that we may take as an approximation

$$\left(1 + \frac{u}{2x}\right)^{n-\frac{1}{2}} \sim 1.$$

Then

$$K_n(x) \sim \frac{\sqrt{\pi}}{\Gamma(n+\tfrac{1}{2})} \frac{1}{\sqrt{(2x)}} e^{-x} \int_0^\infty e^{-u} u^{n-\frac{1}{2}} \, du$$

$$= \frac{\sqrt{\pi}}{\Gamma(n+\tfrac{1}{2})} \frac{1}{\sqrt{(2x)}} e^{-x} \Gamma(n+\tfrac{1}{2})$$

$$\text{(by definition (2.1))}$$

$$= \left(\frac{\pi}{2x}\right)^{\frac{1}{2}} e^{-x}.$$

(iii) From theorem 4.14 we have

$$K_n(x) = \frac{\pi}{2} i^{n+1} H_n^{(1)}(ix)$$

where, if n is non-integral, we take the value of the many-valued function i^{n+1} given by $e^{(i\pi/2)(n+1)}$.

Then

$$H_n^{(1)}(ix) = \frac{2}{\pi} \exp\{(-i\pi/2)(n+1)\} K_n(x)$$

and hence, on replacing x by $-ix$,

$$H_n^{(1)}(x) = \frac{2}{\pi} \exp\{(-i\pi/2)(n+1)\} K_n(-ix)$$

Thus

$$H_n^{(1)}(x) \sim \frac{2}{\pi} \exp\{(-i\pi/2)(n+1)\} \left(\frac{\pi}{-2ix}\right)^{\frac{1}{2}} e^{ix}$$

$$= \left(\frac{2}{\pi x}\right)^{\frac{1}{2}} (-i)^{-\frac{1}{2}} \exp\{(-i\pi/2)(n+1)\} e^{ix}$$

$$= \left(\frac{2}{\pi x}\right)^{\frac{1}{2}} e^{i\pi/4} \exp\{(-i\pi/2)(n+1)\} e^{ix}$$

$$\text{(on writing } -i = e^{-i\pi/2})$$

$$= \left(\frac{2}{\pi x}\right)^{\frac{1}{2}} \exp[i\{x - (n+\tfrac{1}{2})(\pi/2)\}].$$

(iv) Since $H_n^{(2)}(x) = J_n(x) - iY_n(x)$

and $H_n^{(1)}(x) = J_n(x) + iY_n(x)$

we have $H_n^{(2)}(x) = \{H_n^{(1)}(x)\}^*$

$$\sim \left[\left(\frac{2}{\pi x}\right)^{\frac{1}{2}} \exp[i\{x - (n+\tfrac{1}{2})(\pi/2)\}]\right]^*$$

$$= \left(\frac{2}{\pi x}\right)^{\frac{1}{2}} \exp[-i\{(n+\tfrac{1}{2})(\pi/2)\}].$$

(i) We have

$$J_n(x) = \operatorname{Re} H_n^{(1)}(x)$$

$$\sim \operatorname{Re}\left(\frac{2}{\pi x}\right)^{\frac{1}{2}} \exp\left[i\{x - (n + \tfrac{1}{2})(\pi/2)\}\right]$$

$$= \left(\frac{2}{\pi x}\right)^{\frac{1}{2}} \cos\left\{x - (n + \tfrac{1}{2})\frac{\pi}{2}\right\}.$$

(ii) Similarly

$$Y_n(x) = \operatorname{Im} H_n^{(1)}(x)$$

$$\sim \operatorname{Im}\left(\frac{2}{\pi x}\right)^{\frac{1}{2}} \exp\left[i\{x - (n + \tfrac{1}{2})(\pi/2)\}\right]$$

$$= \left(\frac{2}{\pi x}\right)^{\frac{1}{2}} \sin\left\{x - (n + \tfrac{1}{2})\frac{\pi}{2}\right\}.$$

(v) By definition we have $I_n(x) = i^{-n} J_n(ix)$ so that, by part (i) above, we have

$$I_n(x) \sim i^{-n}\left(\frac{2}{\pi i x}\right)^{\frac{1}{2}} \cos\left\{ix - (n + \tfrac{1}{2})\frac{\pi}{2}\right\}$$

$$= i^{-n-\frac{1}{2}}\left(\frac{2}{\pi x}\right)^{\frac{1}{2}} \tfrac{1}{2}[\exp\{-x-(n+\tfrac{1}{2})(\pi/2)i\} + \exp\{x+(n+\tfrac{1}{2})(\pi/2)i\}]$$

$$= i^{-n-\frac{1}{2}} \frac{1}{\sqrt{(2\pi x)}} \exp\{x + (n + \tfrac{1}{2})(\pi/2)i\}$$

(keeping only the dominant term for $x \to \infty$)

$$= i^{-n-\frac{1}{2}} \frac{1}{\sqrt{(2\pi x)}} \exp(x) . i^{n+\frac{1}{2}}$$

(writing $\exp(i\pi/2) = i$)

$$= \frac{1}{\sqrt{(2\pi x)}} e^x.$$

(vii) $\quad j_n(x) = \left(\frac{\pi}{2x}\right)^{\frac{1}{2}} J_{n+\frac{1}{2}}(x)$

(by definition (4.26))

$$\sim \left(\frac{\pi}{2x}\right)^{\frac{1}{2}}\left(\frac{2}{\pi x}\right)^{\frac{1}{2}} \cos\left\{x - (n + 1)\frac{\pi}{2}\right\}$$

(by result (i) above)

$$= \frac{1}{x} \cos\left(x - \frac{n\pi}{2} - \frac{\pi}{2}\right).$$

$$= \frac{1}{x} \sin \left(x - \frac{n\pi}{2} \right).$$

(viii) $y_n(x) = \left(\dfrac{\pi}{2x} \right)^{\frac{1}{2}} Y_{n+\frac{1}{2}}(x)$

(by definition (4.27))

$$\sim \left(\frac{\pi}{2x} \right)^{\frac{1}{2}} \left(\frac{2}{\pi x} \right)^{\frac{1}{2}} \sin \left\{ x - (n+1)\frac{\pi}{2} \right\}$$

(by result (ii) above)

$$= \frac{1}{x} \sin \left(x - \frac{n\pi}{2} - \frac{\pi}{2} \right)$$

$$= -\frac{1}{x} \sin \left\{ \frac{\pi}{2} - \left(x - \frac{n\pi}{2} \right) \right\}$$

$$= -\frac{1}{x} \cos \left(x - \frac{n\pi}{2} \right).$$

(ix) $h_n^{(1)}(x) = j_n(x) + i y_n(x)$

$$\sim \frac{1}{x} \sin \left(x - \frac{n\pi}{2} \right) - \frac{i}{x} \cos \left(x - \frac{n\pi}{2} \right)$$

$$= -\frac{i}{x} \left\{ \cos \left(x - \frac{n\pi}{2} \right) + i \sin \left(x - \frac{n\pi}{2} \right) \right\}$$

$$= -\frac{i}{x} \exp \left[i\{ x - (n\pi/2) \} \right].$$

(x) $h_n^{(2)}(x) = \{ h_n^{(1)}(x) \}^*$

$$\sim \left[-\frac{i}{x} \exp \left[i\{ x - n(\pi/2) \} \right] \right]^*$$

$$= \frac{i}{x} \exp \left[-i\{ x - (n\pi/2) \} \right].$$

Theorem 4.22

As $x \to 0$ we have

(i) $J_n(x) \sim \dfrac{1}{\Gamma(n+1)} \left(\dfrac{x}{2} \right)^n$

S F—K

(ii)
$$Y_n(x) \sim \begin{cases} -\dfrac{1}{\pi}\Gamma(n)\left(\dfrac{2}{x}\right)^n & (n \neq 0) \\[2ex] \dfrac{2}{\pi}\ln x & (n = 0); \end{cases}$$

(iii) $j_n(x) \sim \dfrac{x^n}{(2n+1)!!}$ (n integral);†

(iv) $y_n(x) \sim -\dfrac{(2n-1)!!}{x^{n+1}}$ (n integral).

PROOF

(i) We consider the series (4.6) for $J_n(x)$. As $x \to 0$ only the lowest power of x will be important. But this lowest power of x is just given by the term with $r = 0$, so that we have

$$J_n(x) \sim \frac{1}{\Gamma(n+1)}\left(\frac{x}{2}\right)^n.$$

(ii) When n is not an integer we have

$$Y_n(x) = \frac{\cos n\pi \, J_n(x) - J_{-n}(x)}{\sin n\pi}$$

and we pick out the lowest power of x occurring in this expression. This will be contained in $J_{-n}(x)$ and will be given by the result of (i) above, so that we obtain

$$Y_n(x) \sim -\frac{1}{\sin n\pi}\frac{1}{\Gamma(-n+1)}\left(\frac{x}{2}\right)^{-n}$$

$$= -\frac{\Gamma(n)}{\pi}\left(\frac{2}{x}\right)^n,$$

using the result of theorem (2.12) that

$$\Gamma(n)\Gamma(1-n) = \frac{\pi}{\sin n\pi}.$$

When n is an integer we pick out the dominant term from the series for $Y_n(x)$ given by theorem 4.3. Remembering that a power of x dominates a logarithm, we see that

$$Y_n(x) \sim \frac{2}{\pi}\ln x \qquad (n = 0)$$

---

† By $n!!$ (n double factorial) we mean
$$n(n-2)(n-4)\ldots \begin{cases} 5.3.1 \text{ if } n \text{ is odd} \\ 6.4.2 \text{ if } n \text{ is even.} \end{cases}$$

and
$$Y_n(x) \sim -\frac{1}{\pi}(n-1)!\left(\frac{x}{2}\right)^{-n} \quad (n \neq 0)$$

$$= -\frac{1}{\pi}\Gamma(n)\left(\frac{2}{x}\right)^n.$$

(iii) We have from definition (4.26)

$$j_n(x) = \sqrt{\left(\frac{\pi}{2x}\right)}J_{n+\frac{1}{2}}(x)$$

$$\sim \sqrt{\left(\frac{\pi}{2x}\right)}\frac{1}{\Gamma(n+\frac{3}{2})}\left(\frac{x}{2}\right)^{n+\frac{1}{2}}$$

$$= \frac{(\sqrt{\pi})x^n}{2^{n+1}}\frac{1}{(n+\frac{1}{2})(n-\frac{1}{2})\ldots\frac{3}{2}.\frac{1}{2}\Gamma(\frac{1}{2})}$$

(using repeatedly the fact that $\Gamma(n+1) = n\Gamma(n)$)

$$= \frac{(\sqrt{\pi})x^n}{(2n+1)(2n-1)\ldots3.1.\sqrt{\pi}}$$

(where we have made use of the result of theorem 2.6 that $\Gamma(\frac{1}{2}) = \sqrt{\pi}$)

$$= \frac{x^n}{(2n+1)!!}.$$

(iv)
$$y_n(x) = \sqrt{\left(\frac{\pi}{2x}\right)}Y_{n+\frac{1}{2}}(x)$$

$$\sim \sqrt{\left(\frac{\pi}{2x}\right)}\left\{-\frac{1}{\pi}\Gamma(n+\frac{1}{2})\left(\frac{2}{x}\right)^{n+\frac{1}{2}}\right\}$$

$$= -\frac{1}{\sqrt{\pi}}\frac{2^n}{x^{n+1}}\Gamma(n+\frac{1}{2})$$

$$= -\frac{1}{\sqrt{\pi}}\frac{2^n}{x^{n+1}}(n-\frac{1}{2})(n-\frac{3}{2})\ldots\frac{3}{2}.\frac{1}{2}\Gamma(\frac{1}{2})$$

$$= -\frac{1}{\sqrt{\pi}}\frac{(2n-1)(2n-3)\ldots3.1.\sqrt{\pi}}{x^{n+1}}$$

$$= -\frac{(2n-1)!!}{x^{n+1}}.$$

4.13 GRAPHS OF THE BESSEL FUNCTIONS

We give here some graphs of various Bessel functions; they bring out rather clearly the behaviour for large and small x discussed in the previous section.

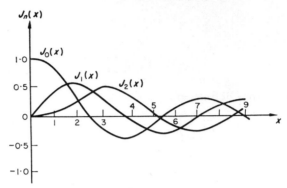

FIG. 4.1 $J_n(x)$, $n = 0, 1, 2$

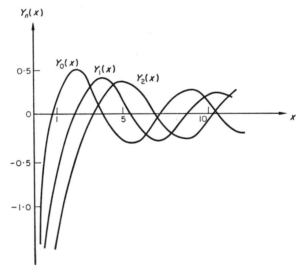

FIG. 4.2 $Y_n(x)$, $n = 0, 1, 2$

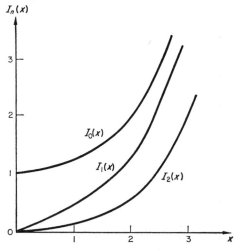

FIG. 4.3 $I_n(x)$, $n = 0, 1, 2$

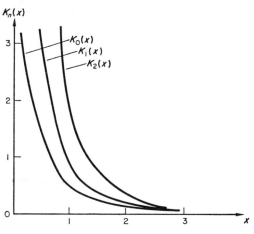

FIG. 4.4 $K_n(x)$, $n = 0, 1, 2$

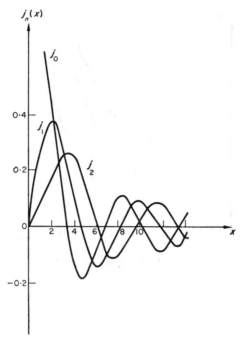

FIG. 4.5 $j_n(x)$, $n = 0, 1, 2$

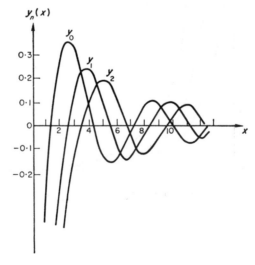

FIG. 4.6 $y_n(x)$, $n = 0, 1, 2$

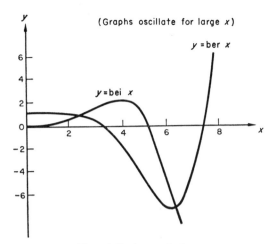

FIG. 4.7   ber x, bei x

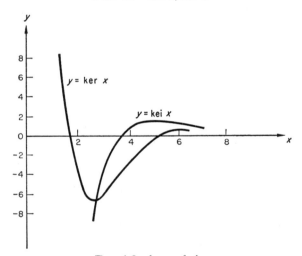

FIG. 4.8   ker x, kei x

4.14   ORTHONORMALITY OF THE BESSEL FUNCTIONS; BESSEL SERIES

Theorem 4.23

$$\int_0^a x J_n(\xi_i x) J_n(\xi_j x)\,\mathrm{d}x = \frac{a^2}{2}\{J_{n+1}(\xi_i a)\}^2 \delta_{ij}$$

if ξ_i and ξ_j are roots of the equation $J_n(\xi a) = 0$.

PROOF

We first show that if ξ_i and ξ_j are distinct roots of the equation $J_n(\xi a) = 0$ then

$$\int_0^a x J_n(\xi_i x) J_n(\xi_j x) \, dx = 0.$$

$J_n(\xi_i x)$ and $J_n(\xi_j x)$, being Bessel functions, must satisfy the following equations

$$x^2 \frac{d^2}{dx^2} J_n(\xi_i x) + x \frac{d}{dx} J_n(\xi_i x) + (\xi_i^2 x^2 - n^2) J_n(\xi_i x) = 0$$

and

$$x^2 \frac{d^2}{dx^2} J_n(\xi_j x) + x \frac{d}{dx} J_n(\xi_j x) + (\xi_j^2 x^2 - n^2) J_n(\xi_j x) = 0,$$

which may be written in the form

$$x \frac{d}{dx} \left\{ x \frac{d}{dx} J_n(\xi_i x) \right\} + (\xi_i^2 x^2 - n^2) J_n(\xi_i x) = 0 \qquad (4.32)$$

and

$$x \frac{d}{dx} \left\{ x \frac{d}{dx} J_n(\xi_j x) \right\} + (\xi_j^2 x^2 - n^2) J_n(\xi_j x) = 0. \qquad (4.33)$$

Multiplying equation (4.32) by $(1/x) J_n(\xi_j x)$, equation (4.33) by $(1/x) J_n(\xi_i x)$ and subtracting, we obtain

$$J_n(\xi_j x) \frac{d}{dx} \left\{ x \frac{d}{dx} J_n(\xi_i x) \right\} - J_n(\xi_i x) \frac{d}{dx} \left\{ x \frac{d}{dx} J_n(\xi_j x) \right\}$$

$$+ (\xi_i^2 - \xi_j^2) \, x J_n(\xi_i x) J_n(\xi_j x) = 0.$$

Applying the result $u(dv/dx) = (d/dx)(uv) - v(du/dx)$ to both first and second terms gives

$$\frac{d}{dx} \left\{ J_n(\xi_j x) x \frac{d}{dx} J_n(\xi_i x) \right\} - \left\{ \frac{d}{dx} J_n(\xi_j x) \right\} x \frac{d}{dx} J_n(\xi_i x)$$

$$- \frac{d}{dx} \left\{ J_n(\xi_i x) x \frac{d}{dx} J_n(\xi_j x) \right\} + \left\{ \frac{d}{dx} J_n(\xi_i x) \right\} x \frac{d}{dx} J_n(\xi_j x)$$

$$+ (\xi_i^2 - \xi_j^2) x J_n(\xi_i x) J_n(\xi_j x) = 0$$

and thus

$$\frac{d}{dx} \left\{ J_n(\xi_j x) x \frac{d}{dx} J_n(\xi_i x) \right\} - \frac{d}{dx} \left\{ J_n(\xi_i x) x \frac{d}{dx} J_n(\xi_j x) \right\}$$

$$+ (\xi_i^2 - \xi_j^2) x J_n(\xi_i x) J_n(\xi_j x) = 0.$$

Integrating from 0 to a, we obtain

$$\left[J_n(\xi_j x) x \frac{\mathrm{d}}{\mathrm{d}x} J_n(\xi_i x) - J_n(\xi_i x) x \frac{\mathrm{d}}{\mathrm{d}x} J_n(\xi_j x) \right]_0^a$$

$$+ (\xi_i^2 - \xi_j^2) \int_0^a x J_n(\xi_i x) J_n(\xi_j x) \, \mathrm{d}x = 0.$$

The first term will now vanish at the upper limit since

$$J_n(\xi_i a) = J_n(\xi_j a) = 0,$$

and at the lower limit because it contains a factor x.

Accordingly $(\xi_i^2 - \xi_j^2) \displaystyle\int_0^a x J_n(\xi_i x) J_n(\xi_j x) \, \mathrm{d}x = 0$

and hence $\displaystyle\int_0^a x J_n(\xi_i x) J_n(\xi_j x) \, \mathrm{d}x = 0$

provided $\xi_i \neq \xi_j$.

To complete the proof we require to prove that

$$\int_0^a x \{ J_n(\xi x) \}^2 \, \mathrm{d}x = \frac{a^2}{2} \{ J_{n+1}(\xi a) \}^2$$

if $J_n(\xi a) = 0.$

Now, if we denote $J_n(\xi x)$ by z we have

$$x^2 z'' + x z' + (\xi^2 x^2 - n^2) z = 0$$

which, on multiplication by $2z'$, becomes

$$2x^2 z'' z' + 2x z'^2 + 2(\xi^2 x^2 - n^2) z z' = 0$$

and this is readily seen to be equivalent to

$$\frac{\mathrm{d}}{\mathrm{d}x} \{ x^2 z'^2 - n^2 z^2 + \xi^2 x^2 z^2 \} - 2\xi^2 x z^2 = 0.$$

Integrating this equation from 0 to a gives

$$[x^2 z'^2 - n^2 z^2 + \xi^2 x^2 z^2]_0^a - 2\xi^2 \int_0^a x z^2 \, \mathrm{d}x = 0$$

which, on replacing z by $J_n(\xi x)$, becomes

$$\left[x^2 \left\{ \frac{\mathrm{d}}{\mathrm{d}x} J_n(\xi x) \right\}^2 - n^2 \{ J_n(\xi x) \}^2 + \xi^2 x^2 \{ J_n(\xi x) \}^2 \right]_0^a$$

$$- 2\xi^2 \int_0^a x \{ J_n(\xi x) \}^2 \, \mathrm{d}x = 0$$

and hence, using the facts that $J_n(\xi a) = 0$ and $n J_n(0) = 0$,

$$\left[a^2 \left\{ \frac{\mathrm{d}}{\mathrm{d}x} J_n(\xi x) \right\}^2 \right]_{x=a} - 2\xi^2 \int_0^a x \{ J_n(\xi x) \}^2 \, \mathrm{d}x = 0.$$

Hence

$$\int_0^a x\{J_n(\xi x)\}^2 \, dx = \frac{1}{2\xi^2}\left[a^2\left\{\frac{d}{dx}J_n(\xi x)\right\}^2\right]_{x=a}.$$

But, by theorem 4.8(iv), we have

$$\frac{d}{d(\xi x)}J_n(\xi x) = \frac{n}{\xi x}J_n(\xi x) - J_{n+1}(\xi x)$$

which may be rewritten in the form

$$\frac{d}{dx}J_n(\xi x) = \frac{n}{x}J_n(\xi x) - \xi J_{n+1}(\xi x)$$

so that

$$\int_0^a x\{J_n(\xi x)\}^2 \, dx = \frac{1}{2\xi^2}\left[a^2\left\{\frac{n}{x}J_n(\xi x) - \xi J_{n+1}(\xi x)\right\}^2\right]_{x=a}$$

$$= \frac{1}{2\xi^2}a^2\xi^2\{J_{n+1}(\xi a)\}^2$$

(again using the fact that $J_n(\xi a) = 0$)

$$= \frac{a^2}{2}\{J_{n+1}(\xi a)\}^2.$$

Theorem 4.24

If $f(x)$ is defined in the region $0 \leqslant x \leqslant a$ and can be expanded in the form $\sum_{i=1}^{\infty} c_i J_n(\xi_i x)$ where the ξ_i are the roots of the equation $J_n(\xi a) = 0$, then

$$c_i = \frac{2\int_0^a xf(x)J_n(\xi_i x) \, dx}{a^2\{J_{n+1}(\xi_i a)\}^2}.$$

PROOF

We have

$$f(x) = \sum_{i=1}^{\infty} c_i J_n(\xi_i x)$$

so that

$$xf(x)J_n(\xi_j x) = \sum_{i=1}^{\infty} c_i x J_n(\xi_i x)J_n(\xi_j x)$$

and hence

$$\int_0^a x f(x) J_n(\xi_j x) \, dx = \sum_{i=1}^{\infty} c_i \int_0^a x J_n(\xi_i x) J_n(\xi_j x) \, dx$$

$$= \sum_{i=1}^{\infty} c_i \frac{a^2}{2} J_{n+1}(\xi_i a)^2 \delta_{ij}$$

(by theorem 4.23)

$$= c_j \frac{a^2}{2} \{J_{n+1}(\xi_j a)\}^2.$$

Thus

$$c_j = \frac{2 \int_0^a x f(x) J_n(\xi_j x) \, dx}{a^2 \{J_{n+1}(\xi_j a)\}^2}$$

which completes the proof.

The series $\sum_{i=1}^{\infty} c_i J_n(\xi_i x)$, with c_i as given above, is called the Bessel series for $f(x)$. The conditions under which $f(x)$ may be expanded in this way are given in the next theorem, which we quote without proof.

Theorem 4.25

If $f(x)$ is defined for $0 < x < a$ and $\int_0^a (\sqrt{x}) f(x) \, dx$ is finite, then

$$\sum_{i=1}^{\infty} c_i J_n(\xi_i x)$$

(with c_i as defined above) is convergent and has sum $f(x)$ if $f(x)$ is continuous at x and $\frac{1}{2} \{f(x+) + f(x-)\}$ if $f(x)$ is discontinuous at x.

4.15 INTEGRALS INVOLVING BESSEL FUNCTIONS

Theorem 4.26

$$J_n(x) = \frac{2(x/2)^{n-m}}{\Gamma(n-m)} \int_0^1 (1 - t^2)^{n-m-1} t^{m+1} J_m(xt) \, dt$$

$$(n > m > -1).$$

PROOF

Consider the integral

$$I = \int_0^1 (1 - t^2)^{n-m-1} t^{m+1} J_m(xt) \, dt$$

and substitute the series (4.6) for J_m to obtain

$$I = \int_0^1 (1 - t^2)^{n-m-1} t^{m+1} \sum_{r=0}^{\infty} (-1)^r \frac{(xt/2)^{m+2r}}{r!\Gamma(m+r+1)} \, dt$$

$$= \sum_{r=0}^{\infty} (-1)^r \frac{(x/2)^{m+2r}}{r!\Gamma(m+r+1)} \int_0^1 (1 - t^2)^{n-m-1} t^{2m+2r+1} \, dt$$

$$= \sum_{r=0}^{\infty} (-1)^r \frac{(x/2)^{m+2r}}{r!\Gamma(m+r+1)} \frac{1}{2} \int_0^1 (1 - u)^{n-m-1} u^{m+r} \, du$$

(on making the substitution $u = t^2$).

But $\int_0^1 (1 - u)^{n-m-1} u^{m+r} \, du$

$$= B(n - m, m + r + 1)$$

(by the definition of the beta function, provided $n - m > 0$ and $m + r + 1 > 0$. This last condition is equivalent to $m > -1$, since r takes on values between zero and infinity.)

$$= \frac{\Gamma(n - m)\Gamma(m + r + 1)}{\Gamma(n + r + 1)}$$

(by theorem 2.7).

Hence $$I = \tfrac{1}{2}\Gamma(n - m) \sum_{r=0}^{\infty} (-1)^r \frac{(x/2)^{m+2r}}{r!\Gamma(n + r + 1)}$$

$$= \tfrac{1}{2}\Gamma(n - m)\left(\frac{x}{2}\right)^{m-n} \sum_{r=0}^{\infty} (-1)^r \frac{(x/2)^{n+2r}}{r!\Gamma(n + r + 1)}$$

$$= \tfrac{1}{2}\Gamma(n - m)\left(\frac{x}{2}\right)^{m-n} J_n(x).$$

Thus

$$J_n(x) = 2\frac{(x/2)^{n-m}}{\Gamma(n - m)} I$$

which is the required result.

Theorem 4.27

$$\int_0^{\infty} e^{-ax} J_0(bx) \, dx = \frac{1}{\sqrt{(a^2 + b^2)}} \qquad (a > 0).$$

PROOF

From theorem 4.6 we have

$$J_0(x) = \frac{1}{\pi} \int_0^\pi \cos(x \sin \phi)\, d\phi.$$

Hence

$$\int_0^\infty e^{-ax} J_0(bx)\, dx = \int_0^\infty e^{-ax} \frac{1}{\pi} \int_0^\pi \cos(bx \sin \phi)\, d\phi\, dx$$

$$= \frac{1}{\pi} \int_0^\pi \left[\int_0^\infty e^{-ax} \tfrac{1}{2}\{\exp(ibx \sin \phi) + \exp(-ibx \sin \phi)\}\, dx \right] d\phi$$

(interchanging the order of integration)

$$= \frac{1}{2\pi} \int_0^\pi \left[\frac{\exp\{-(a - ib \sin \phi)x\}}{-a + ib \sin \phi} + \frac{\exp\{-(a + ib \sin \phi)x\}}{-a - ib \sin \phi} \right]_0^\infty d\phi$$

$$= \frac{1}{2\pi} \int_0^\pi \left\{ \frac{1}{a - ib \sin \phi} + \frac{1}{a + ib \sin \phi} \right\} d\phi$$

$$= \frac{a}{\pi} \int_0^\pi \frac{1}{a^2 + b^2 \sin^2 \phi}\, d\phi.$$

But this last integral may be evaluated by elementary means (e.g., by the substitution $u = \cot \phi$) to give

$$\int_0^\infty e^{-ax} J_0(bx)\, dx = \frac{a}{\pi} \frac{\pi}{a\sqrt{(a^2 + b^2)}}$$

$$= \frac{1}{\sqrt{(a^2 + b^2)}}.$$

Theorem 4.28

$$\int_0^\infty J_n(bx)\, dx = \frac{1}{b} \quad (\textit{if } n \textit{ is a non-negative integer}).$$

PROOF

We first prove the result for $n = 0$ and $n = 1$, and then show that if the result is true for $n = N$, it is also true for $n = N + 2$, thus proving the result for all non-negative integral n.

For $n = 0$ we take the limit as $a \to 0$ of the result of theorem 4.27, obtaining

$$\int_0^\infty J_0(bx)\, dx = \frac{1}{b}.$$

For $n = 1$ we make use of theorem 4.8(ii), which says that

$$\frac{d}{dx}\{x^{-n}J_n(x)\} = -x^{-n}J_{n+1}(x)$$

so that, by taking $n = 0$, we have

$$\frac{d}{dx}J_0(x) = -J_1(x),$$

and replacing x by bx gives

$$\frac{d}{d(bx)}J_0(bx) = -J_1(bx)$$

which is equivalent to

$$\frac{1}{b}\frac{d}{dx}J_0(bx) = -J_1(bx).$$

Hence
$$\int_0^\infty J_1(bx)\,dx = -\frac{1}{b}\left[J_0(bx)\right]_0^\infty$$

$$= \frac{1}{b},$$

since $J_0(\infty) = 0$ and $J_0(0) = 1$, results which are implied by theorems 4.21(i) and 4.22(i).

If we now use theorem 4.8(v) and integrate from 0 to ∞, we obtain

$$\left[J_n(x)\right]_0^\infty = \frac{1}{2}\int_0^\infty \{J_{n-1}(x) - J_{n+1}(x)\}\,dx.$$

Remembering that $n > 0$ so that $J_n(\infty) = J_n(0) = 0$, we have

$$0 = \frac{1}{2}\int_0^\infty \{J_{n-1}(x) - J_{n+1}(x)\}\,dx$$

and thus

$$\int_0^\infty J_{n+1}(x)\,dx = \int_0^\infty J_{n-1}(x)\,dx.$$

Replacing $n - 1$ by N and x by bx gives the result

$$\int_0^\infty J_{N+2}(bx)\,dx = \int_0^\infty J_N(bx)\,dx.$$

Thus if $\int_0^\infty J_N(bx)\,dx = \frac{1}{b}$, we also have $\int_0^\infty J_{N+2}(bx)\,dx = \frac{1}{b}$, and hence the proof is complete.

Theorem 4.29

(i) $\displaystyle\int_0^\infty J_n(bx)x^n\, e^{-ax}\, dx = \frac{2^n\Gamma(n+\frac12)}{\sqrt{\pi}} \frac{b^n}{(a^2+b^2)^{n+\frac12}};$

(ii) $\displaystyle\int_0^\infty J_n(bx)x^{n+1}\, e^{-ax}\, dx = \frac{2^{n+1}\Gamma(n+\frac32)}{\sqrt{\pi}} \frac{ab^n}{(a^2+b^2)^{n+\frac32}};$

$$(a > 0).$$

PROOF

(i) From equation (4.6) we have

$$J_n(bx) = \sum_{r=0}^{\infty} (-1)^r \frac{1}{r!\,\Gamma(n+r+1)} \left(\frac{bx}{2}\right)^{2r+n}$$

so that

$$\int_0^\infty J_n(bx)x^n\, e^{-ax}\, dx$$

$$= \sum_{r=0}^{\infty} (-1)^r \frac{1}{r!\,\Gamma(n+r+1)}\left(\frac{b}{2}\right)^{2r+n} \int_0^\infty e^{-ax}x^{2r+2n}\, dx.$$

But $\displaystyle\int_0^\infty e^{-ax}x^{2r+2n}\, dx$

$$= \int_0^\infty e^{-t} \frac{t^{2r+2n}}{a^{2r+2n+1}}\, dt$$

$$(\text{writing } t = ax)$$

$$= \frac{1}{a^{2r+2n+1}}\Gamma(2r+2n+1),$$

$$(\text{by definition (2.1) of the gamma function}),$$

so that

$$\int_0^\infty J_n(bx)x^n\, e^{-ax}\, dx$$

$$= \sum_{r=0}^{\infty}(-1)^r \frac{1}{r!\,\Gamma(n+r+1)}\left(\frac{b}{2}\right)^{2r+n} \frac{1}{a^{2r+2n+1}}\Gamma(2r+2n+1)$$

$$= \sum_{r=0}^{\infty}(-1)^r \frac{1}{r!}\frac{2\Gamma(2r+2n)}{\Gamma(r+n)}\left(\frac{b}{2}\right)^{2r+n} \frac{1}{a^{2r+2n+1}}$$

(using the result of theorem 2.2 that $\Gamma(n+1) = n\Gamma(n)$).

But by theorem 2.10 we have

$$\frac{\Gamma(2x)}{\Gamma(x)} = \Gamma(x + \tfrac{1}{2})\frac{2^{2x-1}}{\sqrt{\pi}}$$

so that

$$\int_0^\infty J_n(bx)x^n\,e^{-ax}\,dx$$

$$= \sum_{r=0}^\infty (-1)^r \frac{1}{r!} 2\Gamma(r + n + \tfrac{1}{2})\frac{2^{2r+2n-1}}{\sqrt{\pi}}\left(\frac{b}{2}\right)^{2r+n}\frac{1}{a^{2r+2n+1}}$$

$$= \frac{2^n b^n}{\sqrt{\pi}} \sum_{r=0}^\infty (-1)^r \frac{\Gamma(r + n + \tfrac{1}{2})\,b^{2r}}{a^{2r+2n+1}\,r!}$$

$$= \frac{2^n b^n}{(\sqrt{\pi})a^{2n+1}} \sum_{r=0}^\infty (-1)^r \frac{\Gamma(r + n + \tfrac{1}{2})}{r!}\left(\frac{b^2}{a^2}\right)^r.$$

But $\dfrac{1}{(a^2 + b^2)^{n+\frac{1}{2}}} = \dfrac{1}{a^{2n+1}}\left(1 + \dfrac{b^2}{a^2}\right)^{-n-\frac{1}{2}}$

$$= \frac{1}{a^{2n+1}}\left\{1 + (-n - \tfrac{1}{2})\left(\frac{b^2}{a^2}\right) + \frac{(-n - \tfrac{1}{2})(-n - \tfrac{3}{2})}{2!}\left(\frac{b^2}{a^2}\right)^2 + \cdots \right.$$

$$\left. + \frac{(-n - \tfrac{1}{2})(-n - \tfrac{3}{2})\cdots(-n - \tfrac{1}{2} - r + 1)}{r!}\left(\frac{b^2}{a^2}\right)^r + \cdots\right\}$$

(by the binomial theorem)

$$= \frac{1}{a^{2n+1}} \sum_{r=0}^\infty (-1)^r \frac{(n + \tfrac{1}{2})(n + \tfrac{3}{2})\cdots(n + r - \tfrac{1}{2})}{r!}\left(\frac{b^2}{a^2}\right)^r$$

$$= \frac{1}{a^{2n+1}} \sum_{r=0}^\infty (-1)^r \frac{\Gamma(n + \tfrac{1}{2})(n + \tfrac{1}{2})(n + \tfrac{3}{2})\cdots(n + r - \tfrac{1}{2})}{\Gamma(n + \tfrac{1}{2})\,r!}\left(\frac{b^2}{a^2}\right)^r$$

$$= \frac{1}{a^{2n+1}} \sum_{r=0}^\infty (-1)^r \frac{\Gamma(n + r + \tfrac{1}{2})}{\Gamma(n + \tfrac{1}{2})\,r!}\left(\frac{b^2}{a^2}\right)^r,$$

on repeated use of the result $x\Gamma(x) = \Gamma(x + 1)$ (theorem 2.2).

Hence $\qquad \displaystyle\int_0^\infty J_n(bx)x^n\,e^{-ax}\,dx = \frac{2^n b^n}{\sqrt{\pi}}\Gamma(n + \tfrac{1}{2})\frac{1}{(a^2 + b^2)^{n+\frac{1}{2}}}$

$$= \frac{2^n \Gamma(n + \tfrac{1}{2})}{\sqrt{\pi}}\frac{b^n}{(a^2 + b^2)^{n+\frac{1}{2}}}.$$

(ii) This result follows immediately from result (i) if we differentiate both sides with respect to a.

Theorem 4.30

(i) $\int_0^\infty J_n(bx)x^{n+1} \exp(-ax^2) \, dx = \dfrac{b^n}{(2a)^{n+1}} \exp(-b^2/4a);$

(ii) $\int_0^\infty J_n(bx)x^{n+3} \exp(-ax^2) \, dx = \dfrac{b^n}{2^{n+1}a^{n+2}}\left(n + 1 - \dfrac{b^2}{4a}\right) \exp(-b^2/4a);$

$$(a > 0).$$

PROOF

The proof is very similar to the proof of theorem 4.29; so we shall not give it here.

Theorem 4.31

(i) $\int_0^\infty \sin ax \, J_0(bx) \, dx = \begin{cases} 0 & (b > a) \\ \dfrac{1}{\sqrt{(a^2 - b^2)}} & (b < a). \end{cases}$

(ii) $\int_0^\infty \cos ax \, J_0(bx) \, dx = \begin{cases} \dfrac{1}{\sqrt{(b^2 - a^2)}} & (b > a) \\ 0 & (b < a). \end{cases}$

PROOF

We shall obtain these results by replacing the a occurring in theorem 4.27 by ia, although it should be noted that strictly speaking this is not allowed, since the proof of theorem 4.27 depended on having the real part of a positive. It is possible to give a procedure justifying taking the real part of a zero, but we shall not describe it here.

Thus we have

$$\int_0^\infty e^{-iax} J_0(bx) \, dx = \frac{1}{\sqrt{(b^2 - a^2)}}$$

so that

$$\int_0^\infty \cos ax \, J_0(bx) \, dx - i \int_0^\infty \sin ax \, J_0(bx) \, dx = \frac{1}{\sqrt{(b^2 - a^2)}}.$$

Equating imaginary parts of both sides gives

$$\int_0^\infty \sin ax \, J_0(bx) \, dx = \frac{1}{\sqrt{(a^2 - b^2)}} \qquad \text{if } a > b$$

$$\int_0^\infty \sin ax \, J_0(bx) \, dx = 0 \qquad \text{if } a < b.$$

Equating real parts of both sides gives

$$\int_0^\infty \cos ax\, J_0(bx)\, dx = \frac{1}{\sqrt{(b^2 - a^2)}} \quad \text{if } b > a$$

$$\int_0^\infty \cos ax\, J_0(bx)\, dx = 0 \quad \text{if } b < a.$$

4.16 EXAMPLES

Example 1

Use the generating function to prove that

$$J_n(x + y) = \sum_{r=-\infty}^{\infty} J_r(x) J_{n-r}(y).$$

We have from theorem 4.5 that

$$\exp\left\{\tfrac{1}{2}(x + y)\left(t - \frac{1}{t}\right)\right\} = \sum_{n=-\infty}^{\infty} J_n(x + y)t^n$$

so that $J_n(x + y)$ is the coefficient of t^n in the expansion

of $\qquad \exp\left\{\tfrac{1}{2}(x + y)\left(t - \frac{1}{t}\right)\right\}.$

But

$$\exp\left\{\tfrac{1}{2}(x + y)\left(t - \frac{1}{t}\right)\right\} = \exp\left\{\tfrac{1}{2}x\left(t - \frac{1}{t}\right)\right\} \cdot \exp\left\{\tfrac{1}{2}y\left(t - \frac{1}{t}\right)\right\}$$

$$= \sum_{r=-\infty}^{\infty} J_r(x)t^r \cdot \sum_{s=-\infty}^{\infty} J_s(y)t^s$$

$$= \sum_{r,s=-\infty}^{\infty} J_r(x)J_s(y)t^{r+s}.$$

For a particular value of r we obtain t^n by taking $s = n - r$, so that, for this value of r, we obtain the coefficient of t^n as $J_r(x)J_{n-r}(y)$; hence the total coefficient of t^n is obtained by summing over all allowed values of r.

Accordingly the coefficient of t^n is equal to $\sum_{r=-\infty}^{\infty} J_r(x)J_{n-r}(y)$ and thus

$$J_n(x + y) = \sum_{r=-\infty}^{\infty} J_r(x)J_{n-r}(y).$$

Example 2

Show that $\int_0^\infty \frac{J_n(x)}{x}\,dx = \frac{1}{n}.$

From theorem 4.28 we have

$$\int_0^\infty J_n(x)\,dx = 1.$$

But from theorem 4.8(vi) we have

$$\frac{2n}{x}J_n(x) = J_{n-1}(x) + J_{n+1}(x)$$

so that $\quad 2n\int_0^\infty \frac{J_n(x)}{x}\,dx = \int_0^\infty J_{n-1}(x)\,dx + \int_0^\infty J_{n+1}(x)\,dx$

$$= 1 + 1,$$

and hence $\quad \int_0^\infty \frac{J_n(x)}{x}\,dx = \frac{1}{n}.$

Example 3

If ξ_i are the solutions of the equation $J_0(\xi) = 0$,

show that $\sum_{i=1}^\infty \frac{J_0(\xi_i x)}{\{\xi_i J_1(\xi_i)\}^2} = -\tfrac{1}{2}\ln x \qquad (0 < x < 1).$

We use theorem 4.25 to write

$$-\tfrac{1}{2}\ln x = \sum_{i=1}^\infty c_i J_0(\xi_i x)$$

with

$$c_i = \frac{2\int_0^1 x(-\tfrac{1}{2}\ln x)J_0(\xi_i x)\,dx}{\{J_1(\xi_i)\}^2}$$

$$= -\frac{\int_0^1 x\ln x\, J_0(\xi_i x)\,dx}{\{J_1(\xi_i)\}^2}.$$

To evaluate the integral appearing in the numerator we use the series (4.6) for J_0:

$$J_0(\xi_i x) = \sum_{r=0}^\infty (-1)^r \frac{1}{r!\,\Gamma(r+1)}\left(\frac{\xi_i x}{2}\right)^{2r}$$

$$= \sum_{r=0}^{\infty} (-1)^r \frac{1}{(r!)^2} \left(\frac{\xi_i}{2}\right)^{2r} x^{2r}$$

(and we note that since $J_0(\xi_i) = 0$ we shall have

$$\sum_{r=0}^{\infty} (-1)^r \frac{1}{(r!)^2} \left(\frac{\xi_i}{2}\right)^{2r} = 0). \qquad (4.34)$$

We shall also require the integral $\int_0^1 x^n \ln x \, dx$.

Integrating by parts gives

$$\int_0^1 x^n \ln x \, dx = \left[\frac{1}{n+1} x^{n+1} \ln x\right]_0^1 - \int_0^1 \frac{1}{n+1} x^{n+1} \cdot \frac{1}{x} \, dx$$

$$= 0 - \int_0^1 \frac{1}{n+1} x^n \, dx$$

$$= -\frac{1}{(n+1)^2}. \qquad (4.35)$$

Thus $\int_0^1 x \ln x \, J_0(\xi_i x) \, dx$

$$= \sum_{r=0}^{\infty} (-1)^r \frac{1}{(r!)^2} \left(\frac{\xi_i}{2}\right)^{2r} \int_0^1 x^{2r+1} \ln x \, dx$$

$$= \sum_{r=0}^{\infty} (-1)^r \frac{1}{(r!)^2} \left(\frac{\xi_i}{2}\right)^{2r} \left\{-\frac{1}{(2r+2)^2}\right\}$$

(using equation (4.35))

$$= \frac{1}{\xi_i^2} \sum_{r=0}^{\infty} (-1)^{r+1} \frac{1}{\{(r+1)!\}^2} \left(\frac{\xi_i}{2}\right)^{2r+2}$$

$$= \frac{1}{\xi_i^2} \sum_{r=1}^{\infty} (-1)^r \frac{1}{(r!)^2} \left(\frac{\xi_i}{2}\right)^{2r}$$

$$= \frac{1}{\xi_i^2} \left\{\sum_{r=0}^{\infty} (-1)^r \frac{1}{(r!)^2} \left(\frac{\xi_i}{2}\right)^{2r} - 1\right\}$$

$$= -\frac{1}{\xi_i^2},$$

(using equation (4.34)).

Thus we have

$$c_i = \frac{1}{\xi_i^2 \{J_1(\xi_i)\}^2}$$

and hence

$$-\tfrac{1}{2} \ln x = \sum_{i=1}^{\infty} \frac{J_0(\xi_i x)}{\{\xi_i J_1(\xi_i)\}^2}$$

Example 4

Show that $J_n(x) Y_n'(x) - J_n'(x) Y_n(x) = \dfrac{A}{x}$

where A is a constant, and by considering the behaviour for small x show that
$A = 2/\pi.$

We have

$$\frac{d}{dx}\{J_n Y_n' - J_n' Y_n\}$$

$$= J_n Y_n'' + J_n' Y_n' - J_n'' Y_n - J_n' Y_n'$$
$$= J_n Y_n'' - J_n'' Y_n$$

(all functions having argument x);

but both $J_n(x)$ and $Y_n(x)$ satisfy the equation

$$x^2 y'' + x y' + (x^2 - n^2)y = 0$$

so that

$$x^2 \frac{d}{dx}\{J_n Y_n' - J_n' Y_n\}$$

$$= J_n\{-x Y_n' - (x^2 - n^2) Y_n\} - \{-x J_n' - (x^2 - n^2)J_n\} Y_n$$
$$= -x\{J_n Y_n' - J_n' Y_n\}.$$

Hence, writing $J_n Y_n' - J_n' Y_n = z$, we have

$$\frac{dz}{dx} = -\frac{z}{x}$$

or

$$\frac{dz}{z} + \frac{dx}{x} = 0.$$

When integrated this gives

$$\ln z + \ln x = \text{constant}$$

which is equivalent to

$$\ln zx = \text{constant}$$

and hence $zx = \text{constant} = A$, say.

Thus $z = \dfrac{A}{x}$ so that, by the definition of z,

$$J_n Y_n' - J_n' Y_n = \frac{A}{x}.$$

For small values of x, we have, by theorem 4.22,

$$J_0(x) \sim 1, \quad Y_0(x) \sim \frac{2}{\pi} \ln x$$

so that, considering the relationship for $n = 0$, we have

$$J_n Y_n' - J_n' Y_n \sim 1.\frac{2}{\pi}.\frac{1}{x} - 0.\frac{2}{\pi} \ln x$$

$$= \frac{2}{\pi x}.$$

Hence

$$\frac{2}{\pi x} = \frac{A}{x},$$

giving

$$A = \frac{2}{\pi}$$

and thus

$$J_n(x) Y_n'(x) - J_n'(x) Y_n(x) = \frac{2}{\pi x}.$$

Example 5

$$\int_0^x t\{J_n(t)\}^2 \, dt = \frac{x^2}{2}\{J_n{}^2(x) - J_{n-1}(x)J_{n-1}(x)\}.\dagger$$

We shall show this by first proving that

$$t\{J_n(t)\}^2 = \frac{d}{dt}\left[\frac{t^2}{2}\{J_n{}^2(t) - J_{n-1}(t)J_{n+1}(t)\}\right]$$

and then integrating this relationship from 0 to x.
  We have

$$\frac{d}{dt}\left\{\frac{t^2}{2}(J_n^2 - J_{n-1}J_{n+1})\right\}$$

$\dagger\ J_n^2(x) \equiv \{J_n(x)\}^2.$

$$= t(J_n^2 - J_{n-1}J_{n+1}) + \frac{t^2}{2}(2J_nJ_n' - J_{n-1}'J_{n+1} - J_{n-1}J_{n+1}')$$

(it being understood that the argument of all Bessel functions here is t)

$$= t(J_n^2 - J_{n-1}J_{n+1}) + \frac{t^2}{2}\left\{2J_n \tfrac{1}{2}(J_{n-1} - J_{n+1})\right.$$

$$\left. - \left(\frac{n-1}{t}J_{n-1} - J_n\right)J_{n+1} - J_{n-1}\left(J_n - \frac{n+1}{t}J_{n+1}\right)\right\}$$

(using theorem 4.8(iii), (iv) and (v))

$$= t(J_n^2 - J_{n-1}J_{n+1}) + \frac{t^2}{2}\cdot\frac{2}{t}J_{n-1}J_{n+1}$$

$$= tJ_n^2.$$

Integrating from 0 to x now gives

$$\int_0^x tJ_n^2 \, dt = \left[\frac{t^2}{2}\{J_n^2(t) - J_{n-1}(t)J_{n+1}(t)\}\right]_0^x$$

$$= \frac{x^2}{2}\{J_n^2(x) - J_{n-1}(x)J_{n+1}(x)\}.$$

Example 6

Use the generating function to show that $J_n(-x) = (-1)^nJ_n(x)$.

We have, from theorem 4.5,

$$\exp\left\{\frac{x}{2}\left(t - \frac{1}{t}\right)\right\} = \sum_{n=-\infty}^{\infty} J_n(x)t^n$$

so that

$$\sum_{n=-\infty}^{\infty} J_n(-x)t^n = \exp\left[\frac{1}{2}\left\{-x\left(t - \frac{1}{t}\right)\right\}\right]$$

$$= \exp\left[\frac{x}{2}\left\{(-t) - \frac{1}{(-t)}\right\}\right]$$

$$= \sum_{n=-\infty}^{\infty} J_n(x)(-t)^n$$

$$= \sum_{n=-\infty}^{\infty} (-1)^n t^n J_n(x).$$

Equating the coefficients of t^n on both sides gives

$$J_n(-x) = (-1)^nJ_n(x).$$

PROBLEMS

(1) Show that

$$\frac{d}{dx}\{xJ_n(x)J_{n+1}(x)\} = x\{J_n^2(x) - J_{n+1}^2(x)\}.$$

(2) Show that (i) $\displaystyle\int_0^{\pi/2} J_0(x\cos\theta)\cos\theta\,d\theta = \frac{\sin x}{x}$;

(ii) $\displaystyle\int_0^{\pi/2} J_1(x\cos\theta)\,d\theta = \frac{1-\cos x}{x}.$

(3) Show that $J_n'(x)J_{-n}(x) - J_n(x)J_{-n}'(x) = A/x$ where A is a constant; by considering the behaviour for large values of x, show that

$$A = (2\sin n\pi)/\pi.$$

(4) Find the solution of the differential equation

$$(\sqrt{x})\frac{d^2y}{dx^2} + \lambda y = 0$$

which is zero at $x = 0$.

(5) Show that $\displaystyle\sum_{n=0}^{\infty} \frac{x^n}{n!}J_n(a) = J_0\{\sqrt{(a^2 - 2ax)}\}.$

(6) Use the generating function to prove that

$$1 = \{J_0(x)\}^2 + 2\{J_1(x)\}^2 + 2\{J_2(x)\}^2 + \dots$$

and deduce that $|J_0(x)| \leqslant 1,\ |J_n(x)| \leqslant 1/\sqrt{2}\quad (n = 1, 2, 3 \dots).$

(7) Show that $\displaystyle\int_0^{\infty} \frac{J_{n+1}(x)}{x^n}\,dx = \frac{1}{2^n\Gamma(n+1)}$ if $n > -\tfrac{1}{2}.$

(8) Prove that $\displaystyle\sum_{n=-\infty}^{\infty} J_n(kx)t^n = \exp\left\{\frac{x}{2t}\left(k - \frac{1}{k}\right)\right\}\sum_{n=-\infty}^{\infty} k^n t^n J_n(x)$

and deduce that $\displaystyle I_n(x) = \sum_{m=0}^{\infty} \frac{x^m}{m!}J_{n+m}(x).$

(9) Show that $\displaystyle\exp\left\{\frac{x}{2}\left(t + \frac{1}{t}\right)\right\} = \sum_{n=-\infty}^{\infty} I_n(x)t^n.$

(10) Show that $J_n(x)$, $Y_n(x)$, $K_n(x)$ and $I_n(x)$ all satisfy the differential equation

$$\frac{d^4y}{dx^4} + \frac{2}{x}\frac{d^3y}{dx^3} - \frac{2n^2+1}{x^2}\frac{d^2y}{dx^2} + \frac{2n^2+1}{x^3}\frac{dy}{dx} + \left(\frac{n^4-4n^2}{x^4} - 1\right)y = 0.$$

(11) Expand x^2 in a series of the form $\sum\limits_{r=1}^{\infty} c_r J_0(\lambda_r x)$ valid for the region $0 \leqslant x \leqslant a$, where λ_r are the roots of the equation $J_0(\lambda a) = 0$.

(12) Use the differential equation satisfied by $j_n(x)$ to show that

$$\{n(n+1) - m(m+1)\}j_n(x)j_m(x) = \frac{d}{dx}\{x^2 j_n'(x)j_m(x) - j_n(x)j_m'(x)\}.$$

Hence show that

$$\int_0^{\infty} j_m(x)j_n(x)\,dx = \frac{\sin\{(n-m)\pi/2\}}{n(n+1) - m(m+1)}$$

if $m \neq n$, and use L'Hôpital's rule to deduce that

$$\int_0^{\infty} \{j_n(x)\}^2\,dx = \frac{\pi}{2(2n+1)}.$$

Determine also the values of $\int_{-\infty}^{\infty} j_m(x)j_n(x)\,dx$ $(m \neq n)$ and

$$\int_{-\infty}^{\infty} \{j_n(x)\}^2\,dx.$$

(13) Show that

(i) $\operatorname{ber}_n x = \sum\limits_{k=0}^{\infty} (-1)^k \dfrac{(x/2)^{n+2k} \cos\{\frac{3}{4}(n+2k)\pi\}}{k!(n+k)!}$;

(ii) $\operatorname{bei}_n x = \sum\limits_{k=0}^{\infty} (-1)^k \dfrac{(x/2)^{n+2k} \sin\{\frac{3}{4}(n+2k)\pi\}}{k!(n+k)!}$.

(14) Prove that

(i) $\int_0^x t\,\operatorname{ber} t\,dt = x\,\operatorname{bei}' x$;

(ii) $\int_0^x t\,\operatorname{bei} t\,dt = -x\,\operatorname{ber}' x$.

(15) Show that, for large values of x,

(i) $\operatorname{ber} x \sim \dfrac{1}{\sqrt{(2\pi x)}} e^{x/\sqrt{2}} \cos\left(\dfrac{x}{\sqrt{2}} - \dfrac{\pi}{8}\right)$;

(ii) $\operatorname{bei} x \sim \dfrac{1}{\sqrt{(2\pi x)}} e^{x/\sqrt{2}} \sin\left(\dfrac{x}{\sqrt{2}} - \dfrac{\pi}{8}\right)$.

5

HERMITE POLYNOMIALS

5.1 HERMITE'S EQUATION AND ITS SOLUTION

Hermite's equation is given by

$$\frac{d^2y}{dx^2} - 2x\frac{dy}{dx} + 2ny = 0, \tag{5.1}$$

and in applications we are required to find solutions which are finite for all finite values of x and are such that $\exp\left(\frac{1}{2}x^2\right) y(x) \to 0$ as $x \to \infty$.

The methods of Chapter 1 are applicable, and if we try for a solution of the form

$$z(x, s) = \sum_{r=0}^{\infty} a_r x^{s+r}$$

we find that the indicial equation has roots $s = 0$ and $s = 1$, with a_1 indeterminate when $s = 0$, so that $s = 0$ gives the two independent series solutions. The recurrence relation for the coefficients then has the form

$$\frac{a_{r+2}}{a_r} = \frac{2(r - n)}{(r + 1)(r + 2)}. \tag{5.2}$$

This recurrence relation may now be used to construct the two series solutions. However, from these series it can be shown that both solutions behave like $\exp(x^2)$ for large values of x. Thus they cannot satisfy the requirement that $\exp\left(\frac{1}{2}x^2\right) y(x) \to 0$ as $x \to \infty$; this can only be satisfied if the series terminate. From equation (5.2) we see that this will be so if, and only if, n is a non-negative integer, for then a_{n+2} and all subsequent coefficients in the corresponding series will vanish. We shall now write the series in descending powers of x. Using equation (5.2), rewritten in the form

$$a_r = -\frac{(r+1)(r+2)}{2(n-r)}a_{r+2},$$

we obtain the series

$$y = a_n\left\{x^n - \frac{n(n-1)}{2.2}x^{n-2} + \frac{n(n-1)(n-2)(n-3)}{2^2.2.4}x^{n-4} + \ldots\right.$$

$$\left. + (-1)^r\frac{n(n-1)\ldots(n-2r+1)}{2^r.2.4\ldots 2r}x^{n-2r} + \ldots\right\}$$

$$= a_n\sum_{r=0}^{[\frac{1}{2}n]}(-1)^r\frac{n(n-1)\ldots(n-2r+1)}{2^r.2.4\ldots 2r}x^{n-2r}$$

$$\text{(where } [\tfrac{1}{2}n] = \begin{cases} \tfrac{1}{2}n \text{ if } n \text{ is even} \\ \tfrac{1}{2}(n-1) \text{ if } n \text{ is odd}) \end{cases}$$

$$= a_n\sum_{r=0}^{[\frac{1}{2}n]}(-1)^r\frac{n!}{2^{2r}r!(n-2r)!}x^{n-2r}.$$

The standard solution is obtained by making the choice of 2^n for the arbitrary constant a_n; the solution is then denoted by $H_n(x)$ and called the Hermite polynomial of order n:

$$H_n(x) = \sum_{r=0}^{[\frac{1}{2}n]}(-1)^r\frac{n!}{r!(n-2r)!}(2x)^{n-2r}. \tag{5.3}$$

5.2　GENERATING FUNCTION

Theorem 5.1

$$e^{2tx-t^2} = \sum_{n=0}^{\infty}\frac{t^n}{n!}H_n(x).$$

PROOF

We wish to pick out the coefficient of t^n in the power series expansion of $\exp(2tx - t^2)$.

Now,

$$e^{2tx-t^2} = e^{2tx}\,e^{-t^2}$$

$$= \sum_{r=0}^{\infty}\frac{(2tx)^r}{r!}\sum_{s=0}^{\infty}\frac{(-t^2)^s}{s!}$$

$$= \sum_{r,s=0}^{\infty}(-1)^s\frac{(2x)^r}{r!s!}t^{r+2s}.$$

For a fixed value of s we obtain t^n by taking $r + 2s = n$, i.e., $r = n - 2s$, so that for this value of s the coefficient of t^n is just given by

$$(-1)^s \frac{(2x)^{n-2s}}{(n-2s)!s!}.$$

The total coefficient of t^n is obtained by summing over all allowed values of s, and, since $r = n - 2s$, this implies that we must have $n - 2s \geqslant 0$, i.e., $s \leqslant \frac{1}{2}n$. Thus, if n is even, s goes from 0 to $\frac{1}{2}n$, while if n is odd, s goes from 0 to $\frac{1}{2}(n-1)$; that is, in all cases, s goes from 0 to $[\frac{1}{2}n]$ with $[\frac{1}{2}n]$ defined as above.

Thus we have:

$$\text{coefficient of } t^n = \sum_{s=0}^{[\frac{1}{2}n]} (-1)^s \frac{1}{(n-2s)!s!}(2x)^{n-2s}$$

$$= \frac{1}{n!}H_n(x),$$

(by definition (5.3)).

5.3   OTHER EXPRESSIONS FOR THE HERMITE POLYNOMIALS

Theorem 5.2

$$H_n(x) = (-1)^n\, e^{x^2} \frac{d^n}{dx^n}\, e^{-x^2}.$$

PROOF

By use of the generating function of theorem 5.1 and Taylor's theorem, which states that

$$F(t) = \sum_{n=0}^{\infty} \left(\frac{d^n F}{dt^n}\right)_{t=0} \frac{t^n}{n!},$$

we have

$$H_n(x) = \left[\frac{\partial^n}{\partial t^n}\, e^{2tx - t^2}\right]_{t=0}$$

$$= \left[\frac{\partial^n}{\partial t^n}\, e^{x^2 - (x-t)^2}\right]_{t=0}$$

$$= e^{x^2}\left[\frac{\partial^n}{\partial t^n}\, e^{-(x-t)^2}\right]_{t=0}.$$

But

$$\frac{\partial}{\partial t}f(x-t) = -\frac{\partial}{\partial x}f(x-t),$$

so that

$$\frac{\partial^n}{\partial t^n} f(x - t) = (-1)^n \frac{\partial^n}{\partial x^n} f(x - t)$$

and we have

$$H_n(x) = (-1)^n e^{x^2} \left[\frac{\partial^n}{\partial x^n} e^{-(x-t)^2} \right]_{t=0}$$

$$= (-1)^n e^{x^2} \frac{\partial^n}{\partial x^n} e^{-x^2}$$

$$= (-1)^n e^{x^2} \frac{d^n}{dx^n} e^{-x^2}$$

Theorem 5.3

$$H_n(x) = 2^n \left\{ \exp\left(-\frac{1}{4} \frac{d^2}{dx^2} \right) \right\} x^n . \dagger$$

PROOF

We have

$$\frac{1}{2} \frac{d}{dx} e^{2tx} = t\, e^{2tx}$$

and hence

$$\left(\frac{1}{2} \frac{d}{dx} \right)^n e^{2tx} = t^n\, e^{2tx}.$$

Thus

$$\exp\left(-\frac{1}{4} \frac{d^2}{dx^2} \right) \exp(2tx) = \sum_{n=0}^{\infty} \frac{1}{n!} \left(-\frac{1}{4} \frac{d^2}{dx^2} \right)^n e^{2tx}$$

$$= \sum_{n=0}^{\infty} \frac{(-1)^n}{n!} \left(\frac{1}{2} \frac{d}{dx} \right)^{2n} e^{2tx}$$

$$= \sum_{n=0}^{\infty} \frac{(-1)^n}{n!} t^{2n} e^{2tx}$$

$$= e^{-t^2} . e^{2tx}$$

$$= e^{-t^2 + 2tx}.$$

Expanding both sides in powers of t, we have

$$\exp\left(-\frac{1}{4} \frac{d^2}{dx^2} \right) \sum_{n=0}^{\infty} \frac{2^n x^n t^n}{n!} = \sum_{n=0}^{\infty} H_n(x) \frac{t^n}{n!}$$

(using the generating function property of theorem 5.1).

---

† The exponential of an operator is defined by its power series expansion. Thus, for example, $\exp\left(\dfrac{d}{dx} \right) = \displaystyle\sum_{n=0}^{\infty} \frac{1}{n!} \left(\frac{d}{dx} \right)^n = \displaystyle\sum_{n=0}^{\infty} \frac{1}{n!} \frac{d^n}{dx^n}$ so that $\exp\left(\dfrac{d}{dx} \right) f(x) = \displaystyle\sum_{n=0}^{\infty} \frac{1}{n!} \frac{d^n f}{dx^n}$.

Equating the coefficients of t^n on both sides now gives

$$\left\{\exp\left(-\frac{1}{4}\frac{d^2}{dx^2}\right)\right\}\frac{2^n x^n}{n!} = \frac{H_n(x)}{n!}$$

and hence

$$H_n(x) = 2^n \left\{\exp\left(-\frac{1}{4}\frac{d^2}{dx^2}\right)\right\} x^n.$$

5.4   EXPLICIT EXPRESSIONS FOR, AND SPECIAL VALUES OF, THE HERMITE POLYNOMIALS

We may use either the definition (5.3), or theorem 5.2 or theorem 5.3 to write down an explicit expression for the Hermite polynomial of any order we choose. For the first few orders we obtain

$$H_0(x) = 1$$
$$H_1(x) = 2x$$
$$H_2(x) = 4x^2 - 2$$
$$H_3(x) = 8x^3 - 12x$$
$$H_4(x) = 16x^4 - 48x^2 + 12$$
$$H_5(x) = 32x^5 - 160x^3 + 120x.$$

Theorem 5.4

$$H_{2n}(0) = (-1)^n \frac{(2n)!}{n!}; \quad H_{2n+1}(0) = 0.$$

PROOF

From the generating function of theorem 5.1 with $x = 0$, we have

$$e^{-t^2} = \sum_{n=0}^{\infty} H_n(0)\frac{t^n}{n!}$$

which, on expanding the left-hand side in powers of t, reduces to

$$\sum_{n=0}^{\infty} (-1)^n \frac{t^{2n}}{n!} = \sum_{n=0}^{\infty} H_n(0)\frac{t^n}{n!}.$$

Equating coefficients of corresponding powers of t on both sides gives

$$H_n(0) = 0 \text{ if } n \text{ is odd}$$

(which is equivalent to $H_{2n+1}(0) = 0$ with n a non-negative integer) and

$$(-1)^n \frac{1}{n!} = H_{2n}(0) \frac{1}{(2n)!} \text{ (with } n \text{ a non-negative integer)}$$

which yields

$$H_{2n}(0) = (-1)^n \frac{(2n)!}{n!}.$$

5.5 ORTHOGONALITY PROPERTIES OF THE HERMITE POLYNOMIALS

Theorem 5.5

$$\int_{-\infty}^{\infty} e^{-x^2} H_n(x) H_m(x) \, dx = 2^n n! (\sqrt{\pi}) \delta_{nm}.$$

PROOF

We have
$$e^{-t^2 + 2tx} = \sum_{n=0}^{\infty} H_n(x) \frac{t^n}{n!}$$

and
$$e^{-s^2 + 2sx} = \sum_{m=0}^{\infty} H_m(x) \frac{s^m}{m!}$$

so that $\int_{-\infty}^{\infty} e^{-x^2} H_n(x) H_m(x) \, dx$ is the coefficient of $(t^n s^m)/(n! m!)$ in the expansion of $\int_{-\infty}^{\infty} e^{-x^2} e^{-t^2 + 2tx} e^{-s^2 + 2sx} \, dx.$

But
$$\int_{-\infty}^{\infty} e^{-x^2} e^{-t^2 + 2tx} e^{-s^2 + 2sx} \, dx$$

$$= e^{-t^2 - s^2} \int_{-\infty}^{\infty} \exp\{-x^2 + 2(s + t)x\} \, dx$$

$$= e^{-t^2 - s^2} \int_{-\infty}^{\infty} \exp[-\{x - (s + t)\}^2 + (s + t)^2] \, dx$$

$$= e^{2st} \int_{-\infty}^{\infty} \exp[-\{x - (s + t)\}^2] \, dx$$

$$= e^{2st} \int_{-\infty}^{\infty} \exp(-u^2) \, du$$

(changing the variable of integration to $u = x - (s + t)$)

$$= e^{2st} \sqrt{\pi}$$

(by the corollary to theorem 2.6)

$$= \sum_{n=0}^{\infty} (\sqrt{\pi}) \frac{2^n s^n t^n}{n!}.$$

Hence the coefficient of $(t^n s^m)/(n!m!)$ is zero if $m \neq n$ and is $(\sqrt{\pi})2^n n!$ when $m = n$.

Hence
$$\int_{-\infty}^{\infty} e^{-x^2} H_n(x)H_m(x) \, dx = \begin{cases} 0 & \text{if } m \neq n \\ (\sqrt{\pi})2^n n! & \text{if } m = n \end{cases}$$

or, making use of the Kronecker delta,

$$\int_{-\infty}^{\infty} e^{-x^2} H_n(x)H_m(x) \, dx = (\sqrt{\pi})2^n n! \delta_{mn}.$$

5.6 RELATIONS BETWEEN HERMITE POLYNOMIALS AND THEIR DERIVATIVES; RECURRENCE RELATIONS

Theorem 5.6

  (i) $H_n'(x) = 2nH_{n-1}(x) \ (n \geqslant 1); \quad H_0'(x) = 0.$
  (ii) $H_{n+1}(x) = 2xH_n(x) - 2nH_{n-1}(x) \ (n \geqslant 1); \quad H_1(x) = 2xH_0(x).$

PROOF

(i) If we differentiate both sides of the generating function relationship with respect to x, we obtain

$$\sum_{n=0}^{\infty} H_n'(x)\frac{t^n}{n!} = \frac{d}{dx} \exp(2tx - t^2)$$

$$= 2t \exp(2tx - t^2)$$

$$= 2t \sum_{n=0}^{\infty} H_n(x)\frac{t^n}{n!}$$

$$= 2 \sum_{n=0}^{\infty} H_n(x)\frac{t^{n+1}}{n!}$$

$$= 2 \sum_{n=1}^{\infty} H_{n-1}(x)\frac{t^n}{(n-1)!}.$$

Equating coefficients of t^n gives for $n = 0$
$$H_0'(x) = 0$$

and, for $n \geqslant 1$,

$$\frac{H_n'(x)}{n!} = \frac{2H_{n-1}(x)}{(n-1)!}$$

which reduces to

$$H_n'(x) = 2nH_{n-1}(x).$$

(ii) Differentiating both sides of the generating function relationship with respect to t gives

$$\frac{d}{dt} \exp(2tx - t^2) = \frac{d}{dt} \sum_{n=0}^{\infty} \frac{t^n}{n!} H_n(x)$$

and thus, performing the differentiations,

$$(2x - 2t) \exp(2tx - t^2) = \sum_{n=0}^{\infty} \frac{nt^{n-1}}{n!} H_n(x).$$

We now note that the term with $n = 0$ does not contribute to the summation on the right-hand side (we remember that $0! = 1$) and thus, on use of theorem 5.1, the above equation becomes

$$2(x - t) \sum_{n=0}^{\infty} \frac{t^n}{n!} H_n(x) = \sum_{n=1}^{\infty} \frac{t^{n-1}}{(n-1)!} H_n(x)$$

which is equivalent to

$$2x \sum_{n=0}^{\infty} \frac{t^n}{n!} H_n(x) - 2 \sum_{n=0}^{\infty} \frac{t^{n+1}}{n!} H_n(x) = \sum_{n=1}^{\infty} \frac{t^{n-1}}{(n-1)!} H_n(x)$$

which may be written in the form

$$2x \sum_{n=0}^{\infty} \frac{t^n}{n!} H_n(x) - 2 \sum_{n=1}^{\infty} \frac{t^n}{(n-1)!} H_{n-1}(x) = \sum_{n=0}^{\infty} \frac{t^n}{n!} H_{n+1}(x).$$

Thus, equating coefficients of t^n for $n \geqslant 1$, we have

$$2x \frac{1}{n!} H_n(x) - \frac{2H_{n-1}(x)}{(n-1)!} = \frac{1}{n!} H_{n+1}(x)$$

which on multiplying throughout by $n!$ becomes

$$2xH_n(x) - 2nH_{n-1}(x) = H_{n+1}(x).$$

Similarly, equating coefficients of t^0 gives

$$2xH_0(x) = H_1(x).$$

5.7   WEBER-HERMITE FUNCTIONS

An equation closely related to Hermite's equation is

$$\frac{d^2y}{dx^2} + (\lambda - x^2)y = 0. \tag{5.4}$$

If we make the substitution

$$y = z \, e^{-x^2/2}$$

S F—M

we find that the above equation reduces to

$$\frac{d^2z}{dx^2} - 2x\frac{dz}{dx} + (\lambda - 1)z = 0. \tag{5.5}$$

This is Hermite's equation of order n with $2n = \lambda - 1$. If, as is usually the case in applications, we are looking for solutions of equation (5.4) which are finite for all values of x, we must have a solution of equation (5.5) which does not tend to infinity any faster than $\exp(x^2/2)$ as x tends to infinity, and by the discussion of Section 5.1 this implies that $\frac{1}{2}(\lambda - 1)$ must be integral. With $n = \frac{1}{2}(\lambda - 1)$ the solution of equation (5.4) is then given by

$$\Psi_n(x) = e^{-x^2/2}\, H_n(x).$$

$\Psi_n(x)$ is called the Weber-Hermite function of order n.

5.8 EXAMPLES

Example 1

Prove that, if $m < n$,

$$\frac{d^m}{dx^m}\{H_n(x)\} = \frac{2^m n!}{(n-m)!}H_{n-m}(x).$$

From the generating function of theorem 5.1 we have that

$$\left(\frac{d^m}{dx^m}\right)\{H_n(x)\}$$

is the coefficient of $t^n/n!$ in the expansion of

$$\left(\frac{d^m}{dx^m}\right)\exp(2tx - t^2).$$

But $$\frac{d^m}{dx^m}\exp(2tx - t^2) = (2t)^m \exp(2tx - t^2)$$

$$= 2^m t^m \sum_{n=0}^{\infty} \frac{t^n}{n!}H_n(x)$$

$$= 2^m \sum_{n=0}^{\infty} \frac{1}{n!}H_n(x)t^{n+m}$$

$$= 2^m \sum_{r=m}^{\infty} \frac{1}{(r-m)!}H_{r-m}(x)t^r,$$

setting $r = m + n$.

The coefficient of t^n is therefore

$$2^m \frac{1}{(n-m)!}H_{n-m}(x)$$

and hence the coefficient of $t^n/n!$ is

$$2^m \frac{n!}{(n-m)!} H_{n-m}(x),$$

which proves the required result.

Example 2

Evaluate $\displaystyle\int_{-\infty}^{\infty} x\,e^{-x^2}\, H_n(x)H_m(x)\, dx.$

We have, from theorem 5.6(ii)

$$xH_n(x) = nH_{n-1}(x) + \tfrac{1}{2}H_{n+1}(x)$$

so that

$$\int_{-\infty}^{\infty} x\,e^{-x^2}\, H_n(x)H_m(x)\, dx$$

$$= \int_{-\infty}^{\infty} e^{-x^2} \{nH_{n-1}(x) + \tfrac{1}{2}H_{n+1}(x)\}H_m(x)\, dx$$

$$= n2^{n-1}(n-1)!(\sqrt{\pi})\delta_{n-1,\,m} + \tfrac{1}{2}.2^{n+1}(n+1)!(\sqrt{\pi})\delta_{n+1,\,m}$$
$$\text{(by theorem 5.5)}$$

$$= (\sqrt{\pi})2^{n-1}n!\delta_{n-1,\,m} + (\sqrt{\pi})2^n(n+1)!\delta_{n+1,\,m}.$$

Example 3

Show that $\displaystyle P_n(x) = \frac{2}{(\sqrt{\pi})n!} \int_0^{\infty} t^n\,e^{-t^2}\, H_n(xt)\, dt.$

From equation (5.3) we have

$$H_n(xt) = \sum_{r=0}^{[\frac{1}{2}n]} (-1)^r \frac{n!}{r!(n-2r)!}(2xt)^{n-2r}$$

so that

$$\frac{2}{(\sqrt{\pi})n!} \int_0^{\infty} t^n\,e^{-t^2}\, H_n(xt)\, dt$$

$$= \frac{2}{(\sqrt{\pi})n!} \int_0^{\infty} t^n\,e^{-t^2} \sum_{r=0}^{[\frac{1}{2}n]} (-1)^r \frac{n!}{r!(n-2r)!}2^{n-2r}x^{n-2r}t^{n-2r}\, dt$$

$$= \sum_{r=0}^{[\frac{1}{2}n]} \frac{2^{n-2r+1}(-1)^r x^{n-2r}}{(\sqrt{\pi})r!(n-2r)!} \int_0^{\infty} e^{-t^2}\, t^{2n-2r}\, dt$$

$$= \sum_{r=0}^{[\frac{1}{2}n]} \frac{2^{n-2r+1}(-1)^r x^{n-2r}}{(\sqrt{\pi})r!(n-2r)!} \tfrac{1}{2}\Gamma(n-r+\tfrac{1}{2})$$
$$\text{(by theorem 2.4)}$$

$$= \sum_{r=0}^{[\frac{1}{2}n]} \frac{2^{n-2r}(-1)^r x^{n-2r}}{(\sqrt{\pi})r!(n-2r)!} \frac{(2n-2r)!}{2^{2n-2r}(n-r)!}\sqrt{\pi}$$

(by the corollary to theorem 2.10)

$$= \sum_{r=0}^{[\frac{1}{2}n]} (-1)^r \frac{(2n-2r)!}{2^n r!(n-2r)!(n-r)!} x^{n-2r}$$

$$= P_n(x),$$

(by equation (3.17)).

PROBLEMS

(1) Show that $\int_{-\infty}^{\infty} x^2 e^{-x^2} \{H_n(x)\}^2 dx = (\sqrt{\pi})2^n n!(n+\frac{1}{2}).$

(2) If $f(x)$ is a polynomial of degree m, show that $f(x)$ may be written in the form

$$f(x) = \sum_{r=0}^{m} c_r H_r(x)$$

where $\qquad c_r = \frac{1}{2^r r!\sqrt{\pi}} \int_{-\infty}^{\infty} e^{-x^2} f(x)H_r(x) dx.$

Deduce that $\int_{-\infty}^{\infty} e^{-x^2} f(x)H_n(x) dx = 0$ if $f(x)$ is a polynomial of degree less than n.

(3) Show that $e^{-x^2} = \frac{2}{\sqrt{\pi}} \int_0^{\infty} e^{-t^2} \cos 2xt \, dt.$

By differentiating this result $2n$ times with respect to x, show that

$$H_{2n}(x) = \frac{2^{2n+1}(-1)^n e^{x^2}}{\sqrt{\pi}} \int_0^{\infty} e^{-t^2} t^{2n} \cos 2xt \, dt,$$

and obtain a similar expression for $H_{2n+1}(x)$.

Deduce that $H_n(x) = \frac{2^n(-i)^n e^{x^2}}{\sqrt{\pi}} \int_{-\infty}^{\infty} e^{-t^2+2itx} t^n \, dt.$

(4) Use the result of problem 3 to show that

$$\sum_{n=0}^{\infty} \frac{H_n(x)H_n(y)}{2^n n!} t^n = (1-t^2)^{-1/2} \exp\left\{\frac{2xyt-(x^2+y^2)t^2}{1-t^2}\right\}$$

and deduce that

$$\sum_{n=0}^{\infty} \frac{\{H_n(x)\}^2}{2^n n!} t^n = (1-t^2)^{-1/2} \exp\{2x^2 t/(1+t)\}.$$

(5) Use the result of problem 4 to show that

(i) $\displaystyle\int_{-\infty}^{\infty} \{H_n(x)\}^2 \, e^{-2x^2} \, dx = 2^{n-\frac{1}{2}}\Gamma(n + \tfrac{1}{2});$

(ii) $\displaystyle\frac{1}{2^n n!} \int_{-\infty}^{\infty} \frac{\{H_n(x)\}^2 \, e^{-x^2}}{1 + x^2} \, dx = \int_{-\infty}^{\infty} \left(\frac{1 - x^2}{1 + x^2}\right)^n \frac{e^{-x^2}}{1 + x^2} \, dx.$

(6) Prove that

(i) $2n\Psi_{n-1}(x) = x\Psi_n(x) + \Psi_n'(x);$
(ii) $2x\Psi_n(x) - 2n\Psi_{n-1}(x) = \Psi_{n+1}(x);$
(iii) $\Psi_n'(x) = x\Psi_n(x) - \Psi_{n+1}(x).$

(7) Evaluate

(i) $\displaystyle\int_{-\infty}^{\infty} \Psi_m(x)\Psi_n(x) \, dx;$

(ii) $\displaystyle\int_{-\infty}^{\infty} \Psi_m(x)\Psi_n'(x) \, dx.$

6

LAGUERRE POLYNOMIALS

6.1 LAGUERRE'S EQUATION AND ITS SOLUTION

Laguerre's equation is

$$x\frac{d^2y}{dx^2} + (1 - x)\frac{dy}{dx} + ny = 0 \tag{6.1}$$

and in applications we usually require a solution which is finite for all finite values of x and which tends to infinity no faster than $e^{x/2}$ as x tends to infinity.

The methods of Chapter 1 apply, and if we look for a solution of the form $z(x, s) = \sum_{r=0}^{\infty} a_r x^{s+r}$ we obtain an indicial equation with double root $s = 0$, and the recurrence relation

$$a_{r+1} = a_r \frac{(s + r - n)}{(s + r + 1)^2}.$$

The two independent solutions are then given by

$$z(x, 0) \quad \text{and} \quad \left[\frac{\partial z}{\partial s}\right]_{s=0}.$$

The second of these we know from Chapter 1 contains a term of the form $\ln x$, and so is infinite when $x = 0$. Since we require a solution finite for all finite x we can only obtain this from $z(x, 0)$. In this case the recurrence relation takes the form

$$a_{r+1} = a_r \frac{(r - n)}{(r + 1)^2}. \tag{6.2}$$

However, the infinite series obtained from this relation may be shown to behave like e^x for large values of x, so that, from our remarks above, it does not behave well enough as x tends to infinity. The way round this difficulty is to make the series terminate, and from equation (6.2) we see that this happens if n is a positive integer. For, in this case, $a_n \neq 0$ but a_{n+1} and all subsequent coefficients will vanish. In such a case the relation (6.2) is best written in the form

$$a_{r+1} = -a_r \frac{(n-r)}{(r+1)^2}$$

and we obtain the solution

$$y = a_0 \left\{ 1 - \frac{n}{1^2}x + \frac{n(n-1)}{(2!)^2}x^2 + \dots \right.$$
$$\left. + (-1)^r \frac{n(n-1)\dots(n-r+1)}{(r!)^2}x^2 + \dots \right\}$$

(the highest power of x being x^n)

$$= a_0 \sum_{r=0}^{n} (-1)^r \frac{n(n-1)\dots(n-r+1)}{(r!)^2} x^r$$

$$= a_0 \sum_{r=0}^{n} (-1)^r \frac{n!}{(n-r)!(r!)^2} x^r.$$

We define the standard solution as that for which $a_0 = 1$; we shall call it the Laguerre polynomial of order n, and denote it by $L_n(x)$:

$$L_n(x) = \sum_{r=0}^{n} (-1)^r \frac{n!}{(n-r)!(r!)^2} x^r. \tag{6.3}$$

6.2 GENERATING FUNCTION

Theorem 6.1

$$\frac{\exp\{-xt/(1-t)\}}{(1-t)} = \sum_{n=0}^{\infty} L_n(x)t^n.$$

PROOF

We have

$$\frac{1}{(1-t)} \exp\{-xt/(1-t)\} = \frac{1}{(1-t)} \sum_{r=0}^{\infty} \frac{1}{r!}\left(-\frac{xt}{1-t}\right)^r$$

$$= \sum_{r=0}^{\infty} \frac{(-1)^r}{r!} \frac{x^r t^r}{(1-t)^{r+1}}.$$

But $\dfrac{1}{(1-t)^{r+1}}$

$$= 1 + (r+1)t + \frac{(r+1)(r+2)}{2!}t^2 + \frac{(r+1)(r+2)(r+3)t^3}{3!}$$

$$+ \dots$$

(by the binomial theorem)

$$= \sum_{s=0}^{\infty} \frac{(r+s)!}{r!s!}t^s,$$

so that we now have

$$\frac{1}{1-t}\exp\{-xt/(1-t)\} = \sum_{r,\,s=0}^{\infty}(-1)^r\frac{(r+s)!}{(r!)^2s!}x^r t^{r+s}.$$

For a fixed value of r the coefficient of t^n in this expansion is obtained by taking $r+s = n$, i.e., $s = n-r$. Thus, for this value of r, the coefficient of t^n is given by

$$(-1)^r\frac{n!}{(r!)^2(n-r)!}x^r.$$

The total coefficient of t^n is obtained by summing over all allowed values of r. Since $s = n-r$, and we require $s \geqslant 0$, we must have $r \leqslant n$. Hence the total coefficient of t^n is given by

$$\sum_{r=0}^{n}(-1)^r\frac{n!}{(r!)^2(n-r)!}x^r = L_n(x)$$

(by equation (6.3)),

which proves the required result.

6.3   ALTERNATIVE EXPRESSION FOR THE LAGUERRE POLYNOMIALS

Theorem 6.2

$$L_n(x) = \frac{e^x}{n!}\frac{d^n}{dx^n}(x^n\,e^{-x}).$$

PROOF

Leibniz's theorem for the nth derivative of a product states that

$$\frac{d^n}{dx^n}(uv) = \sum_{r=0}^{n}\frac{n!}{(n-r)!r!}\frac{d^{n-r}u}{dx^{n-r}}\frac{d^r v}{dx^r},$$

so that we have

$$\frac{e^x}{n!}\frac{d^n}{dx^n}(x^n\, e^{-x}) = \frac{e^x}{n!}\sum_{r=0}^{n}\frac{n!}{(n-r)!r!}\frac{d^{n-r}}{dx^{n-r}}x^n\frac{d^r}{dx^r}e^{-x}.$$

But

$$\frac{d^p}{dx^p}x^q = q(q-1)\ldots(q-p+1)x^{q-p}$$

$$= \frac{q!}{(q-p)!}x^{q-p},$$

and hence we obtain

$$\frac{e^x}{n!}\frac{d^n}{dx^n}(x^n e^{-x}) = \frac{e^x}{n!}\sum_{r=0}^{n}\frac{n!}{(n-r)!r!}\frac{n!}{r!}x^r(-1)^r e^{-x}$$

$$= \sum_{r=0}^{n}(-1)^r\frac{n!}{(r!)^2(n-r)!}x^r$$

$$= L_n(x)$$

(by definition (6.3)).

6.4   EXPLICIT EXPRESSIONS FOR, AND SPECIAL VALUES OF, THE LAGUERRE POLYNOMIALS

We have an explicit series for $L_n(x)$ given by equation (6.3). For the first few Laguerre polynomials this gives

$$L_0(x) = 1$$
$$L_1(x) = -x + 1$$
$$L_2(x) = \frac{1}{2!}(x^2 - 4x + 2)$$
$$L_3(x) = \frac{1}{3!}(-x^3 + 9x^2 - 18x + 6)$$
$$L_4(x) = \frac{1}{4!}(x^4 - 16x^3 + 72x^2 - 96x + 24).$$

Theorem 6.3

(i) $L_n(0) = 1$.

(ii) $L_n'(0) = -n$.

PROOF

(i) Set $x = 0$ in the generating function of theorem 6.1 and we obtain

$$\sum_{n=0}^{\infty} L_n(0)t^n = \frac{1}{1-t}$$

$$= \sum_{n=0}^{\infty} t^n$$

(using the binomial theorem)

so that equating coefficients of t^n on both sides gives $L_n(0) = 1$.

(ii) $L_n(x)$ satisfies Laguerre's equation (6.1), so that we have

$$x\frac{d^2}{dx^2}L_n(x) + (1-x)\frac{d}{dx}L_n(x) + nL_n(x) = 0.$$

Setting $x = 0$ in this equation and using part (i) above we obtain

$$L_n'(0) + n = 0$$

and hence

$$L_n'(0) = -n.$$

6.5   ORTHOGONALITY PROPERTIES OF THE LAGUERRE POLYNOMIALS

Theorem 6.4

$$\int_0^{\infty} e^{-x} L_n(x)L_m(x)dx = \delta_{nm}.$$

PROOF

From the generating function of theorem 6.1 we have

$$\frac{\exp\{-xt/(1-t)\}}{1-t} = \sum_{n=0}^{\infty} L_n(x)t^n$$

and

$$\frac{\exp\{-xs/(1-s)\}}{1-s} = \sum_{m=0}^{\infty} L_m(x)s^m,$$

so that

$$\sum_{n,\,m=0}^{\infty} e^{-x}L_n(x)L_m(x)t^n s^m = e^{-x} \cdot \frac{\exp\{-xt/(1-t)\}}{1-t} \cdot \frac{\exp\{-xs/(1-s)\}}{1-s}.$$

Thus $\int_0^{\infty} e^{-x}L_n(x)L_m(x)\,dx$ is the coefficient of $t^n s^m$ in the expansion of

$$I = \int_0^{\infty} e^{-x} \cdot \frac{\exp\{-xt/(1-t)\}}{1-t} \cdot \frac{\exp\{-xs/(1-s)\}}{1-s}\,dx.$$

But $I = \dfrac{1}{(1-t)(1-s)} \displaystyle\int_0^\infty \exp\left\{-x\left(1 + \dfrac{t}{1-t} + \dfrac{s}{1-s}\right)\right\} dx$

$ = \dfrac{1}{(1-t)(1-s)} \left[-\dfrac{1}{1 + \{t/(1-t)\} + \{s/(1-s)\}} \cdot \right.$

$ \left. \exp\left\{-x\left(1 + \dfrac{t}{1-t} + \dfrac{s}{1-s}\right)\right\}\right]_0^\infty$

$ = \dfrac{1}{(1-t)(1-s)} \dfrac{1}{1 + \{t/(1-t)\} + \{s/(1-s)\}}$

$ = \dfrac{1}{(1-t)(1-s) + t(1-s) + s(1-t)}$

$ = \dfrac{1}{1-st}$

$ = \displaystyle\sum_{n=0}^\infty s^n t^n.$

Thus the coefficient of $t^n s^m$ is 1 if $n = m$ and 0 if $n \neq m$, i.e. it is δ_{nm}.
Hence $\displaystyle\int_0^\infty e^{-x} L_n(x) L_m(x) \, dx = \delta_{nm}.$

6.6 RELATIONS BETWEEN LAGUERRE POLYNOMIALS AND THEIR DERIVATIVES: RECURRENCE RELATIONS

Theorem 6.5

(i) $(n+1)L_{n+1}(x) = (2n + 1 - x)L_n(x) - nL_{n-1}(x).$

(ii) $xL_n'(x) = nL_n(x) - nL_{n-1}(x).$

(iii) $L_n'(x) = -\displaystyle\sum_{r=0}^{n-1} L_r(x).$

PROOF

(i) If we differentiate the generating function with respect to t and use the fact that

$$\frac{d}{dt}\frac{t}{1-t} = \frac{1}{(1-t)^2}$$

we obtain

$$\sum_{n=0}^\infty L_n(x).nt^{n-1} = \frac{1}{(1-t)^2}\exp\{-xt/(1-t)\} - \frac{x}{(1-t)^2}\frac{\exp\{-xt/(1-t)\}}{(1-t)}$$

which, on further use of theorem 5.1, becomes

$$\sum_{n=0}^\infty L_n(x).nt^{n-1} = \frac{1}{(1-t)}\sum_{n=0}^\infty L_n(x)t^n - \frac{x}{(1-t)^2}\sum_{n=0}^\infty L_n(x)t^n.$$

Multiplying throughout by $(1 - t)^2$ gives

$$(1 - t)^2 \sum_{n=0}^{\infty} L_n(x)nt^{n-1} = (1 - t) \sum_{n=0}^{\infty} L_n(x)t^n - x \sum_{n=0}^{\infty} L_n(x)t^n$$

and hence

$$\sum_{n=0}^{\infty} L_n(x)nt^{n-1} - 2 \sum_{n=0}^{\infty} L_n(x)nt^n + \sum_{n=0}^{\infty} L_n(x)nt^{n+1}$$

$$= \sum_{n=0}^{\infty} L_n(x)t^n - \sum_{n=0}^{\infty} L_n(x)t^{n+1} - x \sum_{n=0}^{\infty} L_n(x)t^n.$$

Relabelling the summations so that the general power appears as t^n in each gives

$$\sum_{n=-1}^{\infty} L_{n+1}(x)(n + 1)t^n - 2 \sum_{n=0}^{\infty} L_n(x)nt^n + \sum_{n=1}^{\infty} L_{n-1}(x)(n - 1)t^n$$

$$= \sum_{n=0}^{\infty} L_n(x)t^n - \sum_{n=1}^{\infty} L_{n-1}(x)t^n - x \sum_{n=0}^{\infty} L_n(x)t^n$$

and then equating the coefficients of t^n on both sides of the above equation gives

$$(n + 1)L_{n+1}(x) - 2nL_n(x) + (n - 1)L_{n-1}(x)$$
$$= L_n(x) - L_{n-1}(x) - xL_n(x) \quad (n \geqslant 1)$$

which reduces to

$$(n + 1)L_{n+1}(x) = (2n + 1 - x)L_n(x) - nL_{n-1}(x).$$

(ii) If we differentiate the generating function with respect to x we obtain

$$\sum_{n=0}^{\infty} L_n'(x)t^n = -\frac{t}{1 - t} \frac{\exp\{-xt/(1 - t)\}}{1 - t}$$

$$= -\frac{t}{1 - t} \sum_{n=0}^{\infty} L_n(x)t^n. \tag{6.4}$$

Thus

$$(1 - t) \sum_{n=0}^{\infty} L_n'(x)t^n = -t \sum_{n=0}^{\infty} L_n(x)t^n$$

and hence

$$\sum_{n=0}^{\infty} L_n'(x)t^n - \sum_{n=0}^{\infty} L_n'(x)t^{n+1} = -\sum_{n=0}^{\infty} L_n(x)t^{n+1}$$

which, on relabelling, becomes

$$\sum_{n=0}^{\infty} L_n'(x)t^n - \sum_{n=1}^{\infty} L_{n-1}'(x)t^n = -\sum_{n=1}^{\infty} L_{n-1}(x)t^n.$$

Equating coefficients of t^n on both sides of the above equation gives

$$L_n'(x) - L_{n-1}'(x) = -L_{n-1}(x) \quad (n \geqslant 1). \tag{6.5}$$

If we now differentiate result (i) above with respect to x we obtain

$$(n+1)L_{n+1}'(x) = (2n+1-x)L_n'(x) - L_n(x) - nL_{n-1}'(x)$$

and if we use equation (6.5) in the rewritten forms

$$L_{n+1}'(x) = L_n'(x) - L_n(x)$$

and
$$L_{n-1}'(x) = L_n'(x) + L_{n-1}(x),$$

we shall have

$$(n+1)\{L_n'(x) - L_n(x)\} = (2n+1-x)L_n'(x) - L_n(x)$$
$$- n\{L_n'(x) + L_{n-1}(x)\}.$$

This simplifies to give

$$-nL_n(x) = -xL_n'(x) - nL_{n-1}(x)$$

and hence

$$xL_n'(x) = nL_n(x) - nL_{n-1}(x).$$

(iii) If, in equation (6.4), we expand $1/(1-t)$ in the form $\sum_{r=0}^{\infty} t^r$ we

obtain

$$\sum_{n=0}^{\infty} L_n'(x)t^n = -t \sum_{r=0}^{\infty} t^r \sum_{s=0}^{\infty} L_s(x)t^s$$
$$= -\sum_{r,s=0}^{\infty} L_s(x)t^{r+s+1},$$

so that $L_n'(x)$ is given by the coefficient of t^n on the right-hand side of the above equation. For a fixed value of s we obtain t^n by taking $r+s+1 = n$, i.e., $r = n-s-1$, and then the coefficient of t^n is $-L_s(x)$. We obtain the total coefficient of t^n by summing over all allowed values of s, which, since we require $r \geqslant 0$, implies that $n-s-1 \geqslant 0$, i.e., $s \leqslant n-1$.

This means that we have

$$\text{coefficient of } t^n = \sum_{s=0}^{n-1} -L_s(x),$$

and hence
$$L_n'(x) = -\sum_{s=0}^{n-1} L_s(x).$$

6.7 ASSOCIATED LAGUERRE POLYNOMIALS

Laguerre's associated equation is

$$x\frac{d^2y}{dx^2} + (k + 1 - x)\frac{dy}{dx} + ny = 0. \tag{6.6}$$

Theorem 6.6

If z is a solution of Laguerre's equation of order $n + k$ then $d^k z/dx^k$ satisfies Laguerre's associated equation.

PROOF

Since z is a solution of Laguerre's equation (6.1) of order $n + k$, we have

$$x\frac{d^2z}{dx^2} + (1 - x)\frac{dz}{dx} + (n + k)z = 0.$$

Differentiating this equation k times and using Leibniz's rule for the kth derivative of a product gives

$$x\frac{d^{k+2}}{dx^{k+2}}z + k\frac{d^{k+1}}{dx^{k+1}}z + (1 - x)\frac{d^{k+1}}{dx^{k+1}}z + k.-1.\frac{d^k}{dx^k}z$$

$$+ (n + k)\frac{d^k}{dx^k}z = 0.$$

Thus

$$x\frac{d^2}{dx^2}\frac{d^k z}{dx^k} + (k + 1 - x)\frac{d}{dx}\frac{d^k z}{dx^k} + n\frac{d^k z}{dx^k} = 0$$

which just states that $d^k z/dx^k$ satisfies equation (6.6).

From the above theorem and the fact that the Laguerre polynomials $L_n(x)$ satisfy Laguerre's equation, it follows that $(d^k/dx^k)L_{n+k}(x)$ satisfies Laguerre's associated equation. We define the associated Laguerre polynomials by this solution together with the constant factor $(-1)^k$:

$$L_n^k(x) = (-1)^k \frac{d^k}{dx^k} L_{n+k}(x). \tag{6.7}$$

Theorem 6.7

$$L_n^k(x) = \sum_{r=0}^{n} (-1)^r \frac{(n + k)!}{(n - r)!(k + r)!r!}x^r.$$

PROOF

From equation (6.3) we have

$$L_{n+k}(x) = \sum_{r=0}^{n+k} (-1)^r \frac{(n + k)!}{(n + k - r)!(r!)^2}x^r$$

so that, by equation (6.7),

$$L_n^k(x) = (-1)^k \frac{d^k}{dx^k} \sum_{r=0}^{n+k} (-1)^r \frac{(n+k)!}{(n+k-r)!(r!)^2} x^r$$

$$= (-1)^k \frac{d^k}{dx^k} \sum_{r=k}^{n+k} (-1)^r \frac{(n+k)!}{(n+k-r)!(r!)^2} x^r$$

(since (d^k/dx^k) operating on powers of x less than k gives zero)

$$= (-1)^k \sum_{r=k}^{n+k} (-1)^r \frac{(n+k)!}{(n+k-r)!(r!)^2} \frac{r!}{(r-k)!} x^{r-k}$$

$$\left(\text{since } (d^k/dx^k)x^r = r(r-1)\dots(r-k+1)x^{r-k} \right.$$

$$= \left. \frac{r!}{(r-k)!} x^{r-k} \right)$$

$$= (-1)^k \sum_{s=0}^{n} (-1)^{k+s} \frac{(n+k)!}{(n+k-k-s)!(k+s)!s!} x^s$$

(changing the variable of summation to $s = r - k$)

$$= \sum_{s=0}^{n} (-1)^s \frac{(n+k)!}{(n-s)!(k+s)!s!} x^s,$$

which is the required result.

6.8   PROPERTIES OF THE ASSOCIATED LAGUERRE POLYNOMIALS

Theorem 6.8 (Generating function)

$$\frac{\exp\{-xt/(1-t)\}}{(1-t)^{k+1}} = \sum_{n=0}^{\infty} L_n^k(x)t^n.$$

PROOF

From theorem 6.1

$$\frac{\exp -xt/(1\{-t)\}}{(1-t)} = \sum_{n=0}^{\infty} L_n(x)t^n.$$

Differentiating both sides k times with respect to x, we have

$$\frac{d^k}{dx^k} \frac{\exp\{-xt/(1-t)\}}{(1-t)} = \frac{d^k}{dx^k} \sum_{n=k}^{\infty} L_n(x)t^n$$

(since $L_n(x)$ is a polynomial of degree n and so, if $n < k$, will give zero when differentiated k times).

Carrying out the differentiation on the left-hand side, we obtain

$$\left(-\frac{t}{1-t}\right)^k \frac{\exp\{-xt/(1-t)\}}{1-t} = \frac{d^k}{dx^k} \sum_{n=0}^{\infty} L_{n+k}(x)t^{n+k}$$

and thus, using equation (6.7),

$$(-1)^k \frac{t^k}{(1-t)^{k+1}} \exp\{-xt/(1-t)\} = \sum_{n=0}^{\infty} (-1)^k L_n^k(x)t^{n+k}$$

which, on cancelling a common factor of $(-1)^k t^k$, becomes

$$\frac{\exp\{-xt/(1-t)\}}{(1-t)^{k+1}} = \sum_{n=0}^{\infty} L_n^k(x)t^n.$$

Theorem 6.9

$$L_n^k(x) = \frac{e^x x^{-k}}{n!} \frac{d^n}{dx^n}(e^{-x}x^{n+k}).$$

PROOF

Since this is almost the same as that of theorem 6.2, we shall not give it here.

Theorem 6.10 (Orthogonality property)

$$\int_0^{\infty} e^{-x} x^k L_n^k(x) L_m^k(x) \, dx = \frac{(n+k)!}{n!} \delta_{nm}.$$

PROOF

Again this proof is very similar to a previous one (that of theorem 6.4) and will be omitted.

Theorem 6.11 (Recurrence relations)

   (i) $L_{n-1}^k(x) + L_n^{k-1}(x) = L_n^k(x)$.

   (ii) $(n+1)L_{n+1}^k(x) = (2n+k+1-x)L_n^k(x) - (n+k)L_{n-1}^k(x)$.

   (iii) $xL_n^{k\prime}(x) = nL_n^k(x) - (n+k)L_{n-1}^k(x)$.

   (iv) $L_n^{k\prime}(x) = -\sum_{r=0}^{n-1} L_r^k(x)$.

   (v) $L_n^{k\prime}(x) = -L_{n-1}^{k+1}(x)$.

   (vi) $L_n^{k+1}(x) = \sum_{r=0}^{n} L_r^k(x)$.

PROOF

(i) Using theorem 6.7 we have

$$L_{n-1}^k(x) + L_n^{k-1}(x)$$

$$= \sum_{r=0}^{n-1}(-1)^r\frac{(n-1+k)!}{(n-1-r)!(k+r)!r!}x^r + \sum_{r=0}^{n}(-1)^r\frac{(n+k-1)!}{(n-r)!(k-1+r)!r!}x^r$$

$$= \sum_{r=0}^{n-1}(-1)^r\frac{(n+k-1)!}{(n-r-1)!(k+r)!r!}x^r + \sum_{r=0}^{n-1}(-1)^r\frac{(n+k-1)!}{(n-r)!(k+r-1)!r!}x^r$$

$$+ (-1)^n\frac{(n+k-1)!}{(n-n)!(k-1+n)!n!}x^n$$

$$= \sum_{r=0}^{n-1}(-1)^r\frac{(n+k-1)!}{(n-r-1)!(k+r-1)!r!}\left\{\frac{1}{(k+r)}+\frac{1}{(n-r)}\right\}x^r$$

$$+ (-1)^n\frac{1}{n!}x^n$$

$$= \sum_{r=0}^{n-1}(-1)^r\frac{(n+k-1)!}{(n-r-1)!(k+r-1)!r!}\frac{(n-r)+(k+r)}{(k+r)(n-r)}x^r$$

$$+ (-1)^n\frac{x^n}{n!}$$

$$= \sum_{r=0}^{n-1}(-1)^r\frac{(n+k)!}{(n-r)!(k+r)!r!}x^r + (-1)^n\frac{x^n}{n!}$$

$$= \sum_{r=0}^{n}(-1)^r\frac{(n+k)!}{(n-r)!(k+r)!r!}x^n$$

$$= L_n^k(x)$$

(again using theorem 6.7).

(ii) Differentiate k times the result of theorem 6.5(i) with n replaced by $n+k$, and we obtain

$$(n+k+1)\frac{d^k}{dx^k}L_{n+k+1}(x) = (2n+2k+1)\frac{d^k}{dx^k}L_{n+k}(x)$$

$$- \frac{d^k}{dx^k}\{xL_{n+k}(x)\} - (n+k)\frac{d^k}{dx^k}L_{n+k-1}(x)$$

and thus, using Leibniz's theorem for the kth derivative of a product,

S F—N

$$(n + k + 1)\frac{\mathrm{d}^k}{\mathrm{d}x^k}L_{n+1+k}(x) = (2n + 2k + 1)\frac{\mathrm{d}^k}{\mathrm{d}x^k}L_{n+k}(x)$$

$$- x\frac{\mathrm{d}^k}{\mathrm{d}x^k}L_{n+k}(x) - k\frac{\mathrm{d}^{k-1}}{\mathrm{d}x^{k-1}}L_{n+k}(x)$$

$$- (n + k)\frac{\mathrm{d}^k}{\mathrm{d}x^k}L_{n-1+k}(x).$$

Making use of definition (6.7) we now have

$$(n + k + 1)(-1)^k L_{n+1}^k(x)$$
$$= (2n + 2k + 1)(-1)^k L_n^k(x) - x(-1)^k L_n^k(x) - k(-1)^{k-1}L_{n+1}^{k-1}(x)$$
$$- (n + k)(-1)^k L_{n-1}^k(x)$$

which, when we take account of part (i) above with n replaced by $n + 1$, gives

$$(n + k + 1)L_{n+1}^k(x) = (2n + 2k + 1)L_n^k(x) - xL_n^k(x)$$
$$+ k\{L_{n+1}^k(x) - L_n^k(x)\} - (n + k)L_{n-1}^k(x)$$

and this simplifies to

$$(n + 1)L_{n+1}^k(x) = (2n + k + 1 - x)L_n^k(x) - (n + k)L_{n-1}^k(x).$$

(iii) If we differentiate k times with respect to x the result of theorem 6.5(ii) with n replaced by $n + k$, we obtain

$$\frac{\mathrm{d}^k}{\mathrm{d}x^k}\{xL_{n-k}'(x)\} = (n + k)\frac{\mathrm{d}^k}{\mathrm{d}x^k}L_{n+k}(x) - (n + k)\frac{\mathrm{d}^k}{\mathrm{d}x^k}L_{n+k-1}(x)$$

which, on use of Leibniz's theorem for the kth derivative of a product, becomes

$$x\frac{\mathrm{d}^k}{\mathrm{d}x^k}L_{n+k}'(x) + k\frac{\mathrm{d}^k}{\mathrm{d}x^k}L_{n+k}(x) = (n + k)\frac{\mathrm{d}^k}{\mathrm{d}x^k}L_{n+k}(x)$$

$$- (n + k)\frac{\mathrm{d}^k}{\mathrm{d}x^k}L_{n+k-1}(x).$$

Then, by equation (6.7), we have

$$xL_n^{k'}(x) + kL_n^k(x) = (n + k)L_n^k(x) - (n + k)L_{n-1}^k(x)$$

and thus

$$xL_n^{k'}(x) = nL_n^k(x) - (n + k)L_{n-1}^k(x).$$

(iv) If we differentiate k times with respect to x the result of theorem 6.5(iii) with n replaced by $n + k$, we obtain

$$\frac{\mathrm{d}^k}{\mathrm{d}x^k}L_{n+k}'(x) = -\sum_{r=0}^{n+k-1}\frac{\mathrm{d}^k}{\mathrm{d}x^k}L_r(x)$$

so that
$$(-1)^k L_n^{k'}(x) = -\sum_{r=k}^{n+k-1} \frac{d^k}{dx^k} L_r(x)$$

(since for $r < k$ $L_r(x)$ is a polynomial of degree less than k and so when differentiated k times just gives zero)

$$= -\sum_{s=0}^{n-1} \frac{d^k}{dx^k} L_{s+k}(x)$$

(changing the variable of summation to $s = r - k$)

$$= -\sum_{s=0}^{n-1} (-1)^k L_s^k(x).$$

Therefore
$$L_n^{k'}(x) = -\sum_{r=0}^{n-1} L_r^k(x).$$

(v) By theorem 6.7 we have

$$L_n^{k'}(x) = \frac{d}{dx} \sum_{r=0}^{n} (-1)^r \frac{(n+k)!}{(n-r)!(k+r)!r!} x^r$$

$$= \sum_{r=1}^{n} (-1)^r \frac{(n+k)!}{(n-r)!(k+r)!(r-1)!} x^{r-1}$$

(the term with $r = 0$ vanishing on differentiation)

$$= \sum_{s=0}^{n-1} (-1)^{s+1} \frac{(n+k)!}{(n-s-1)!(k+s+1)!s!} x^s$$

(changing the variable of summation to $s = r - 1$)

$$= -\sum_{s=0}^{n-1} (-1)^s \frac{(n-1+k+1)!}{(n-1-s)!(k+1+s)!s!} x^s$$

$$= -L_{n-1}^{k+1}(x)$$

(from theorem 6.7).

(vi) Comparing results (iv) and (v) above, we have

$$-\sum_{r=0}^{n-1} L_r^k(x) = -L_{n-1}^{k+1}(x)$$

which, when n is replaced by $n + 1$, gives

$$L_n^{k+1}(x) = \sum_{r=0}^{n} L_r^k(x).$$

6.9   NOTATION

It is important to note that certain authors use different definitions for the Laguerre and associated Laguerre polynomials from those given here.

Sometimes the Laguerre polynomials are defined such that the generating function has the form

$$\frac{\exp\{-xt/(1-t)\}}{1-t} = \sum_{n=0}^{\infty} \mathscr{L}_n(x)\frac{t^n}{n!}$$

so that $\mathscr{L}_n(x)$ thus defined is equal to $n!L_n(x)$.†

The associated Laguerre polynomials may be defined by

$$\mathscr{L}_n^k(x) = \frac{d^k}{dx^k}\mathscr{L}_n(x)$$

giving the relationship $\mathscr{L}_n^k(x) = (-1)^k L_{n-k}^k(x)$.

6.10   EXAMPLES

Example 1

Prove that $L_n^{\alpha+\beta+1}(x+y) = \sum_{r=0}^{n} L_r^{\alpha}(x)L_{n-r}^{\beta}(y)$.

We have, from theorem 6.8,

$$\sum_{n=0}^{\infty} L_n^{\alpha+\beta+1}x+y).t^n = \frac{\exp\{-(x+y)t/(1-t)\}}{(1-t)^{\alpha+\beta+2}}$$

so that $L_n^{\alpha+\beta+1}(x+y)$ is the coefficient of t^n in the power series expansion of

$$\frac{\exp\{-(x+y)t/(1-t)\}}{(1-t)^{\alpha+\beta+2}}.$$

But

$$\frac{\exp\{-(x+y)t/(1-t)\}}{(1-t)^{\alpha+\beta+2}} = \frac{\exp\{-xt/(1-t)\}}{(1-t)^{\alpha+1}}\frac{\exp\{-yt/(1-t)\}}{(1-t)^{\beta+1}}$$

$$= \sum_{r=0}^{\infty} L_r^{\alpha}(x)t^r \sum_{s=0}^{\infty} L_s^{\beta}(y)t^s$$

(again using theorem 6.8)

$$= \sum_{r,s=0}^{\infty} L_r^{\alpha}(x)L_s^{\beta}(y)t^{r+s}.$$

---

† We use $\mathscr{L}$ to denote alternative definitions, in order to distinguish them from ours, but it must be remembered that authors adopting these alternative definitions will use L.

We obtain t^n by taking $r + s = n$; so that for a fixed value of r we have $s = n - r$, and hence, for this value of r, the coefficient of t^n is $L_r^\alpha(x)L_{n-r}^\beta(y)$. The total coefficient of t^n is obtained by summing over all allowed values of r, which, since $s = n - r$ and we require $s \geqslant 0$, implies that $r \leqslant n$.

Hence the coefficient of t^n is $\displaystyle\sum_{r=0}^{n} L_r^\alpha(x)L_{n-r}^\beta(y)$

so that $$L_n^{\alpha+\beta+1}(x + y) = \sum_{r=0}^{n} L_r^\alpha(x)L_{n-r}^\beta(y).$$

Example 2

Show that $J_m\{2\sqrt{(xt)}\} = e^{-t}(xt)^{m/2}\displaystyle\sum_{n=0}^{\infty} \dfrac{L_n^m(x)}{(n + m)!}t^n$

(where J_m is the Bessel function of integral order m).

We shall prove the equivalent result that

$$e^t(xt)^{-m/2}J_m\{2\sqrt{(xt)}\} = \sum_{n=0}^{\infty} \frac{L_n^m(x)}{(n + m)!}t^n.$$

From equation (4.6) we have

$$J_m\{2\sqrt{(xt)}\} = \sum_{r=0}^{\infty} (-1)^r \frac{1}{r!(m + r)!}\left\{\frac{2\sqrt{(xt)}}{2}\right\}^{2r+m}$$

so that

$$e^t(xt)^{-m/2}J_m\{2\sqrt{(xt)}\} = e^t(xt)^{-m/2}\sum_{r=0}^{\infty} (-1)^r \frac{1}{r!(m + r)!}(xt)^{r+(m/2)}$$

$$= e^t\sum_{r=0}^{\infty} (-1)^r \frac{1}{r!(m + r)!}(xt)^r$$

$$= \sum_{s=0}^{\infty} \frac{t^s}{s!}\sum_{r=0}^{\infty} (-1)^r \frac{1}{r!(m + r)!}x^rt^r$$

$$= \sum_{r,s=0}^{\infty} (-1)^r \frac{1}{r!(m + r)!s!}x^rt^{r+s}.$$

We wish to show that the coefficient of t^n in this expansion is

$$L_n^m(x)/(n + m)!.$$

To obtain the coefficient of t^n we take $r + s = n$ so that for a fixed value of r we have $s = n - r$, and for this value of r the coefficient is

$$(-1)^r \frac{1}{r!(m + r)!(n - r)!}x^r.$$

The total coefficient is obtained by summing over all allowed values of r, which, since $s = n - r$ and we require $s \geqslant 0$, is given by $n - r \geqslant 0$, i.e., $r \leqslant n$.

Hence the coefficient of t^n is

$$\sum_{r=0}^{n} (-1)^r \frac{1}{r!(m + r)!(n - r)!} x^r$$

$$= \frac{1}{(n + m)!} \sum_{r=0}^{n} (-1)^r \frac{(n + m)!}{r!(m + r)(n - r)!} x^r$$

$$= \frac{1}{(n + m)!} L_n^m(x)$$

(using theorem 6.7),

and the required result follows.

Example 3

Show that $\int_x^\infty e^{-t} L_n^k(t)\, dt = e^{-x}\{L_n^k(x) - L_{n-1}^k(x)\}.$

Integrating by parts, we have

$$\int_x^\infty e^{-t} L_n^k(t)\, dt = \left[-e^{-t} L_n^k(t) \right]_x^\infty - \int_x^\infty -e^{-t} . L_n^{k'}(t)\, dt$$

$$= e^{-x} L_n^k(x) + \int_x^\infty e^{-t} L_n^{k'}(t)\, dt$$

$$= e^{-x} L_n^k(x) - \int_x^\infty e^{-t} \left\{ \sum_{r=0}^{n-1} L_r^k(t) \right\} dt$$

(by theorem 6.11(iv)).

Thus

$$\int_x^\infty e^{-t} L_n^k(t)\, dt + \sum_{r=0}^{n-1} \int_x^\infty e^{-t} L_r^k(t)\, dt = e^{-x} L_n^k(x)$$

and hence

$$\sum_{r=0}^{n} \int_x^\infty e^{-t} L_r^k(t)\, dt = e^{-x} L_n^k(x). \tag{6.8}$$

Therefore

$$\int_x^\infty e^{-t}L_n^k(t)\,dt = \sum_{r=0}^{n}\int_x^\infty e^{-t}L_r^k(t)\,dt - \sum_{r=0}^{n-1}\int_x^\infty e^{-t}L_r^k(t)\,dt$$

$$= e^{-x}L_n^k(x) - e^{-x}L_{n-1}^k(x)$$

(by equation (6.8) above)

$$= e^{-x}\{L_n^k(x) - L_{n-1}^k(x)\}.$$

PROBLEMS

(1) Show that $L_n''(0) = \frac{1}{2}n(n-1)$.

(2) If $f(x)$ is a polynomial of degree m, show that $f(x)$ may be expressed in the form

$$f(x) = \sum_{r=0}^{m} c_r L_r(x)$$

with
$$c_r = \int_0^\infty e^{-x}L_r(x)f(x)\,dx.$$

Deduce that $\displaystyle\int_0^\infty e^{-x}x^k L_n(x)\,dx = \begin{cases} 0 \text{ if } k < n \\ (-1)^n n! \text{ if } k = n. \end{cases}$

(3) Prove that

$$\int_0^x (x-t)^m L_n(t)\,dt = \frac{m!\,n!}{(m+n+1)!}x^{m+1}L_n^{m+1}(x).$$

(4) Show that

$$L_n^k(x) = (-1)^n\,\frac{2^{2k}k!(n+k)!}{\pi(2k)!(2n)!}\int_{-1}^1 (1-t^2)^{k-\frac{1}{2}}H_{2n}\{(\sqrt{x})t\}\,dt.$$

(5) Prove that

$$n!\frac{d^m}{dx^m}\{e^{-x}x^k L_n^k(x)\} = (m+n)!e^{-x}\,x^{k-m}\,L_{m+n}^{k-m}(x).$$

(6) Show that

$$\int_0^\infty e^{-x}x^{k+1}\{L_n^k(x)\}^2\,dx = \frac{(n+k)!}{n!}(2n+k+1).$$

(7) If $L_n^k(x)$ is defined for non-integral k by the generalisation of the result of theorem 6.7

$$L_n^k(x) = \sum_{r=0}^{n} (-1)^r \frac{\Gamma(n+k+1)}{(n-r)!\Gamma(k+r+1)r!} x^r$$

show that $L_n^{1/2}(x) = (-1)^n \dfrac{1}{2^{2n+1}n!x} H_{2n+1}(\sqrt{x})$

and $L_n^{-1/2}(x) = (-1)^n \dfrac{1}{2^{2n}n!} H_{2n}(\sqrt{x}).$

(8) With $L_n^k(x)$ defined for non-integral k as in problem 7, show that

$$L_n^{k+l}(x) = \frac{\Gamma(n+k+l+1)}{\Gamma(l)\Gamma(n+k+1)} \int_0^1 t^k(1-t)^{l-1} L_n^k(xt) \; \mathrm{d}t.$$

7

CHEBYSHEV POLYNOMIALS†

7.1 DEFINITION OF CHEBYSHEV POLYNOMIALS; CHEBYSHEV'S EQUATION

We define the Chebyshev polynomials of first kind, $T_n(x)$, and second kind, $U_n(x)$, by

$$T_n(x) = \cos(n \cos^{-1} x) \qquad (7.1)$$

and
$$U_n(x) = \sin(n \cos^{-1} x),‡ \qquad (7.2)$$

for n a non-negative integer.

Theorem 7.1

(i) $T_n(x) = \frac{1}{2}[\{x + i\sqrt{(1 - x^2)}\}^n + \{x - i\sqrt{(1 - x^2)}\}^n]$.

(ii) $U_n(x) = -\frac{1}{2}i[\{x + i\sqrt{(1 - x^2)}\}^n - \{x - i\sqrt{(1 - x^2)}\}^n]$.

PROOF

(i) Let us write $x = \cos\theta$ and we obtain

$$\begin{aligned}
T_n(x) &= \cos(n \cos^{-1} \cos\theta) \\
&= \cos n\theta \\
&= \tfrac{1}{2}\{e^{in\theta} + e^{-in\theta}\} \\
&= \tfrac{1}{2}\{(e^{i\theta})^n + (e^{-i\theta})^n\} \\
&= \tfrac{1}{2}\{(\cos\theta + i\sin\theta)^n + (\cos\theta - i\sin\theta)^n\} \\
&= \tfrac{1}{2}[\{x + i\sqrt{(1 - x^2)}\}^n + \{x - i\sqrt{(1 - x^2)}\}^n].
\end{aligned}$$

(ii) The proof is similar to that of (i), and so will not be given.

---

† The transliterations Tchebichef, Tchebicheff and Tschebyscheff are also found.

‡ Sometimes the Chebyshev polynomial of the second kind is defined by
$$\mathscr{U}_n(x) = \sin\{(n+1)\cos^{-1} x\}/\sqrt{(1 - x^2)} = \{1/\sqrt{(1 - x^2)}\}/U_{n+1}(x).$$

Theorem 7.2

(i) $T_n(x) = \displaystyle\sum_{r=0}^{[\frac{1}{2}n]} (-1)^r \frac{n!}{(2r)!(n-2r)!}(1-x^2)^r x^{n-2r}.$

(ii) $U_n(x) = \displaystyle\sum_{r=0}^{[\frac{1}{2}(n-1)]} (-1)^r \frac{n!}{(2r+1)!(n-2r-1)!}(1-x^2)^{r+\frac{1}{2}} x^{n-2r-1}.$

PROOF

(i) From theorem 7.1(i) we have

$T_n(x) = \frac{1}{2}[\{x + i\sqrt{(1-x^2)}\}^n + \{x - i\sqrt{(1-x^2)}\}^n]$

$= \frac{1}{2}\left[\displaystyle\sum_{r=0}^{n} {}^nC_r x^{n-r}\{i\sqrt{(1-x^2)}\}^r + \sum_{r=0}^{n} {}^nC_r x^{n-r}\{-i\sqrt{(1-x^2)}\}^r \right]$

(by the binomial theorem)

$= \frac{1}{2}\displaystyle\sum_{r=0}^{n} {}^nC_r x^{n-r}(1-x^2)^{r/2}\, i^r\{1 + (-1)^r\}.$

Now, when r is odd $(-1)^r = -1$, so that $1 + (-1)^r = 0$, and when r is even $(-1)^r = 1$, so that $1 + (-1)^r = 2$. Hence we have

$$T_n(x) = \frac{1}{2} \sum_{r \text{ even, } \leqslant n} {}^nC_r x^{n-r}(1-x^2)^{r/2}\, i^r\, 2.$$

But if r is even we may write $r = 2s$ with s integral, and the requirement $r \leqslant n$ means that $s \leqslant n/2$. This, since s is an integer, is equivalent to $s \leqslant [n/2]$ with $[n/2]$ as defined before, namely the greatest integer less than or equal to $n/2$. Thus,

$$T_n(x) = \sum_{s=0}^{[\frac{1}{2}n]} {}^nC_{2s} x^{n-2s}(1-x^2)^s\, i^{2s}$$

$$= \sum_{s=0}^{[\frac{1}{2}n]} \frac{n!}{(n-2s)!(2s)!} x^{n-2s}(1-x^2)^s(-1)^s.$$

(ii) The proof is similar to (i) above.

We may use theorem 7.2 to write down the first few Chebyshev polynomials:

$T_0(x) = 1,$ $\qquad\qquad$ $U_0(x) = 0;$

$T_1(x) = x,$ $\qquad\qquad$ $U_1(x) = \sqrt{(1-x^2)};$

$$T_2(x) = 2x^2 - 1, \qquad\qquad U_2(x) = \sqrt{(1 - x^2)}2x;$$
$$T_3(x) = 4x^3 - 3x, \qquad\qquad U_3(x) = \sqrt{(1 - x^2)}(4x^2 - 1);$$
$$T_4(x) = 8x^4 - 8x^2 + 1, \qquad\quad U_4(x) = \sqrt{(1 - x^2)}(8x^3 - 4x);$$
$$T_5(x) = 16x^5 - 20x^3 + 5x, \quad U_5(x) = \sqrt{(1 - x^2)}(16x^4 - 12x^2 + 1).$$

We note that $U_n(x)$ is not actually a polynomial, but is instead a polynomial multiplied by the factor $\sqrt{(1 - x^2)}$, whereas $\mathscr{U}_n(x)$ as defined above *is* a polynomial of degree n.

Since $T_n(\cos\theta) = \cos n\theta$ and $U_n(\cos\theta) = \sin n\theta$, we note that the Chebyshev polynomials provide expansions of $\cos n\theta$ and $\sin n\theta/\sin\theta$ in terms of powers of $\cos\theta$.

Theorem 7.3

$T_n(x)$ and $U_n(x)$ are independent solutions of Chebyshev's equation

$$(1 - x^2)\frac{d^2y}{dx^2} - x\frac{dy}{dx} + n^2y = 0.$$

PROOF

We give the proof for $T_n(x)$; the proof for $U_n(x)$ is similar.
We have, from definition (7.1),

$$\frac{d}{dx}T_n(x) = \frac{d}{dx}\cos(n\cos^{-1}x)$$

$$= -\sin(n\cos^{-1}x).n.\frac{-1}{\sqrt{(1 - x^2)}}$$

(remembering that $(d/dx)\cos^{-1}x = -1/\sqrt{(1 - x^2)}$)

$$= n\frac{1}{\sqrt{(1 - x^2)}}\sin(n\cos^{-1}x).$$

Also,

$$\frac{d^2}{dx^2}T_n(x)$$

$$= \frac{d}{dx}\left\{\frac{n}{\sqrt{(1 - x^2)}}\sin(n\cos^{-1}x)\right\}$$

$$= \frac{nx}{(1 - x^2)^{3/2}}\sin(n\cos^{-1}x) + \frac{n}{(1 - x^2)^{1/2}}\cos(n\cos^{-1}x).\frac{-n}{(1 - x^2)^{1/2}}$$

$$= \frac{nx}{(1 - x^2)^{3/2}}\sin(n\cos^{-1}x) - \frac{n^2}{(1 - x^2)}\cos(n\cos^{-1}x).$$

Hence

$$(1 - x^2)\frac{d^2 T_n(x)}{dx^2} - x\frac{d T_n(x)}{dx} + n^2 T_n(x)$$

$$= \frac{nx}{(1 - x^2)^{1/2}} \sin (n \cos^{-1} x) - n^2 \cos (n \cos^{-1} x)$$

$$- \frac{nx}{(1 - x^2)^{1/2}} \sin (n \cos^{-1} x) + n^2 \cos (n \cos^{-1} x)$$

$$= 0,$$

which proves the required result.

The fact that $U_n(x)$ and $T_n(x)$ are independent solutions follows from observing that $T_n(1) = 1$ while $U_n(1) = 0$, so that $U_n(x)$ cannot be a constant multiple of $T_n(x)$.

7.2 GENERATING FUNCTION

Theorem 7.4

(i) $\dfrac{1 - t^2}{1 - 2tx + t^2} = T_0(x) + 2 \displaystyle\sum_{n=1}^{\infty} T_n(x)t^n.$

(ii) $\dfrac{\sqrt{(1 - x^2)}}{1 - 2tx + t^2} = \displaystyle\sum_{n=0}^{\infty} U_{n+1}(x)t^n.$

PROOF

Again we prove only result (i), the proof of (ii) being similar.

Let us write $x = \cos \theta = \frac{1}{2}(e^{i\theta} + e^{-i\theta})$, so that we have

$$\frac{1 - t^2}{1 - 2tx + t^2} = \frac{1 - t^2}{1 - (e^{i\theta} + e^{-i\theta})t + t^2}$$

$$= \frac{1 - t^2}{(1 - e^{i\theta}t)(1 - e^{-i\theta}t)}$$

$$= (1 - t^2) \sum_{r=0}^{\infty} (e^{i\theta}t)^r \sum_{s=0}^{\infty} (e^{-i\theta}t)^s$$

$$\text{(by the binomial theorem)}$$

$$= (1 - t^2) \sum_{r,s=0}^{\infty} e^{i(r-s)\theta} t^{r+s}$$

$$= \sum_{r,s=0}^{\infty} e^{i(r-)\theta} t^{r+s} - \sum_{r,s=0}^{\infty} e^{i(r-s)\theta} t^{r+s+2}.$$

We wish to pick out the coefficient of t^n in this summation and show that it is $T_0(x)$ when $n = 0$ and $2T_n(x)$ otherwise.

We consider the cases $n = 0$ and $n = 1$ separately, since for these values of n we obtain t^n from the first summation only, whereas for $n \geqslant 2$ we obtain t^n from both summations.

$n = 0$ is obtained only by taking $r = 0$ and $s = 0$ in the first summation, so that the coefficient of t^0 is

$$e^{i(0-0)\theta} = 1 = T_0(x).$$

$n = 1$ is obtained by taking either $r = 1$ and $s = 0$ or $r = 0$ and $s = 1$, so that the coefficient of t^1 is

$$e^{i\theta} + e^{-i\theta} = 2 \cos \theta$$
$$= 2T_1(x)$$

(remembering that $T_n(x) = T_n(\cos \theta) = \cos n\theta$).

For $n \geqslant 2$ we obtain the coefficient of t^n by taking $r + s = n$ (i.e., $s = n - r$) in the first summation and $r + s + 2 = n$ (i.e., $s = n - r - 2$) in the second summation. The coefficient of t^n is therefore

$$\sum_{r=0}^{n} e^{i\{r-(n-r)\}\theta} - \sum_{r=0}^{n-2} e^{i\{r-(n-r-2)\}\theta}$$

$$= e^{-in\theta} \sum_{r=0}^{n} e^{i2r\theta} - e^{-i(n-2)\theta} \sum_{r=0}^{n-2} e^{i2r\theta}$$

$$= e^{-in\theta} \frac{1 - (e^{i2\theta})^{n+1}}{1 - e^{2i\theta}} - e^{-i(n-2)\theta} \frac{1 - (e^{i2\theta})^{n-1}}{1 - e^{2i\theta}}$$

(summing to $n + 1$ and $n - 1$ terms, respectively, the two geometric series which both have the common ratio $e^{2i\theta}$)

$$= \frac{e^{-in\theta} - e^{i(n+2)\theta}}{1 - e^{2i\theta}} - \frac{e^{-i(n-2)\theta} - e^{in\theta}}{1 - e^{2i\theta}}$$

$$= \frac{e^{-in\theta}(1 - e^{2i\theta})}{1 - e^{2i\theta}} + \frac{e^{in\theta}(1 - e^{2i\theta})}{1 - e^{2i\theta}}$$

(on rearranging the terms)

$$= e^{in\theta} + e^{-in\theta}$$
$$= 2 \cos n\theta$$
$$= 2T_n(x),$$

(again remembering that $T_n(x) = T_n(\cos \theta) = \cos n\theta$)

Theorem 7.5 (Special values of the Chebyshev polynomials)

  (i) $T_n(1) = 1$,
   $T_n(-1) = (-1)^n$,
   $T_{2n}(0) = (-1)^n$,
   $T_{2n+1}(0) = 0$.
  (ii) $U_n(1) = 0$,
   $U_n(-1) = 0$,
   $U_{2n}(0) = 0$,
   $U_{2n+1}(0) = (-1)^n$.

PROOF

Again we prove results (i) only.
Setting $x = 1$ in definition (7.1) gives

$$T_n(1) = \cos(n \cos^{-1} 1) = \cos n.0 = \cos 0 = 1.$$

Setting $x = -1$ gives

$$T_n(-1) = \cos(n \cos^{-1} -1) = \cos n\pi = (-1)^n.$$

Setting $x = 0$ gives

$$T_n(0) = \cos(n \cos^{-1} 0) = \cos n\frac{\pi}{2}$$

$$= \begin{cases} 0 & \text{if } n \text{ is odd} \\ (-1)^{n/2} & \text{if } n \text{ is even.} \end{cases}$$

Thus all four results are proved.

7.3 ORTHOGONALITY PROPERTIES

Theorem 7.6

(i) $\displaystyle \int_{-1}^{1} \frac{T_m(x)T_n(x)}{\sqrt{(1-x^2)}}\, dx = \begin{cases} 0 & m \neq n \\ \pi/2 & m = n \neq 0 \\ \pi & m = n = 0. \end{cases}$

(ii) $\displaystyle \int_{-1}^{1} \frac{U_m(x)U_n(x)}{\sqrt{(1-x^2)}}\, dx = \begin{cases} 0 & m \neq n \\ \pi/2 & m = n \neq 0 \\ 0 & m = n = 0. \end{cases}$

PROOF

We prove result (i) only, the proof of (ii) being similar.
If we set $x = \cos\theta$ we have

$$\int_{-1}^{1} \frac{T_m(x)T_n(x)}{\sqrt{(1-x^2)}} \, dx = \int_{\pi}^{0} \frac{T_m(\cos\theta)T_n(\cos\theta)}{\sin\theta}(-\sin\theta \, d\theta)$$

$$= \int_{0}^{\pi} \cos n\theta \cos m\theta \, d\theta \qquad (7.3)$$

$$\text{(by definition (7.1))}$$

$$= \int_{0}^{\pi} \tfrac{1}{2}\{\cos(n+m)\theta + \cos(n-m)\theta\} \, d\theta$$

$$= \frac{1}{2}\left[-\frac{1}{n+m}\sin(n+m)\theta - \frac{1}{n-m}\sin(n-m)\theta\right]_{0}^{\pi}$$

$$\text{(provided } n \quad m \neq 0)$$

$$= 0.$$

If $n - m = 0$ we have from equation (7.3)

$$\int_{-1}^{1} \frac{T_n(x)T_m(x)}{\sqrt{(1-x^2)}} \, dx = \int_{0}^{\pi} \cos^2 n\theta \, d\theta \qquad (7.4)$$

$$= \int_{0}^{\pi} \tfrac{1}{2}(1 + \cos 2n\theta) \, d\theta$$

$$= \frac{1}{2}\left[\theta - \frac{1}{2n}\sin 2n\theta\right]_{0}^{\pi}$$

$$\text{(provided } n \neq 0)$$

$$= \tfrac{1}{2}\pi.$$

If $n = m = 0$ we have from equation (7.4)

$$\int_{-1}^{1} \frac{T_0(x)T_0(x)}{\sqrt{(1-x^2)}} \, dx = \int_{0}^{\pi} 1 \, d\theta$$

$$= \pi,$$

and thus the proof is complete.

7.4 RECURRENCE RELATIONS

Theorem 7.7

(i) $T_{n+1}(x) - 2xT_n(x) + T_{n-1}(x) = 0$.

(ii) $(1 - x^2)T_n'(x) = -nxT_n(x) + nT_{n-1}(x)$.

(iii) $U_{n+1}(x) - 2xU_n(x) + U_{n-1}(x) = 0$.

(iv) $(1 - x^2)U_n'(x) = -nxU_n(x) + nU_{n-1}(x)$.

PROOF

Again we provide proofs for the polynomials of first kind only.

(i) By writing $x = \cos \theta$, the required result is

$$\cos (n + 1)\theta - 2 \cos \theta \cos n\theta + \cos (n - 1)\theta = 0.$$

However,

$$\cos (n + 1)\theta - 2 \cos \theta \cos n\theta + \cos (n - 1)\theta$$
$$= \cos n\theta \cos \theta - \sin n\theta \sin \theta - 2 \cos \theta \cos n\theta$$
$$+ \cos n\theta \cos \theta + \sin n\theta \sin \theta$$
$$= 0,$$

the result which was to be proved.

(ii) By writing $x = \cos \theta$, the required result is

$$(1 - \cos^2 \theta)\frac{d}{d(\cos \theta)} \cos n\theta = -n \cos \theta \cos n\theta + n \cos (n - 1)\theta.$$

But

$$(1 - \cos^2 \theta)\frac{d}{d(\cos \theta)} \cos n\theta = \sin^2 \theta \left(-\frac{1}{\sin \theta}\frac{d}{d\theta} \cos n\theta \right)$$
$$= -\sin \theta(-n \sin n\theta)$$
$$= n \sin \theta \sin n\theta$$

and $-n \cos \theta \cos n\theta + n \cos (n - 1)\theta$

$$= -n \cos \theta \cos n\theta + n(\cos n\theta \cos \theta + \sin n\theta \sin \theta)$$
$$= n \sin n\theta \sin \theta,$$

so that the required result is proved.

7.5   EXAMPLES

Example 1

Show that $\sqrt{(1 - x^2)}T_n(x) = U_{n+1}(x) - xU_n(x).$

If we replace x by $\cos \theta$ and use the consequences of definitions (7.1) and (7.2) that

$$T_n(\cos \theta) = \cos n\theta$$

and
$$U_n(\cos \theta) = \sin n\theta,$$

we find that the result we require to prove is just

$$\sin \theta \cos n\theta = \sin (n + 1)\theta - \cos \theta \sin n\theta.$$

But $\sin (n + 1)\theta - \cos \theta \sin n\theta$

$$= \sin n\theta \cos \theta + \cos n\theta \sin \theta - \cos \theta \sin n\theta$$
$$= \cos n\theta \sin \theta,$$

which proves the result.

Example 2

Show that $\displaystyle\sum_{r=0}^{n} T_{2r}(x) = \frac{1}{2}\Big\{1 + \frac{1}{\sqrt{(1 - x^2)}} U_{2n+1}(x)\Big\}.$

Again we write $x = \cos\theta$, so that we have

$$\sum_{r=0}^{n} T_{2r}(x)$$

$$= \sum_{r=0}^{n} T_{2r}(\cos\theta)$$

$$= \sum_{r=0}^{n} \cos 2r\theta$$

$$= \mathrm{Re} \sum_{r=0}^{n} e^{i2r\theta}$$

$$= \mathrm{Re}\ \frac{1 - e^{i(2n+2)\theta}}{1 - e^{i2\theta}}$$

(using the result for the sum to $n + 1$ terms of a geometric progression)

$$= \mathrm{Re}\ \frac{(1 - e^{i(2n+2)\theta})(1 - e^{-2i\theta})}{(1 - e^{i2\theta})(1 - e^{-2i\theta})}$$

$$= \mathrm{Re}\ \frac{\{1 - \cos(2n+2)\theta - i\sin(2n+2)\theta\}\{1 - \cos 2\theta + i\sin 2\theta\}}{1 + 1 - e^{i2\theta} - e^{-i2\theta}}$$

$$= \frac{1}{2 - 2\cos 2\theta}\ [(1 - \cos 2\theta)\{1 - \cos(2n+2)\theta\} + \sin 2\theta \sin(2n+2)\theta]$$

$$= \frac{1}{2}\Big\{1 - \cos(2n+2)\theta + \frac{\sin 2\theta}{2\sin^2\theta}\sin(2n+2)\theta\Big\}$$

$$= \frac{1}{2}\Big\{1 + \frac{\sin(2n+2)\theta\cos\theta - \cos(2n+2)\theta\sin\theta}{\sin\theta}\Big\}$$

$$= \frac{1}{2}\Big[1 + \frac{\sin\{(2n+2)\theta - \theta\}}{\sin\theta}\Big]$$

$$= \frac{1}{2}\Big\{1 + \frac{\sin(2n+1)\theta}{\sin\theta}\Big\}$$

$$= \frac{1}{2}\Big\{1 + \frac{U_{2n+1}(x)}{\sqrt{(1 - x^2)}}\Big\}.$$

S F—O

PROBLEMS

(1) Show that $\sqrt{(1 - x^2)}U_n(x) = xT_n(x) - T_{n+1}(x)$.

(2) Show that $T_{m+n}(x) + T_{m-n}(x) = 2T_m(x)T_n(x)$.

(3) Prove that $T_n'(x) = \dfrac{n}{\sqrt{(1 - x^2)}}U_n(x)$.

(4) Show that $2\{T_n(x)\}^2 = 1 + T_{2n}(x)$.

(5) Show that $\{T_n(x)\}^2 - T_{n+1}(x)T_{n-1}(x) = 1 - x^2$.

(6) Show that $T_m\{T_n(x)\} = T_n\{T_m(x)\} = T_{mn}(x)$.

(7) Show that $\{1/\sqrt{(1 - x^2)}\}U_n(x)$ satisfies the differential equation

$$(1 - x^2)\frac{d^2y}{dx^2} - 3x\frac{dy}{dx} + (n^2 - 1)y = 0.$$

(8) Use Chebyshev's differential equation and the equation in problem (7) above to show that

$$T_n(x) = \frac{n}{2}\sum_{r=0}^{[\frac{1}{2}n]}(-1)^r\frac{(n - r - 1)!}{r!(n - 2r)!}(2x)^{n-2r}$$

and

$$U_n(x) = \sqrt{(1 - x^2)}\sum_{r=0}^{[\frac{1}{2}(n-1)]}(-1)^r\frac{(n - r - 1)!}{r!(n - 2r - 1)!}(2x)^{n-2r-1}.$$

8

GEGENBAUER AND JACOBI POLYNOMIALS

8.1 GEGENBAUER POLYNOMIALS

It is possible to define new sets of polynomials by generalizing some of the results already proved for the Legendre, Hermite, Laguerre or Chebyshev polynomials. We give here only two particularly useful sets; those obtained by generalizing in two different ways the generating function of the Legendre polynomials, given in theorem 3.1. We shall define the Gegenbauer polynomial† of degree n and order λ, $C_n^\lambda(x)$, as the coefficient of t^n in the expansion of

$$\frac{1}{(1 - 2xt + t^2)^\lambda}.$$

(Note that the Legendre polynomial $P_n(x)$ is in fact equal to $C_n^{\frac{1}{2}}(x)$.)
Thus

$$\frac{1}{(1 - 2xt + t^2)^\lambda} = \sum_{n=0}^{\infty} C_n^\lambda(x)t^n. \qquad (8.1)$$

It may be shown that such a power series expansion is valid for $|t| < 1$, $|x| \leqslant 1$ and $\lambda > -\frac{1}{2}$.

We shall omit proofs of the following properties. All the results may be obtained by methods similar to those used in preceding chapters.

---

† Also sometimes called the ultraspherical polynomial.

Theorem 8.1 (Power series expansion)

$$C_n^\lambda(x) = \sum_{r=0}^{[\frac{1}{2}n]} (-1)^r \frac{\Gamma(n-r+\lambda)}{\Gamma(\lambda)r!(n-2r)!} (2x)^{n-2r}.$$

Theorem 8.2 (Orthogonality property)

$$\int_{-1}^{1} (1-x^2)^{\lambda-\frac{1}{2}} C_n^\lambda(x) C_m^\lambda(x)\, dx = 2^{1-2\lambda}\pi \frac{\Gamma(n+2\lambda)}{(n+\lambda)\{\Gamma(\lambda)\}^2\Gamma(n+1)} \delta_{nm}.$$

Theorem 8.3 (Recurrence relations)

(i) $(n+2)C_{n+2}^\lambda(x) = 2(\lambda+n+1)xC_{n+1}^\lambda(x) - (2\lambda+n)C_n^\lambda(x).$
(ii) $nC_n^\lambda(x) = 2\lambda\{xC_{n-1}^{\lambda+1}(x) - C_{n-2}^{\lambda+1}(x)\}.$
(iii) $(n+2\lambda)C_n^\lambda(x) = 2\lambda\{C_n^{\lambda+1}(x) - xC_{n-1}^{\lambda+1}(x)\}.$
(iv) $nC_n^\lambda(x) = (n-1+2\lambda)xC_{n-1}^\lambda(x) - 2\lambda(1-x^2)C_{n-2}^{\lambda-1}(x).$
(v) $C_n^{\lambda'}(x) = 2\lambda C_{n+1}^{\lambda+1}(x).$

Theorem 8.4 (Differential equation)

$C_n^\lambda(x)$ *satisfies the differential equation*

$$(1-x^2)\frac{d^2y}{dx^2} - (2\lambda+1)x\frac{dy}{dx} + n(n+2\lambda)y = 0.$$

8.2 JACOBI POLYNOMIALS

We may generalize the Legendre polynomial generating function even further. We define the Jacobi polynomial $P_n^{(\alpha,\beta)}(x)$ as the coefficient of t^n in the expansion of

$$\frac{2^{\alpha+\beta}}{(1-2xt+t^2)^{1/2}\{1-t+(1-2xt+t^2)^{1/2}\}^\alpha\{1+t+(1-2xt+t^2)^{1/2}\}^\beta},$$

i.e.,
$$\frac{2^{\alpha+\beta}}{(1-2xt+t^2)^{1/2}\{1-t+(1-2xt+t^2)^{1/2}\}^\alpha\{1+t+(1-2xt+t^2)^{1/2}\}^\beta}$$

$$= \sum_{n=0}^{\infty} P_n^{(\alpha,\beta)}(x)t^n. \tag{8.2}$$

We note that the Legendre polynomial $P_n(x)$ is in fact equal to $P_n^{(0,0)}(x)$.

Again the following properties may be proved by methods similar to those used in previous chapters.

Theorem 8.5 (Series expansions)

(i) $P_n^{(\alpha,\beta)}(x)$

$$= \sum_{r=0}^{n} \frac{\Gamma(n+\alpha+1)\Gamma(n+\beta+1)}{\Gamma(\alpha+r+1)\Gamma(n+\beta-r+1)(n-r)!r!}\left(\frac{x-1}{2}\right)^r\left(\frac{x+1}{2}\right)^{n-r}.$$

(ii) $P_n^{(\alpha,\beta)}(x) = \sum_{r=0}^{n} \frac{\Gamma(n+\alpha+1)\Gamma(n+r+\alpha+\beta+1)}{\Gamma(\alpha+r+1)\Gamma(n+\alpha+\beta+1)(n-r)!r!}\left(\frac{x-1}{2}\right)^r.$

(iii) $P_n^{(\alpha,\beta)}(x) = \sum_{r=0}^{n} \frac{(-1)^{n-r}\Gamma(n+\beta+1)\Gamma(n+r+\alpha+\beta+1)}{\Gamma(\beta+r+1)\Gamma(n+\alpha+\beta+1)(n-r)!r!}\left(\frac{x+1}{2}\right)^r.$

Theorem 8.6 (Orthogonality property)

$$\int_{-1}^{1} (1-x)^{\alpha}(1+x)^{\beta}P_n^{(\alpha,\beta)}(x)P_m^{(\alpha,\beta)}(x)\,dx$$

$$= \frac{2^{\alpha+\beta+1}\Gamma(n+\alpha+1)\Gamma(n+\beta+1)}{(2n+\alpha+\beta+1)n!\Gamma(n+\alpha+\beta+1)}\delta_{nm}.$$

Theorem 8.7 (Recurrence relations)

(i) $2n(\alpha+\beta+n)(\alpha+\beta+2n-2)P_n^{(\alpha,\beta)}(x)$
$= (\alpha+\beta+2n-1)\{\alpha^2-\beta^2+x(\alpha+\beta+2n)(\alpha+\beta+2n-2)\}P_{n-1}^{(\alpha,\beta)}(x)$
$\quad - 2(\alpha+n-1)(\beta+n-1)(\alpha+\beta+2n)P_{n-2}^{(\alpha,\beta)}(x).$

(ii) $P_n^{(\alpha,\beta)\prime}(x) = \frac{1}{2}(1+\alpha+\beta+n)P_{n-1}^{(\alpha+1,\beta+1)}(x).$

(iii) $(x+1)P_n^{(\alpha,\beta)\prime}(x) = nP_n^{(\alpha,\beta)}(x)+(\beta+n)P_{n-1}^{(\alpha+1,\beta)}(x).$

(iv) $(x-1)P_n^{(\alpha,\beta)\prime}(x) = nP_n^{(\alpha,\beta)}(x)-(\alpha+n)P_{n-1}^{(\alpha,\beta+1)}(x).$

(v) $P_n^{(\alpha,\beta)\prime}(x) = \frac{1}{2}\{(\beta+n)P_{n-1}^{(\alpha+1,\beta)}(x)+(\alpha+n)P_{n-1}^{(\alpha,\beta+1)}(x)\}.$

(vi) $(\alpha+\beta+2n)P_n^{(\alpha,\beta-1)}(x) = (\alpha+\beta+n)P_n^{(\alpha,\beta)}(x)+(\alpha+n)P_{n-1}^{(\alpha,\beta)}(x).$

(vii) $(\alpha+\beta+2n)P_n^{(\alpha-1,\beta)}(x) = (\alpha+\beta+n)P_n^{(\alpha,\beta)}(x)-(\beta+n)P_{n-1}^{(\alpha,\beta)}(x).$

Theorem 8.8 (Differential equation)

$P_n^{(\alpha,\beta)}(x)$ *satisfies the differential equation*

$$(1-x^2)\frac{d^2y}{dx^2} + \{\beta-\alpha-(\alpha+\beta+2)x\}\frac{dy}{dx} + n(n+\alpha+\beta+1)y = 0.$$

As well as being related to the Legendre functions (recall that $P_n(x) = P_n^{(0\,0)}(x) = C_n^{1/2}(x)$), the Gegenbauer and Jacobi polynomials are related to each other and to the Chebyshev polynomials. In fact, the

Gegenbauer polynomials are just a special case of the Jacobi polynomials and the Chebyshev are just a special case of the Gegenbauer:

$$C_n^\lambda(x) = \frac{\Gamma(\lambda + \tfrac{1}{2})\Gamma(n + 2\lambda)}{\Gamma(2\lambda)\Gamma(n + \lambda + \tfrac{1}{2})} P_n^{(\lambda - \frac{1}{2}, \lambda - \frac{1}{2})}(x); \qquad (8.3)$$

$$T_n(x) = \frac{n}{2} \lim_{\lambda \to 0} \frac{C_n^\lambda(x)}{\lambda} \quad (n \geqslant 1); \qquad (8.4)$$

$$U_n(x) = \sqrt{(1 - x^2)} C_{n-1}^1(x). \qquad (8.5)$$

These results will be proved in the next chapter (Example 5, p. 215).

There also exist relationships with the Laguerre and Hermite polynomials, which we shall state but shall not prove:

$$L_n^\alpha(x) = \lim_{\beta \to \infty} P_n^{(\alpha, \beta)}(1 - 2x/\beta); \qquad (8.6)$$

$$H_n(x) = n! \lim_{\lambda \to \infty} \lambda^{-n/2} C_n^\lambda(x/\sqrt{\lambda}). \qquad (8.7)$$

8.3   EXAMPLES

Example 1

Show that $\dfrac{d^m}{dx^m} C_n^\lambda(x) = 2^m \dfrac{\Gamma(\lambda + m)}{\Gamma(\lambda)} C_{n-m}^{\lambda+m}(x).$

From theorem 8.3(v) we have

$$\frac{d}{dx} C_n^\lambda(x) = 2\lambda C_{n-1}^{\lambda+1}(x),$$

so that

$$\frac{d^2}{dx^2} C_n^\lambda(x) = 2\lambda \frac{d}{dx} C_{n-1}^{\lambda+1}(x)$$

$$= 2\lambda.2(\lambda + 1) C_{n-2}^{\lambda+2}(x)$$

$$= 2^2\lambda(\lambda + 1) C_{n-2}^{\lambda+2}(x),$$

and, if we repeat this process m times in all, we obviously obtain

$$\frac{d^m}{dx^m} C_n^\lambda(x) = 2^m \lambda(\lambda + 1)(\lambda + 2) \dots (\lambda + m - 1) C_{n-m}^{\lambda+m}(x)$$

$$= 2^m \frac{\Gamma(\lambda + m)}{\Gamma(\lambda)} C_{n-m}^{\lambda+m}(x).$$

Example 2

Show that

$$P_n^{(\alpha,\beta)}(x) = \frac{(-1)^n}{2^n n!}(1-x)^{-\alpha}(1+x)^{-\beta}\frac{d^n}{dx^n}\{(1-x)^{\alpha+n}(1+x)^{\beta+n}\}.$$

Leibniz's theorem for the nth derivative of a product gives

$$\frac{d^n}{dx^n}\{(1-x)^{\alpha+n}(1+x)^{\beta+n}\}$$

$$= \sum_{r=0}^{n}\frac{n!}{r!(n-r)!}\left\{\frac{d^r}{dx^r}(1+x)^{\beta+n}\right\}\left\{\frac{d^{n-r}}{dx^{n-r}}(1-x)^{\alpha+n}\right\}$$

$$= \sum_{r=0}^{n}\frac{n!}{r!(n-r)!}(\beta+n)(\beta+n-1)\ldots(\beta+n-r+1)(1+x)^{\beta+n-r}$$

$$\times (-1)^{n-r}(\alpha+n)(\alpha+n-1)\ldots(\alpha+n-n+r+1)(1-x)^{\alpha+n-n+r}$$

$$= \sum_{r=0}^{n}\frac{n!}{r!(n-r)!}(-1)^{n-r}\frac{\Gamma(\beta+n+1)\Gamma(\alpha+n+1)}{\Gamma(\beta+n-r+1)\Gamma(\alpha+r+1)}(1+x)^{\beta+n-r}(1-x)^{\alpha+r}.$$

Hence we have

$$\frac{(-1)^n}{2^n n!}(1-x)^{-\alpha}(1+x)^{-\beta}\frac{d^n}{dx^n}\{(1-x)^{\alpha+n}(1+x)^{\beta+n}\}$$

$$= \frac{(-1)^n}{2^n n!}\sum_{r=0}^{n}(-1)^{n-r}\frac{n!}{r!(n-r)!}\frac{\Gamma(\alpha+n+1)\Gamma(\beta+n+1)}{\Gamma(\alpha+r+1)\Gamma(\beta+n-r+1)}(1-x)^r(1+x)^{n-r}$$

$$= \sum_{r=0}^{n}\frac{\Gamma(\alpha+n+1)\Gamma(\beta+n+1)}{\Gamma(\alpha+r+1)\Gamma(\beta+n-r+1)r!(n-r)!}\left(\frac{x-1}{2}\right)^r\left(\frac{x+1}{2}\right)^{n-r}$$

$$= P_n^{(\alpha,\beta)}(x)$$

(by theorem 8.5(i)).

PROBLEMS

(1) Show that $P_n^{(\alpha,\beta)}(-x) = (-1)^n P_n^{(\beta,\alpha)}(x)$.

(2) Show that $P_n^{(\alpha,\beta)}(1) = \dfrac{\Gamma(\alpha+n+1)}{\Gamma(\alpha+1)n!}$.

(3) Show that

$$\frac{d^m}{dx^m}P_n^{(\alpha,\beta)}(x) = 2^{-m}\frac{\Gamma(m+n+\alpha+\beta+1)}{\Gamma(n+\alpha+\beta+1)}P_{n-m}^{(\alpha+m,\beta+m)}(x).$$

(4) Use the method of induction to show that

$$\sum_{r=0}^{n} (r + \lambda)C_r^{\lambda}(x) = \frac{(n + 2\lambda)C_n^{\lambda}(x) - (n + 1)C_{n+1}^{\lambda}(x)}{2(1 - x)}.$$

(5) Show that

$$P_n^{(\alpha, \beta-1)}(x) - P_n^{(\alpha-1, \beta)}(x) = P_{n-1}^{(\alpha, \beta)}(x).$$

(6) Show that $C_{n-l}^{l+\frac{1}{2}}(x) = \dfrac{1}{(2l - 1)!!} \dfrac{d^l}{dx^l} P_n(x).$

9

HYPERGEOMETRIC FUNCTIONS

9.1 DEFINITION OF HYPERGEOMETRIC FUNCTIONS

Let us define $(\alpha)_r$ (the so-called Pochhammer symbol) by

$$(\alpha)_r = \alpha(\alpha + 1) \ldots (\alpha + r - 1)$$

$$= \frac{\Gamma(\alpha + r)}{\Gamma(\alpha)}; \quad (r \text{ a positive integer})$$

$$(\alpha)_0 = 1.$$

Then we define the general hypergeometric function

$$_mF_n(\alpha_1, \alpha_2, \ldots \alpha_m; \beta_1, \beta_2, \ldots \beta_n; x)$$

by

$$_mF_n(\alpha_1, \alpha_2, \ldots \alpha_m; \beta_1, \beta_2, \ldots \beta_n; x) = \sum_{r=0}^{\infty} \frac{(\alpha_1)_r(\alpha_2)_r \ldots (\alpha_m)_r \, x^r}{(\beta_1)_r(\beta_2)_r \ldots (\beta_n)_r \, r!}. \qquad (9.1)$$

The notation

$$_mF_n\left[\begin{matrix} \alpha_1, \alpha_2, \ldots \alpha_m; \\ \beta_1, \beta_2, \ldots \beta_n; \end{matrix} x \right]$$

is also often used.

We shall show that many of the special functions encountered up to now (and indeed many of the elementary functions) may be expressed in terms of hypergeometric functions. We shall confine ourselves to the two separate cases: $m = n = 1$ (in which case the function will be called the confluent hypergeometric function or Kummer function) and $m = 2$, $n = 1$ (in which case we shall merely call it the hypergeometric function).†

Convergence of the series (9.1) needs to be considered. The following results may be proved using the standard techniques of convergence theory:

(i) The confluent hypergeometric series is convergent for all values of x.

(ii) The hypergeometric series is convergent if $|x| < 1$ and divergent if $|x| > 1$. For $x = 1$ the series converges if $\beta > \alpha_1 + \alpha_2$, while for $x = -1$ it converges if $\beta > \alpha_1 + \alpha_2 - 1$.

The following theorem shows the intimate relationships which exist between the hypergeometric functions and the special functions already considered.

Theorem 9.1

(i) $P_n(x) = {}_2F_1\left(-n, n + 1; 1; \dfrac{1 - x}{2}\right).$

(ii) $P_n^m(x) = \dfrac{(n+m)!}{(n-m)!} \dfrac{(1-x^2)^{m/2}}{2^m m!} \, {}_2F_1\left(m-n, m+n+1; m+1; \dfrac{1 - x}{2}\right).$

(iii) $J_n(x) = \dfrac{e^{-ix}}{n!}\left(\dfrac{x}{2}\right)^n {}_1F_1(n + \tfrac{1}{2}; 2n + 1; 2ix).$

(iv) $H_{2n}(x) = (-1)^n \dfrac{(2n)!}{n!} \, {}_1F_1(-n; \tfrac{1}{2}; x^2).$

(v) $H_{2n+1}(x) = (-1)^n \dfrac{2(2n + 1)!}{n!} x \, {}_1F_1(-n; \tfrac{3}{2}; x^2).$

(vi) $L_n(x) = {}_1F_1(-n; 1; x).$

(vii) $L_n^k(x) = \dfrac{\Gamma(n + k + 1)}{n!\Gamma(k + 1)} \, {}_1F_1(-n; k + 1; x).$

(viii) $T_n(x) = {}_2F_1\left(-n, n; \dfrac{1}{2}; \dfrac{1 - x}{2}\right).$

(ix) $U_n(x) = \sqrt{(1 - x^2)}\, n \, {}_2F_1\left(-n + 1, n + 1; \dfrac{3}{2}; \dfrac{1 - x}{2}\right).$

(x) $C_n^\lambda(x) = \dfrac{\Gamma(n + 2\lambda)}{n!\Gamma(2\lambda)} \, {}_2F_1\left(-n, n + 2\lambda; \lambda + \tfrac{1}{2}; \dfrac{1 - x}{2}\right).$

---

† The confluent hypergeometric function ${}_1F_1(\alpha; \beta; x)$ is often denoted by $M(\alpha, \beta, x)$, and the hypergeometric function ${}_2F_1(\alpha_1, \alpha_2; \beta; x)$ is often denoted by $F(\alpha_1, \alpha_2, \beta, x)$.

(xi) $P_n^{(\alpha, \beta)}(x) = \dfrac{\Gamma(n+\alpha+1)}{n!\Gamma(\alpha+1)} \, _2F_1\left(-n, \, n+\alpha+\beta+1; \, \alpha+1; \, \dfrac{1-x}{2}\right).$

PROOF

In each case the result may be proved by expanding the hypergeometric function as a series, using definition (9.1), and comparing with a known series for the given function. We shall illustrate this method by proving result (i) only.

We have, from definition (9.1),

$$_2F_1\left(-n, \, n+1; \, 1; \, \frac{1-x}{2}\right) = \sum_{r=0}^{\infty} \frac{(-n)_r(n+1)_r\{(1-x)/2\}^r}{(1)_r} \, \frac{}{r!}.$$

We may take n to be a non-negative integer, since it is for only these values of n that the Legendre polynomials are defined.

Then we have

$$
\begin{aligned}
(-n)_r &= (-n)(-n+1)(-n+2) \ldots (-n+r-1) \\
&= (-1)^r n(n-1)(n-2) \ldots (n-r+1) \\
&= (-1)^r n!/(n-r)! \qquad \text{if } r \leqslant n.
\end{aligned}
$$

If $r \geqslant n+1$, then $(-n)_r = 0$, for it will contain a zero factor.

Also

$$
\begin{aligned}
(n+1)_r &= (n+1)(n+2) \ldots (n+r) \\
&= (n+r)!/n!
\end{aligned}
$$

and

$$
\begin{aligned}
(1)_r &= 1.2.3 \ldots r \\
&= r!
\end{aligned}
$$

so that we now have

$$
\begin{aligned}
_2F_1\left(-n, \, n+1; \, 1; \, \frac{1-x}{2}\right) &= \sum_{r=0}^{n} (-1)^r \, \frac{n!}{(n-r)!} \, \frac{(n+r)!}{n!} \, \frac{1}{r!} \, \frac{(1-x)^r}{2^r r!} \\
&= \sum_{r=0}^{n} \frac{(-1)^r}{2^r} \, \frac{(n+r)!}{(n-r)!(r!)^2} \, (1-x)^r \\
&= \sum_{r=0}^{n} \frac{(n+r)!}{2^r(n-r)!(r!)^2} \, (x-1)^r. \qquad (9.2)
\end{aligned}
$$

To show that this is the same as $P_n(x)$, it is easiest to write $P_n(x)$ as a power series in $(x-1)$. We do not as yet have such a power series, but we use Taylor's theorem to write

$$P_n(x) = \sum_{r=0}^{\infty} P_n^{(r)}(1) \frac{(x-1)^r}{r!} \qquad (9.3)$$

where by $P_n^{(r)}(1)$ we mean the rth derivative of $P_n(x)$ evaluated at $x = 1$.

To calculate $P_n^{(r)}(1)$ we use the generating function for the Legendre polynomials given in theorem 3.1:

$$\frac{1}{\sqrt{(1 - 2tx + t^2)}} = \sum_{n=0}^{\infty} P_n(x)t^n,$$

so that, by differentiating r times with respect to x, we have

$$\sum_{n=0}^{\infty} P_n^{(r)}(x)t^n = \frac{d^r}{dx^r}(1 - 2tx + t^2)^{-1/2}$$

$$= (-2t)^r(-\tfrac{1}{2})(-\tfrac{1}{2} - 1)(-\tfrac{1}{2} - 2) \ldots (-\tfrac{1}{2} - r + 1)(1 - 2tx + t^2)^{-\frac{1}{2}-r}$$

$$= 2^r t^r \tfrac{1}{2}(\tfrac{1}{2} + 1)(\tfrac{1}{2} + 2) \ldots (\tfrac{1}{2} + r - 1)(1 - 2tx + t^2)^{-\frac{1}{2}-r}$$

$$= t^r 1.3.5 \ldots (2r - 1)(1 - 2tx + t^2)^{-\frac{1}{2}-r}$$

$$= t^r \frac{(2r)!}{2^r r!}(1 - 2tx + t^2)^{-\frac{1}{2}-r}.$$

Hence, setting $x = 1$, we have

$$\sum_{n=0}^{\infty} P_n^{(r)}(1)t^n = \frac{t^r(2r)!}{2^r r!}(1 - 2t + t^2)^{-\frac{1}{2}-r}$$

$$= \frac{t^r(2r)!}{2^r r!}(1 - t)^{-1-2r}$$

$$= \frac{t^r(2r)!}{2^r r!}\left\{1 + (1 + 2r)t + \frac{(2r + 1)(2r + 2)}{2!}t^2\right.$$

$$\left. + \frac{(2r + 1)(2r + 2)(2r + 3)}{3!}t^3 + \ldots\right\}$$

(by the binomial theorem)

$$= \frac{t^r(2r)!}{2^r r!} \sum_{s=0}^{\infty} \frac{(2r + s)!}{(2r)!s!} t^s$$

$$= \frac{1}{2^r r!} \sum_{s=0}^{\infty} \frac{(2r + s)!}{s!} t^{r+s}$$

$$= \frac{1}{2^r r!} \sum_{n=r}^{\infty} \frac{(r + n)!}{(n - r)!} t^n,$$

writing $r + s = n$.

Equating coefficients of t^n gives

$$P_n^{(r)}(1) = \frac{1}{2^r r!} \frac{(r + n)!}{(n - r)!} \quad \text{for } n \geqslant r$$

$$= 0 \qquad\qquad \text{for } n < r.$$

Hence, from equation (9.3), we have

$$P_n(x) = \sum_{r=0}^{n} \frac{1}{2^r r!} \frac{(n+r)!}{(n-r)!} \frac{(x-1)^r}{r!}$$

$$= \sum_{r=0}^{n} \frac{(n+r)!}{2^r(n-r)!(r!)^2} (x-1)^r$$

$$= {}_2F_1\left(-n,\, n+1;\, 1;\, \frac{1-x}{2}\right)$$

(by equation (9.2)).

9.2 PROPERTIES OF THE HYPERGEOMETRIC FUNCTION

Theorem 9.2

$${}_2F_1(\alpha,\, \beta;\, \gamma;\, x) = {}_2F_1(\beta,\, \alpha;\, \gamma;\, x).$$

PROOF

This follows immediately from definition (9.1):

$${}_2F_1(\alpha,\, \beta;\, \gamma;\, x) = \sum_{r=0}^{n} \frac{(\alpha)_r (\beta)_r}{(\gamma)_r} \frac{x^r}{r!}.$$

Theorem 9.3

The differential equation

$$x(1-x)\frac{d^2y}{dx^2} + \{\gamma - (\alpha+\beta+1)x\}\frac{dy}{dx} - \alpha\beta y = 0$$

(the hypergeometric equation or Gauss's equation) has ${}_2F_1(\alpha, \beta; \gamma; x)$ *as a solution. If* γ *is not an integer a second independent solution is given by* $x^{1-\gamma}{}_2F_1(\alpha+1-\gamma; \beta+1-\gamma; 2-\gamma; x).$

PROOF

These results may be proved by using the series solution method of Chapter 1. It is found that the roots of the indicial equation are 0 and $1 - \gamma$, so that they lead to independent solutions provided γ is non-integral. It is found that these independent series solutions are just the hypergeometric functions given in the theorem.

Theorem 9.4 (Integral representation)

$${}_2F_1(\alpha, \beta; \gamma; x) = \frac{\Gamma(\gamma)}{\Gamma(\beta)\Gamma(\gamma-\beta)} \int_0^1 t^{\beta-1}(1-t)^{\gamma-\beta-1}(1-xt)^{-\alpha}\, dt$$

if $\gamma > \beta > 0.$

PROOF

From definition (9.1) we have

$_2F_1(\alpha, \beta; \gamma; x)$

$$= \sum_{r=0}^{\infty} \frac{(\alpha)_r(\beta)_r}{(\gamma)_r} \frac{x^r}{r!}$$

$$= \sum_{r=0}^{\infty} \frac{\Gamma(\alpha + r)\Gamma(\beta + r)\Gamma(\gamma)}{\Gamma(\alpha)\Gamma(\beta)\Gamma(\gamma + r)} \frac{x^r}{r!}$$

$$= \frac{\Gamma(\gamma)}{\Gamma(\alpha)\Gamma(\beta)\Gamma(\gamma - \beta)} \sum_{r=0}^{\infty} \Gamma(\alpha + r) \frac{\Gamma(\gamma - \beta)\Gamma(\beta + r)}{\Gamma(\gamma + r)} \frac{x^r}{r!}$$

$$= \frac{\Gamma(\gamma)}{\Gamma(\alpha)\Gamma(\beta)\Gamma(\gamma - \beta)} \sum_{r=0}^{\infty} \Gamma(\alpha + r)B(\gamma - \beta, \beta + r) \frac{x^r}{r!}$$

$$\text{(by theorem 2.7)}$$

$$= \frac{\Gamma(\gamma)}{\Gamma(\alpha)\Gamma(\beta)\Gamma(\gamma - \beta)} \sum_{r=0}^{\infty} \Gamma(\alpha + r) \int_0^1 (1 - t)^{\gamma-\beta-1} t^{\beta+r-1} \, dt \frac{x^r}{r!}$$

(by definition (2.2) of the beta function, which is valid if $\gamma - \beta > 0$ and $\beta + r > 0$)

$$= \frac{\Gamma(\gamma)}{\Gamma(\beta)\Gamma(\gamma - \beta)} \int_0^1 (1 - t)^{\gamma-\beta-1} t^{\beta-1} \sum_{r=0}^{\infty} \frac{\Gamma(\alpha + r)}{\Gamma(\alpha)} \frac{(xt)^r}{r!} \, dt$$

$$= \frac{\Gamma(\gamma)}{\Gamma(\beta)\Gamma(\gamma - \beta)} \int_0^1 (1 - t)^{\gamma-\beta-1} t^{\beta-1} (1 - xt)^{-\alpha} \, dt$$

(using the binomial theorem).

Theorem 9.5

Each of the following twenty-four functions is a solution of the hyper-geometric equation:

$V_1 = {}_2F_1(\alpha, \beta; \gamma; x)$

$V_2 = (1 - x)^{\gamma-\alpha-\beta} {}_2F_1(\gamma - \alpha, \gamma - \beta; \gamma; x)$

$V_3 = (1 - x)^{-\alpha} {}_2F_1\left(\alpha, \gamma - \beta; \gamma; \dfrac{x}{x - 1}\right)$

$V_4 = (1 - x)^{-\beta} {}_2F_1\left(\gamma - \alpha, \beta; \gamma; \dfrac{x}{x - 1}\right)$

$V_5 = {}_2F_1(\alpha, \beta; \alpha + \beta + 1 - \gamma; 1 - x)$

$V_6 = x^{1-\gamma} {}_2F_1(\alpha + 1 - \gamma; \beta + 1 - \gamma; \alpha + \beta + 1 - \gamma; 1 - x)$

$$V_7 = x^{-\alpha}{}_2F_1\left(\alpha, \alpha + 1 - \gamma; \alpha + \beta + 1 - \gamma; 1 - \frac{1}{x}\right)$$

$$V_8 = x^{-\beta}{}_2F_1\left(\beta + 1 - \gamma, \beta; \alpha + \beta + 1 - \gamma; 1 - \frac{1}{x}\right)$$

$$V_9 = (-x)^{-\alpha}{}_2F_1\left(\alpha, \alpha + 1 - \gamma; \alpha + 1 - \beta; \frac{1}{x}\right)$$

$$V_{10} = (-x)^{\beta-\gamma}(1 - x)^{\gamma-\alpha-\beta}{}_2F_1\left(1 - \beta, \gamma - \beta; \alpha + 1 - \beta; \frac{1}{x}\right)$$

$$V_{11} = (1 - x)^{-\alpha}{}_2F_1\left(\alpha, \gamma - \beta; \alpha + 1 - \beta; \frac{1}{1 - x}\right)$$

$$V_{12} = (-x)^{1-\gamma}(1 - x)^{\gamma-\alpha-1}{}_2F_1\left(\alpha + 1 - \gamma, 1 - \beta; \alpha + 1 - \beta; \frac{1}{1 - x}\right)$$

$$V_{13} = (-x)^{-\beta}{}_2F_1\left(\beta + 1 - \gamma, \beta; \beta + 1 - \alpha; \frac{1}{x}\right)$$

$$V_{14} = (-x)^{\alpha-\gamma}(1 - x)^{\gamma-\alpha-\beta}{}_2F_1\left(1 - \alpha, \gamma - \alpha; \beta + 1 - \alpha; \frac{1}{x}\right)$$

$$V_{15} = (1 - x)^{-\beta}{}_2F_1\left(\beta, \gamma - \alpha; \beta + 1 - \alpha; \frac{1}{1 - x}\right)$$

$$V_{16} = (-x)^{1-\gamma}(1 - x)^{\gamma-\beta-1}{}_2F_1\left(\beta + 1 - \gamma, 1 - \alpha; \beta + 1 - \alpha; \frac{1}{1 - x}\right)$$

$$V_{17} = x^{1-\gamma}{}_2F_1(\alpha + 1 - \gamma, \beta + 1 - \gamma; 2 - \gamma; x)$$

$$V_{18} = x^{1-\gamma}(1 - x)^{\gamma-\alpha-\beta}{}_2F_1(1 - \alpha, 1 - \beta; 2 - \gamma; x)$$

$$V_{19} = x^{1-\gamma}(1 - x)^{\gamma-\alpha-1}{}_2F_1\left(\alpha + 1 - \gamma, 1 - \beta; 2 - \gamma; \frac{x}{x - 1}\right)$$

$$V_{20} = x^{1-\gamma}(1 - x)^{\gamma-\beta-1}{}_2F_1\left(\beta + 1 - \gamma, 1 - \alpha; 2 - \gamma; \frac{x}{x - 1}\right)$$

$$V_{21} = (1 - x)^{\gamma-\alpha-\beta}{}_2F_1(\gamma - \alpha, \gamma - \beta; \gamma + 1 - \alpha - \beta; 1 - x)$$

$$V_{22} = x^{1-\gamma}(1 - x)^{\gamma-\alpha-\beta}{}_2F_1(1 - \alpha, 1 - \beta; \gamma + 1 - \alpha - \beta; 1 - x)$$

$$V_{23} = x^{\alpha-\gamma}(1 - x)^{\gamma-\alpha-\beta}{}_2F_1\left(\gamma - \alpha, 1 - \alpha; \gamma + 1 - \alpha - \beta; 1 - \frac{1}{x}\right)$$

$$V_{24} = x^{\beta-\gamma}(1 - x)^{\gamma-\alpha-\beta}{}_2F_1\left(\gamma - \beta, 1 - \beta; \gamma + 1 - \alpha - \beta; 1 - \frac{1}{x}\right).$$

PROOF

Each function may be verified to be a solution by means of change of variable, direct substitution and use of theorem 9.3.

Since the hypergeometric equation is of second order, there must be only two independent solutions, so that a linear relation must exist between any three of the twenty-four functions given above. In fact, it may be shown that

$$V_1 = V_2 = V_3 = V_4,$$
$$V_5 = V_6 = V_7 = V_8,$$
$$V_9 = V_{10} = V_{11} = V_{12},$$
$$V_{13} = V_{14} = V_{15} = V_{16},$$
$$V_{17} = V_{18} = V_{19} = V_{20},$$

and
$$V_{21} = V_{22} = V_{23} = V_{24}.$$

For the remaining relations the reader is referred to ERDELYI *et al.*, *Higher Transcendental Functions*, Vol. I, pp. 106–8.

The six hypergeometric functions $_2F_1(\alpha \pm 1, \beta; \gamma; x)$, $_2F_1(\alpha, \beta \pm 1; \gamma; x)$, $_2F_1(\alpha, \beta; \gamma \pm 1; x)$ are said to be contiguous to $_2F_1(\alpha, \beta; \gamma; x)$. It may be shown that between $_2F_1(\alpha, \beta; \gamma; x)$ and any two functions which are contiguous to it, there exists a linear relationship whose coefficients are linear functions of x. Since we can choose 2 from 6 in $^6C_2 = 15$ ways, there will be 15 such relationships altogether. For details the reader is referred to ERDELYI *et al.*, Vol. I, pp. 103–4.

9.3 PROPERTIES OF THE CONFLUENT HYPERGEOMETRIC FUNCTION

Theorem 9.6

The confluent hypergeometric function $_1F_1(\alpha; \beta; x)$ is a solution of the equation

$$x^2 \frac{d^2y}{dx^2} + (\beta - x) \frac{dy}{dx} - \alpha y = 0$$

(the confluent hypergeometric equation or Kummer's equation). If β is not an integer a second independent solution is given by

$$x^{1-\beta} {}_1F_1(\alpha - \beta + 1; 2 - \beta; x).$$

PROOF

As for theorem 9.3 above.

Theorem 9.7 (Integral representation)

$$_1F_1(\alpha;\beta;x) = \frac{\Gamma(\beta)}{\Gamma(\alpha)\Gamma(\beta-\alpha)} \int_0^1 (1-t)^{\beta-\alpha-1} t^{\alpha-1} e^{xt}\, dt$$

for $\beta > \alpha > 0$.

PROOF

Similar to theorem 9.4 above.

Theorem 9.8

Solutions of the equation

$$\frac{d^2y}{dx^2} + \left\{ -\frac{1}{4} + \frac{k}{x} + \frac{\frac{1}{4}-m^2}{x^2} \right\} y = 0 \tag{9.4}$$

are given by

$$y = x^{\frac{1}{2}-m} e^{-x/2} z,$$

where z is a solution of the confluent hypergeometric equation with

$$\alpha = \tfrac{1}{2} - k - m \quad and \quad \beta = 1 - 2m.$$

PROOF

The result follows immediately on direct substitution and use of theorem 9.6.

COROLLARY

The independent solutions of equation (9.4) are given by

$$M_{k,m}(x) = x^{\frac{1}{2}+m} e^{-x/2} {}_1F_1(\tfrac{1}{2} - k + m; 1 + 2m; x)$$

and

$$M_{k,-m}(x) = x^{\frac{1}{2}-m} e^{-x/2} {}_1F_1(\tfrac{1}{2} - k - m; 1 - 2m; x).$$

PROOF

Since the independent solutions of the confluent hypergeometric equation are

$$_1F_1(\alpha;\beta;x)$$

and

$$x^{1-\beta} {}_1F_1(\alpha - \beta + 1; 2 - \beta; x),$$

we have, from the theorem, that two independent choices for z are

$$_1F_1(\tfrac{1}{2} - k - m; 1 - 2m; x)$$

and

$$x^{2m} {}_1F_1(\tfrac{1}{2} - k + m; 1 + 2m; x),$$

SF—P

so that the corresponding solutions are

$$x^{\frac{1}{2}-m} e^{-x/2} {}_1F_1(\tfrac{1}{2} - k - m; 1 - 2m; x)$$

and

$$x^{\frac{1}{2}+m} e^{-x/2} {}_1F_1(\tfrac{1}{2} - k + m; 1 + 2m; x).$$

$M_{k,m}(x)$ and $M_{k,-m}(x)$ are known as Whittaker's confluent hypergeometric functions.

Theorem 9.9

Each of the following four functions is a solution of the confluent hypergeometric equation:

$$V_1 = {}_1F_1(\alpha; \beta; x)$$
$$V_2 = x^{1-\beta} {}_1F_1(1 + \alpha - \beta; 2 - \beta; x)$$
$$V_3 = e^x {}_1F_1(\beta - \alpha; \beta; -x)$$
$$V_4 = x^{1-\beta} e^x {}_1F_1(1 - \alpha; 2 - \beta; -x).$$

PROOF

By change of variable, direct substitution and use of theorem 9.6.

The four confluent hypergeometric functions ${}_1F_1(\alpha \pm 1; \beta; x)$, ${}_1F_1(\alpha; \beta \pm 1; x)$ are said to be contiguous to ${}_1F_1(\alpha; \beta; x)$. It may be shown that between ${}_1F_1(\alpha; \beta; x)$ and any two functions contiguous to it there exists a linear relationship whose coefficients are linear functions of x. Since we can choose 2 from 4 in ${}^4C_2 = 6$ ways, there will be six such contiguous relationships altogether. For details the reader is referred to ERDELYI *et al.*, Vol. I, p. 254 (see *Bibliography*).

9.4 EXAMPLES

Example 1

Show that ${}_2F_1(\alpha, \beta; \gamma; 1) = \dfrac{\Gamma(\gamma)\Gamma(\gamma - \alpha - \beta)}{\Gamma(\gamma - \alpha)\Gamma(\gamma - \beta)}.$

From theorem 9.4 we have

$$
\begin{aligned}
{}_2F_1(\alpha, \beta; \gamma; 1) &= \frac{\Gamma(\gamma)}{\Gamma(\beta)\Gamma(\gamma - \beta)} \int_0^1 t^{\beta-1}(1 - t)^{\gamma-\beta-1}(1 - t)^{-\alpha}\, dt \\
&= \frac{\Gamma(\gamma)}{\Gamma(\beta)\Gamma(\gamma - \beta)} \int_0^1 t^{\beta-1}(1 - t)^{\gamma-\alpha-\beta-1}\, dt \\
&= \frac{\Gamma(\gamma)}{\Gamma(\beta)\Gamma(\gamma - \beta)}\, B(\beta,\, \gamma - \alpha - \beta)
\end{aligned}
$$

(by definition (2.2) of the beta function)

$$= \frac{\Gamma(\gamma)}{\Gamma(\beta)\Gamma(\gamma - \beta)} \frac{\Gamma(\beta)\Gamma(\gamma - \alpha - \beta)}{\Gamma(\gamma - \alpha)}$$

(by theorem 2.7)

$$= \frac{\Gamma(\gamma)\Gamma(\gamma - \alpha - \beta)}{\Gamma(\gamma - \alpha)\Gamma(\gamma - \beta)}.$$

Example 2

Show that

$$\,_2F_1(\alpha, \beta; \gamma; x) = (1 - x)^{-\alpha} \,_2F_1\left(\alpha, \gamma - \beta; \gamma; \frac{x}{x - 1}\right)$$

(*i.e.*, $V_1 = V_3$, *using the notation of theorem* 9.5).

If we set $\tau = 1 - t$ in theorem 9.4 we have

$$\,_2F_1(\alpha, \beta; \gamma; x)$$

$$= \frac{\Gamma(\gamma)}{\Gamma(\beta)\Gamma(\gamma - \beta)} \int_0^1 (1 - \tau)^{\beta - 1} \tau^{\gamma - \beta - 1} \{1 - x(1 - \tau)\}^{-\alpha} \, d\tau$$

$$= \frac{\Gamma(\gamma)}{\Gamma(\beta)\Gamma(\gamma - \beta)} \int_0 (1 - \tau)^{\beta - 1} \tau^{\gamma - \beta - 1} (1 - x)^{-\alpha} \left(1 - \frac{x}{x - 1}\tau\right)^{-\alpha} \, d\tau$$

$$= \frac{\Gamma(\gamma)}{\Gamma(\gamma - \beta)\Gamma\{\gamma - (\gamma - \beta)\}} (1 - x)^{-\alpha} \int_0^1 \tau^{\gamma - \beta - 1} (1 - \tau)^{\beta - 1} \left(1 - \frac{x}{x - 1}\tau\right)^{-\alpha} \, d\tau$$

$$= (1 - x)^{-\alpha} \,_2F_1\left(\alpha, \gamma - \beta; \gamma; \frac{x}{x - 1}\right),$$

on further use of theorem 9.4.

Example 3

Prove the relation of contiguity

$$\gamma\{\gamma - 1 - (2\gamma - 1 - \alpha - \beta)x\} \,_2F_1(\alpha, \beta; \gamma; x)$$
$$+ (\gamma - \alpha)(\gamma - \beta)x \,_2F_1(\alpha, \beta; \gamma + 1; x)$$
$$- \gamma(\gamma - 1)(1 - x) \,_2F_1(\alpha, \beta; \gamma - 1; x) = 0.$$

We prove this result by expanding the hypergeometric functions in power series. Since

$$\,_2F_1(\alpha, \beta; \gamma; x) = \sum_{r=0}^{\infty} \frac{(\alpha)_r (\beta)_r}{(\gamma)_r r!} x^r,$$

we see that the coefficient of x^n on the left-hand side above must be

$$\gamma(\gamma - 1)\frac{(\alpha)_n (\beta)_n}{(\gamma)_n n!} - \gamma(2\gamma - 1 - \alpha - \beta)\frac{(\alpha)_{n-1}(\beta)_{n-1}}{(\gamma)_{n-1}(n - 1)!} +$$

$$+ (\gamma-\alpha)(\gamma-\beta)\frac{(\alpha)_{n-1}(\beta)_{n-1}}{(\gamma+1)_{n-1}(n-1)!} - \gamma(\gamma-1)\frac{(\alpha)_n(\beta)_n}{(\gamma-1)_n n!}$$

$$+ \gamma(\gamma-1)\frac{(\alpha)_{n-1}(\beta)_{n-1}}{(\gamma-1)_{n-1}(n-1)!}$$

$$= \gamma(\gamma-1)\frac{\Gamma(\alpha+n)\Gamma(\beta+n)\Gamma(\gamma)}{\Gamma(\alpha)\Gamma(\beta)\Gamma(\gamma+n)n!}$$

$$- \gamma(2\gamma-1-\alpha-\beta)\frac{\Gamma(\alpha+n-1)\Gamma(\beta+n-1)\Gamma(\gamma)}{\Gamma(\alpha)\Gamma(\beta)\Gamma(\gamma+n-1)(n-1)!}$$

$$+ (\gamma-\alpha)(\gamma-\beta)\frac{\Gamma(\alpha+n-1)\Gamma(\beta+n-1)\Gamma(\gamma+1)}{\Gamma(\alpha)\Gamma(\beta)\Gamma(\gamma+n)(n-1)!}$$

$$- \gamma(\gamma-1)\frac{\Gamma(\alpha+n)\Gamma(\beta+n)\Gamma(\gamma-1)}{\Gamma(\alpha)\Gamma(\beta)\Gamma(\gamma+n-1)n!}$$

$$+ \gamma(\gamma-1)\frac{\Gamma(\alpha+n-1)\Gamma(\beta+n-1)\Gamma(\gamma-1)}{\Gamma(\alpha)\Gamma(\beta)\Gamma(\gamma+n-2)(n-1)!}$$

$$= \frac{\Gamma(\alpha+n-1)\Gamma(\beta+n-1)\Gamma(\gamma-1)}{\Gamma(\alpha)\Gamma(\beta)\Gamma(\gamma+n-2)(n-1)!}\left\{\frac{\gamma(\gamma-1)(\alpha+n-1)(\beta+n-1)\gamma}{(\gamma+n-1)(\gamma+n-2)n}\right.$$

$$- \frac{\gamma(2\gamma-1-\alpha-\beta)(\gamma-1)}{(\gamma+n-2)} + \frac{(\gamma-\alpha)(\gamma-\beta)\gamma(\gamma-1)}{(\gamma+n-1)(\gamma+n-2)}$$

$$\left. - \frac{\gamma(\gamma-1)(\alpha+n-1)(\beta+n-1)}{(\gamma+n-2)n} + \gamma(\gamma-1)\right\}$$

$$= \frac{\Gamma(\alpha+n-1)\Gamma(\beta+n-1)\Gamma(\gamma-1)}{\Gamma(\alpha)\Gamma(\beta)\Gamma(\gamma+n-2)(n-1)!}\frac{1}{n(\gamma+n-1)(\gamma+n-2)}\gamma(\gamma-1)$$

$$\cdot\{\gamma(\alpha+n-1)(\beta+n-1) - n(\gamma+n-1)(2\gamma-1-\alpha-\beta)$$

$$+ n(\gamma-\alpha)(\gamma-\beta) - (\gamma+n-1)(\alpha+n-1)(\beta+n-1)$$

$$+ n(\gamma+n-1)(\gamma+n-2)\}$$

$$= \frac{\Gamma(\alpha+n-1)\Gamma(\beta+n-1)\Gamma(\gamma-1)\gamma(\gamma-1)}{\Gamma(\alpha)\Gamma(\beta)\Gamma(\gamma+n-2)(n-1)!n(\gamma+n-1)(\gamma+n-2)}$$

$$\cdot[\gamma^2(-2n+n+n) + \gamma\{(\alpha+n-1)(\beta+n-1) + n(\alpha+\beta+1)$$

$$- 2(n-1)n - n\alpha - n\beta - (\alpha+n-1)(\beta+n-1)$$

$$+ n(n-2) + n(n-1)\} + n(n-1)(\alpha+\beta+1) + n\alpha\beta$$

$$- (n-1)(\alpha+n-1)(\beta+n-1) + n(n-1)(n-2)]$$

$$= 0.$$

Thus the relation is verified.

Example 4

Show that ${}_1F_1(\alpha; \beta; x) = e^x \, {}_1F_1(\beta - \alpha; \beta; -x).$

From theorem 9.7 we have

$${}_1F_1(\alpha; \beta; x) = \frac{\Gamma(\beta)}{\Gamma(\alpha)\Gamma(\beta - \alpha)} \int_0^1 (1 - t)^{\beta - \alpha - 1} t^{\alpha - 1} \, e^{xt} \, dt.$$

If we make the change of variable $t = 1 - \tau$, we have

$${}_1F_1(\alpha; \beta; x) = \frac{\Gamma(\beta)}{\Gamma(\alpha)\Gamma(\beta - \alpha)} \int_0^1 \tau^{\beta - \alpha - 1}(1 - \tau)^{\alpha - 1} \, e^{x(1 - \tau)} \, d\tau$$

$$= e^x \frac{\Gamma(\beta)}{\Gamma(\beta - \alpha)\Gamma(\alpha)} \int_0^1 (1 - \tau)^{\alpha - 1} \tau^{\beta - \alpha - 1} \, e^{-x\tau} \, d\tau$$

$$= e^x \, {}_1F_1(\beta - \alpha; \alpha; -x)$$

(using theorem 9.7 again).

Example 5

Show that

(i) $\quad C_n^\lambda(x) = \dfrac{\Gamma(\lambda + \frac{1}{2})\Gamma(n + 2\lambda)}{\Gamma(2\lambda)\Gamma(n + \lambda + \frac{1}{2})} \, P_n^{\lambda - \frac{1}{2}, \, \lambda - \frac{1}{2}}(x);$

(ii) $\quad T_n(x) = \dfrac{n}{2} \lim_{\lambda \to 0} \dfrac{C_n^\lambda(x)}{\lambda};$

(iii) $\quad U_n(x) = \sqrt{(1 - x^2)} \, C_{n-1}^1(x).$

(i) From theorem 9.1(xi) we have

$P_n^{\lambda - \frac{1}{2}, \, \lambda - \frac{1}{2}}(x)$

$$= \frac{\Gamma(n + \lambda - \frac{1}{2} + 1)}{n!\Gamma(\lambda - \frac{1}{2} + 1)} \, {}_2F_1\left(-n, \, n + \lambda - \frac{1}{2} + \lambda - \frac{1}{2} + 1; \, \lambda - \frac{1}{2} + 1; \, \frac{1 - x}{2}\right)$$

$$= \frac{\Gamma(n + \lambda + \frac{1}{2})}{n!\Gamma(\lambda + \frac{1}{2})} \, {}_2F_1\left(-n, \, n + 2\lambda; \, \lambda + \frac{1}{2}; \, \frac{1 - x}{2}\right)$$

$$= \frac{\Gamma(n + \lambda + \frac{1}{2})}{n!\Gamma(\lambda + \frac{1}{2})} \, \frac{n!\Gamma(2\lambda)}{\Gamma(n + 2\lambda)} C_n^\lambda(x)$$

(by theorem 9.1(x))

$$= \frac{\Gamma(2\lambda)\Gamma(n + \lambda + \frac{1}{2})}{\Gamma(\lambda + \frac{1}{2})\Gamma(n + 2\lambda)} C_n^\lambda(x).$$

(ii) From theorem 9.1(x) we have

$$C_n^\lambda(x) = \frac{\Gamma(n + 2\lambda)}{n!\Gamma(2\lambda)} \, {}_2F_1\left(-n, \, n + 2\lambda; \, \lambda + \frac{1}{2}; \, \frac{1 - x}{2}\right).$$

The trouble at $\lambda = 0$ comes from $\Gamma(2\lambda)$. Hence we have

$$\frac{n}{2} \lim_{\lambda \to 0} \frac{C_n^\lambda(x)}{\lambda} = \frac{n}{2} \lim_{\lambda \to 0} \frac{1}{\lambda \Gamma(2\lambda)} \cdot \lim_{\lambda \to 0} \frac{\Gamma(n+2\lambda)}{n!} \, {}_2F_1\left(-n, n+2\lambda; \lambda+\tfrac{1}{2}; \frac{1-x}{2}\right)$$

$$= \frac{n}{2} \lim_{\lambda \to 0} \frac{1}{\lambda \Gamma(2\lambda)} \cdot \frac{\Gamma(n)}{n!} \, {}_2F_1\left(-n, n; \tfrac{1}{2}; \frac{1-x}{2}\right)$$

$$= \lim_{\lambda \to 0} \frac{1}{2\lambda\Gamma(2\lambda)} \cdot {}_2F_1\left(-n, n; \tfrac{1}{2}; \frac{1-x}{2}\right)$$

$$= \lim_{\lambda \to 0} \frac{1}{\Gamma(2\lambda+1)} \cdot {}_2F_1\left(-n, n; \tfrac{1}{2}; \frac{1-x}{2}\right)$$

$$= 1 \cdot {}_2F_1\left(-n, n; \tfrac{1}{2}; \frac{1-x}{2}\right)$$

$$= T_n(x)$$

(by theorem 9.1(viii)).

(iii) From theorem 9.1(x) we have

$$C_{n-1}^1(x) = \frac{\Gamma(n-1+2)}{(n-1)!\Gamma(2)} {}_2F_1\left(-n+1, n-1+2; 1+\tfrac{1}{2}; \frac{1-x}{2}\right)$$

$$= \frac{\Gamma(n+1)}{n!\Gamma(2)} n \, {}_2F_1\left(-n+1, n+1; \tfrac{3}{2}; \frac{1-x}{2}\right)$$

$$= n \, {}_2F_1\left(-n+1; n+1; \tfrac{3}{2}; \frac{1-x}{2}\right)$$

$$= \frac{1}{\sqrt{(1-x^2)}} U_n(x)$$

(by theorem 9.1(ix)).

PROBLEMS

(1) Show that

    (i) $(1-x)^{-\alpha} = {}_2F_1(\alpha, \beta; \beta; x)$;

    (ii) $\ln(1-x) = -x \, {}_2F_1(1, 1; 2; x)$;

    (iii) $e^x = {}_1F_1(\alpha; \alpha; x)$.

(2) Show that ${}_1F_1(\alpha; \gamma; x) = \lim_{\beta \to \infty} {}_2F_1(\alpha, \beta; \gamma; x/\beta)$.

(3) Show that

$$_2F_1(\alpha, \beta; \beta - \alpha + 1; -1) = \frac{\Gamma(1+\beta-\alpha)\Gamma(1+\tfrac{1}{2}\beta)}{\Gamma(1+\beta)\Gamma(1+\tfrac{1}{2}\beta-\alpha)}$$

and use Example 2 of Section 9.4 to deduce that

$$_2F_1(\alpha, 1 - \alpha; \gamma; \tfrac{1}{2}) = \frac{\Gamma(\tfrac{1}{2}\gamma)\Gamma(\tfrac{1}{2}\gamma + \tfrac{1}{2})}{\Gamma(\tfrac{1}{2}\alpha + \tfrac{1}{2}\gamma)\Gamma(\tfrac{1}{2} - \tfrac{1}{2}\alpha + \tfrac{1}{2}\gamma)}.$$

(4) Show that

$$\frac{d}{dx} \,_2F_1(\alpha, \beta; \gamma; x) = \frac{\alpha\beta}{\gamma} \,_2F_1(\alpha + 1, \beta + 1; \gamma + 1; x)$$

and deduce that

$$\frac{d^n}{dx^n} \,_2F_1(\alpha, \beta; \gamma; x) = \frac{(\alpha)_n(\beta)_n}{(\gamma)_n} \,_2F_1(\alpha + n, \beta + n; \gamma + n; x).$$

(5) Prove the contiguity relationships

(i) $(\alpha - \beta)_2F_1(\alpha, \beta; \gamma; x)$
$$= \alpha \,_2F_1(\alpha + 1, \beta; \gamma; x) - \beta \,_2F_1(\alpha, \beta + 1; \gamma; x);$$

(ii) $(\alpha - \beta)x_1F_1(\alpha; \beta + 1; x) + \beta(x + \beta - 1)_1F_1(\alpha; \beta; x)$
$$- \beta(\beta - 1)_1F_1(\alpha; \beta - 1; x) = 0.$$

(6) Use the confluent hypergeometric function to show that

$$H_{2n}(x) = (-1)^n 2^{2n} n! L_n^{-\frac{1}{2}}(x^2)$$

and
$$H_{2n+1}(x) = (-1)^n 2^{2n+1} n! x L_n^{\frac{1}{2}}(x^2).$$

(7) Evaluate the integral

$$\int_0^\infty e^{-sx} \,_1F_1(\alpha; \beta; x) \, dx.$$

10

OTHER SPECIAL FUNCTIONS

In this chapter we discuss briefly other special functions which the reader is likely to encounter. Several of these are defined by integrals which are impossible to express in terms of known functions, and of these integrals several have no special properties of interest—all the useful information is contained in a table of values of the function.

10.1 INCOMPLETE GAMMA FUNCTIONS

These are defined by

$$\Gamma(x, \alpha) = \int_{\alpha}^{\infty} e^{-t} t^{x-1} \, dt \qquad (10.1)$$

and

$$\gamma(x, \alpha) = \int_{0}^{\alpha} e^{-t} t^{x-1} \, dt. \qquad (10.2)$$

From definition (2.1) of the gamma function we see that

$$\Gamma(x, \alpha) + \gamma(x, \alpha) = \Gamma(x). \qquad (10.3)$$

10.2 EXPONENTIAL INTEGRAL AND RELATED FUNCTIONS

The exponential integrals are defined by

$$\mathrm{Ei}(x) = \int_{-\infty}^{x} \frac{e^t}{t} \, dt \qquad (10.4)$$

and

$$E_1(x) = \int_{x}^{\infty} \frac{e^{-t}}{t} \, dt. \qquad (10.5)$$

We note that
$$E_1(x) = -\text{Ei}(-x). \tag{10.6}$$
(Some authors use the notation ei(x) for $E_1(x)$.)
The logarithmic integral is defined by
$$\text{li}(x) = \int_0^x \frac{dt}{\ln t}. \tag{10.7}$$

It is easy to see that
$$\text{li}(x) = \text{Ei}(\ln x) = -E_1(-\ln x). \tag{10.8}$$

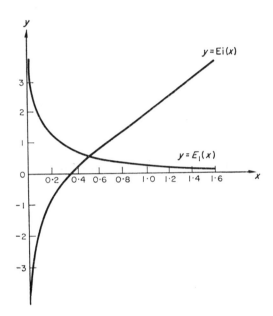

FIG. 10.1   Exponential integrals

The sine and cosine integrals are defined, respectively, by
$$\text{si}(x) = \int_\infty^x \frac{\sin t}{t} \, dt \tag{10.9}$$

$$\text{Si}(x) = \int_0^x \frac{\sin t}{t} \, dt \tag{10.10}$$

and
$$\text{Ci}(x) = \int_\infty^x \frac{\cos t}{t} \, dt; \tag{10.11}$$

(again the reader is warned to beware of different notations).

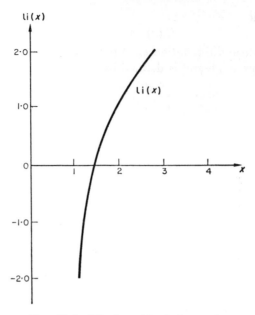

FIG. 10.2   The logarithmic integral

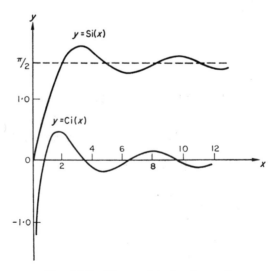

FIG. 10.3   Sine and cosine integrals

The following results may readily be verified:

$$\text{si}(0) = -\frac{\pi}{2}, \tag{10.12}$$

(see Example 1, p. 225)

$$\text{Si}(x) = \frac{\pi}{2} + \text{si}(x), \tag{10.13}$$

$$\text{si}(x) = \frac{1}{2i}\{\text{Ei}(ix) - \text{Ei}(-ix)\}, \tag{10.14}$$

$$\text{Ci}(x) = \tfrac{1}{2}\{\text{Ei}(ix) + \text{Ei}(-ix)\}, \tag{10.15}$$

$$\text{Ei}(\pm ix) = \text{Ci}(x) \pm i\,\text{si}(x). \tag{10.16}$$

The graphs of the above functions are shown in Figs. 10.1–10.3.

10.3   THE ERROR FUNCTION AND RELATED FUNCTIONS

The error function is defined by

$$\text{erf } x = \frac{2}{\sqrt{\pi}} \int_0^x e^{-t^2}\, dt. \tag{10.17}$$

By the corollary to theorem 2.6 we see that

$$\text{erf } \infty = 1. \tag{10.18}$$

As a generalisation of the error function we define the functions

$$E_n(x) = \frac{1}{\Gamma\{(n+1)/n\}} \int_0^x e^{-t^n}\, dt. \tag{10.19}$$

(N.B. $E_1(x)$ given by this equation is not the same as the $E_1(x)$ of the previous section.)

We see that

$$\text{erf } x = E_2(x). \tag{10.20}$$

The Fresnel integrals are defined by

$$S(x) = \int_0^x \sin\frac{\pi}{2}t^2\, dt \tag{10.21}$$

and

$$C(x) = \int_0^x \cos\frac{\pi}{2}t^2\, dt \tag{10.22}$$

It may be shown that

$$S(\infty) = C(\infty) = \tfrac{1}{2} \tag{10.23}$$

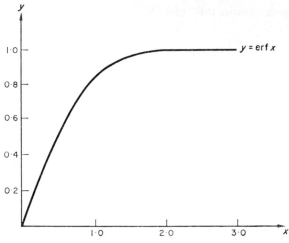

FIG. 10.4   The error function

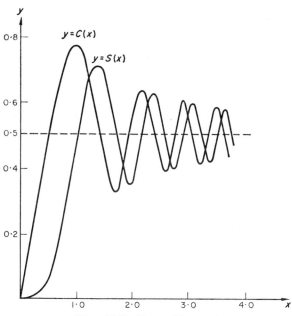

FIG. 10.5   Fresnel integrals

and that the Fresnel integrals are related to the error function by the relationship

$$C(x) + iS(x) = \frac{1+i}{2} \operatorname{erf}\left\{\frac{\sqrt{\pi}}{2}(1-i)x\right\}.$$ (10.24)

The graph of the error function is shown in Fig. 10.4 and the Fresnel integrals in Fig. 10.5.

10.4   RIEMANN'S ZETA FUNCTION

Riemann's zeta function is defined by

$$\zeta(x) = \sum_{n=1}^{\infty} \frac{1}{n^x}.$$ (10.25)

This series is divergent for $x \leqslant 1$, convergent for $x > 1$.
It may be shown that

$$\zeta(2) = \frac{\pi^2}{6},$$

$$\zeta(4) = \frac{\pi^4}{90}$$ (10.26)

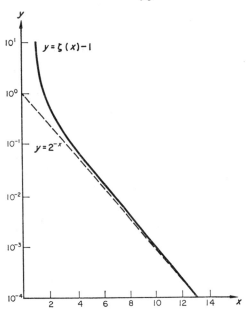

FIG. 10.6   Riemann's zeta function. (The graph is of $\zeta(x) - 1$. Note the logarithmic scale on the vertical axis. For comparison, the dotted line is the graph of 2^{-x}.)

and that in general $\zeta(2n)$, with n integral, may be expressed in closed form.

The graph of $\zeta(x) - 1$ is given in Fig. 10.6. Note the logarithmic scale; for comparison, the graph of 2^{-x} is given by the dotted line.

10.5 DEBYE FUNCTIONS

These are defined by

$$D_n(x) = \int_0^x \frac{t^n}{e^t - 1}\, dt. \tag{10.27}$$

It may be shown that these functions are related to the Riemann zeta function by $D_n(\infty) = n!\,\zeta(n + 1)$.

10.6 ELLIPTIC INTEGRALS

We define the elliptic integrals of the first, second and third kinds respectively by

$$F(k, \phi) = \int_0^\phi \frac{d\theta}{\sqrt{(1 - k^2 \sin^2 \theta)}} \quad (0 < k < 1), \tag{10.28}$$

$$E(k, \phi) = \int_0^\phi \sqrt{(1 - k^2 \sin^2 \theta)}\, d\theta \quad (0 < k < 1), \tag{10.29}$$

$$\Pi(k, \phi, a) = \int_0^\phi \frac{d\theta}{\sqrt{(1 - k^2 \sin^2 \theta)}(1 + a^2 \sin^2 \theta)} \tag{10.30}$$

$$(0 < k < 1,\ a \neq k).$$

Some of the importance of elliptic integrals lies in the following theorem, which we state without proof.

Theorem 10.1

If $R(x, y)$ is a rational function of x and y and if $P(x)$ is a polynomial of degree at most four, with real coefficients, then $\int R[x, \sqrt{\{P(x)\}}]\, dx$ can be expressed in terms of elliptic integrals.

If the upper limit in each of definitions (10.28), (10.29) and (10.30) is $\pi/2$, then we have the definitions of the so-called complete elliptic integrals:

$$K(k) = \int_0^{\pi/2} \frac{d\theta}{\sqrt{(1 - k^2 \sin^2 \theta)}}, \tag{10.31}$$

$$E(k) = \int_0^{\pi/2} \sqrt{(1 - k^2 \sin^2 \theta)}\, d\theta, \tag{10.32}$$

$$\Pi(k, a) = \int_0^{\pi/2} \frac{d\theta}{\sqrt{(1 - k^2 \sin^2 \theta)}(1 + a^2 \sin^2 \theta)}. \tag{10.33}$$

10.7   EXAMPLES

Example 1

Show that si(0) $= -\pi/2$.

From definition (10.9) we have

$$\text{si}(0) = \int_{\infty}^{0} \frac{\sin t}{t}\, dt$$

$$= -\int_{0}^{\infty} \frac{\sin t}{t}\, dt.$$

To evaluate this integral we consider the integral

$$I(\alpha) = \int_{0}^{\infty} \frac{e^{-\alpha t}\sin t}{t}\, dt$$

so that si(0) is given by $-I(0)$.

Now,

$$\frac{dI}{d\alpha} = -\int_{0}^{\infty} e^{-\alpha t}\sin t\, dt$$

$$= -\int_{0}^{\infty} e^{-\alpha t}\frac{1}{2i}(e^{1t} - e^{-1t})\, dt$$

$$= -\frac{1}{2i}\int_{0}^{\infty} \{e^{(-\alpha+i)t} - e^{(-\alpha-i)t}\}\, dt$$

$$= -\frac{1}{2i}\left[\frac{1}{-\alpha+i}\, e^{(-\alpha+i)t} - \frac{1}{-\alpha-i}\, e^{(-\alpha-i)t} \right]_{0}^{\infty}$$

$$= -\frac{1}{2i}\left(\frac{1}{\alpha-i} - \frac{1}{\alpha+i} \right)$$

$$= -\frac{1}{1+\alpha^2}.$$

Hence, by integrating with respect to α we obtain

$$I(\alpha) = -\tan^{-1}\alpha + \text{constant}.$$

But $\qquad\qquad I(\infty) = 0,$

so that we must have $\quad 0 = -\tan^{-1}\infty + \text{constant},$

and hence $\qquad\qquad 0 = -\frac{\pi}{2} + \text{constant},$

giving $\qquad\qquad \text{constant} = \frac{\pi}{2}.$

Thus
$$I(\alpha) = -\tan^{-1}\alpha + \frac{\pi}{2}$$

so that
$$I(0) = -\tan^{-1}0 + \frac{\pi}{2} = \frac{\pi}{2}$$

and hence
$$\mathrm{si}(0) = -I(0) = -\frac{\pi}{2}.$$

Example 2

Show that $\displaystyle\int_0^\infty e^{-st}\,\mathrm{si}(t)\,dt = -\frac{1}{s}\tan^{-1}s.$

Integrating by parts, we have

$$\int_0^\infty e^{-st}\,\mathrm{si}(t)\,dt = \left[-\frac{1}{s}e^{-st}\,\mathrm{si}(t)\right]_0^\infty - \int_0^\infty -\frac{1}{s}e^{-st}\frac{d}{dt}\mathrm{si}(t)\,dt$$

$$= \frac{1}{s}\mathrm{si}(0) + \frac{1}{s}\int_0^\infty e^{-st}\frac{d}{dt}\mathrm{si}(t)\,dt$$

$$= \frac{1}{s}\left(-\frac{\pi}{2}\right) + \frac{1}{s}\int_0^\infty e^{-st}\frac{\sin t}{t}\,dt$$

(using equation (10.12) and definition (10.9))

$$= -\frac{\pi}{2s} + \frac{1}{s}I(s)$$

(with I as defined in Example 1 above)

$$= -\frac{\pi}{2s} + \frac{1}{s}\left(-\tan^{-1}s + \frac{\pi}{2}\right)$$

(as shown in Example 1 above)

$$= -\frac{\tan^{-1}s}{s}.$$

Example 3

Show that (i) $\mathrm{erf}\,(-x) = -\,\mathrm{erf}\,x;$
(ii) $|\,\mathrm{erf}\,x\,| \leqslant 1.$

(i) From definition (10.17) we have

$$\mathrm{erf}\,x = \frac{2}{\sqrt{\pi}}\int_0^x e^{-t^2}\,dt$$

so that

$$\text{erf}\,(-x) = \frac{2}{\sqrt{\pi}} \int_0^{-x} e^{-t^2}\, dt = \frac{2}{\sqrt{\pi}} \int_0^{x} e^{-u^2}.\, -du$$

(on changing the variable to $u = -t$)

$$= -\frac{2}{\sqrt{\pi}} \int_0^{x} e^{-u^2}\, du$$

$$= -\text{erf}\, x.$$

(ii) First suppose $x \geqslant 0$. Then, since $e^{-t^2} > 0$, we have erf $x \geqslant 0$. Also

$$\text{erf}\, x \leqslant \frac{2}{\sqrt{\pi}} \left(\int_0^{x} e^{-t^2}\, dt + \int_x^{\infty} e^{-t^2}\, dt \right)$$

$$= \frac{2}{\sqrt{\pi}} \int_0^{\infty} e^{-t^2}\, dt$$

$$= \text{erf}\, \infty$$

$$= 1$$

(by equation (10.18)).

A similar argument holds if $x < 0$.

Example 4

Show that $\displaystyle\int_0^{\pi/2} \frac{dx}{\sqrt{(2 - \cos x)}} = \frac{2}{\sqrt{3}} \left\{ F\!\left(\sqrt{\tfrac{2}{3}}, \frac{\pi}{2} \right) - F\!\left(\sqrt{\tfrac{2}{3}}, \frac{\pi}{4} \right) \right\}.$

We have

$$\int_0^{\pi/2} \frac{dx}{\sqrt{(2 - \cos x)}} = \int_{\pi}^{\pi/2} \frac{-dy}{\sqrt{\{2 - \cos(\pi - y)\}}}$$

(making the change of variable $y = \pi - x$)

$$= \int_{\pi/2}^{\pi} \frac{dy}{\sqrt{(2 + \cos y)}}$$

$$= \int_{\pi/2}^{\pi} \frac{dy}{\sqrt{\{2 + 1 - 2\sin^2(y/2)\}}}$$

$$= \int_{\pi/4}^{\pi/2} \frac{2dz}{\sqrt{(3 - 2\sin^2 z)}}$$

(making the change of variable $z = y/2$)

$$= \frac{2}{\sqrt{3}} \int_{\pi/4}^{\pi/2} \frac{dz}{\sqrt{(1 - \tfrac{2}{3}\sin^2 z)}}$$

$$= \frac{2}{\sqrt{3}} \left\{ \int_0^{\pi/2} \frac{dz}{\sqrt{(1 - \frac{2}{3}\sin^2 z)}} - \int_0^{\pi/4} \frac{dz}{\sqrt{(1 - \frac{2}{3}\sin^2 z)}} \right\}$$

$$= \frac{2}{\sqrt{3}} \left\{ F\left(\sqrt{\frac{2}{3}}, \frac{\pi}{2}\right) - F\left(\sqrt{\frac{2}{3}}, \frac{\pi}{4}\right) \right\}$$

(by definition (10.28)).

PROBLEMS

(1) Show that

(i) $\displaystyle\int_0^\infty \cos x \, \mathrm{Ci}(x) \, dx = \int_0^\infty \sin x \, \mathrm{si}(x) \, dx = -\frac{\pi}{4};$

(ii) $\displaystyle\int_0^\infty \{\mathrm{Ci}(x)\}^2 \, dx = \int_0^\infty \{\mathrm{si}(x)\}^2 \, dx = \frac{\pi}{2}.$

(2) If $I(\alpha) = \displaystyle\int_0^\infty (1 - e^{-\alpha t}) \frac{\cos t}{t} \, dt$, show that

$$\frac{dI}{d\alpha} = \frac{\alpha}{\alpha^2 + 1}$$

and deduce that $\qquad I(\alpha) = \tfrac{1}{2} \ln (1 + \alpha^2).$

Prove that $\displaystyle\int_0^\infty e^{-st} \, \mathrm{Ci}(t) \, dt = \frac{1}{2s} \ln (1 + s^2).$

(3) Show that $\mathrm{erf}\, x = \dfrac{1}{\sqrt{\pi}} \gamma(\tfrac{1}{2}, x^2) = \dfrac{2x}{\sqrt{\pi}} \, {}_1F_1(\tfrac{1}{2}; \tfrac{3}{2}; -x^2).$

(4) Show that $T(x, t) = C \, \mathrm{erf}\, \{x/\sqrt{(4kt)}\}$ satisfies the following conditions:

     (i) $T(0, t) = 0;$

     (ii) $T(x, 0) = C;$

     (iii) $\dfrac{\partial T}{\partial t} = k \dfrac{\partial^2 T}{\partial x^2}.$

(5) Show that (i) $\displaystyle\int_0^x C(t) \, dt = xC(x) - \frac{1}{\pi} \sin \frac{\pi}{2} x^2;$

     (ii) $\displaystyle\int_0^x S(t) \, dt = xS(x) + \frac{1}{\pi} \cos \frac{\pi}{2} x^2 - \frac{1}{\pi}.$

(6) Show that $\displaystyle\int_0^{\pi/2} \frac{dx}{\sqrt{(\sin x)}} = \int_0^{\pi/2} \frac{dx}{\sqrt{(\cos x)}} = (\sqrt{2})K\left(\frac{1}{\sqrt{2}}\right).$

(7) By making the substitution $x = 2 \sin \theta$, show that

$$\int_0^2 \frac{dx}{\sqrt{\{(4 - x^2)(9 - x^2)\}}} = \tfrac{1}{3}K(\tfrac{2}{3}).$$

(8) Show that

$$\int_0^1 \frac{dx}{\sqrt{\{(1 + x^2)(1 + 2x^2)\}}} = \frac{1}{\sqrt{2}}\left\{K\left(\frac{1}{\sqrt{2}}\right) - F\left(\frac{1}{\sqrt{2}}, \frac{\pi}{4}\right)\right\}.$$

APPENDICES

1 CONVERGENCE OF LEGENDRE SERIES

We wish to investigate the convergence of the series obtained in Section 3.1 as solutions to Legendre's equation.

These series are of the form

$$\sum_{n=0}^{\infty} a_{2n} x^{2n} \tag{A1.1}$$

and

$$\sum_{n=0}^{\infty} a_{2n+1} x^{2n+1} \tag{A1.2}$$

where in both cases we have, from equation (3.7),

$$a_{n+2} = a_n \frac{(n-l)(l+n+1)}{(n+1)(n+2)}. \tag{A1.3}$$

We shall discuss only the series (A1.1), since the discussion of the other series is similar in all respects.

First we note that equation (A1.3) implies that all the terms in the series (A1.1) for $n > l$ have the same sign, so that we may apply tests for series of positive terms.

If $x \neq 1$ we may apply d'Alembert's ratio test:

if $\sum_{n=0}^{\infty} u_n$ is a series of positive terms and if $\lim_{n \to \infty} u_n/u_{n+1} = \alpha$, the series is divergent if $\alpha < 1$, convergent if $\alpha > 1$ and the test provides no information if $\alpha = 1$.

Here $u_n = a_{2n} x^{2n}$, so that we have

$$\frac{u_n}{u_{n+1}} = \frac{a_{2n} x^{2n}}{a_{2n+2} x^{2n+2}}$$

$$= \frac{(2n+1)(2n+2)}{(2n-l)(2n+l+1)} \cdot \frac{1}{x^2}$$

so that

$$\lim_{n \to \infty} \frac{u_n}{u_{n+1}} = \frac{1}{x^2}$$

and the series is hence divergent if $x^2 > 1$ and convergent if $x^2 < 1$; that is, it is divergent if $|x| > 1$ and convergent if $|x| < 1$.

If $x = \pm 1$ we must use Gauss's ratio test:

if $\sum_{n=0}^{\infty} u_n$ is a series of positive terms, and if the ratio u_n/u_{n+1} can, for $n \geqslant$ some fixed N, be expressed in the form

$$\frac{u_n}{u_{n+1}} = 1 + \frac{\mu}{n} + O\left(\frac{1}{n^p}\right)$$

with $p > 1$ (where by $O(1/n^p)$ we mean some function f(n) such that $\lim_{n \to \infty} \{f(n)/(1/n^p)\}$ is finite), then $\sum_{n=0}^{\infty} u_n$ is convergent if $\mu > 1$ and divergent if $\mu \leqslant 1$.

Here, since we are considering $x = \pm 1$, we have

$$\frac{u_n}{u_{n+1}} = \frac{(2n+1)(2n+2)}{(2n-l)(2n+l+1)}$$

and it is a matter of simple algebra to prove that

$$\frac{u_n}{u_{n+1}} = 1 + \frac{1}{n} + \frac{l(l+1)(1+n)}{\{4n^2 + 2n - l(l+1)\}n}.$$

Now, we see that the last term is $O(1/n^2)$, since we have

$$\lim_{n \to \infty} \left[\frac{l(l+1)(1+n)}{\{4n^2 + 2n - l(l+1)\}n} \bigg/ \frac{1}{n^2} \right]$$

$$= \lim_{n \to \infty} \frac{l(l+1)(1+n)n^2}{\{4n^2 + 2n - l(l+1)\}n}$$

$$= l(l+1)/4,$$

which is finite.

Hence the conditions of Gauss's ratio test are satisfied; we have $\mu = 1$ and thus the series is divergent. This means that we have shown that the Legendre series is divergent for $x = \pm 1$.

2 EULER'S CONSTANT

Assuming f(x) to be a continuous, positive and decreasing function, let us consider the sequence

$$u_n = f(1) + f(2) + f(3) + \ldots + f(n) - \int_1^n f(x)\,dx$$

We first show that $u_n > 0$. This follows immediately from Fig. A2.1, since $f(1) + f(2) + \ldots + f(n)$ is the area of the rectangles shown, while

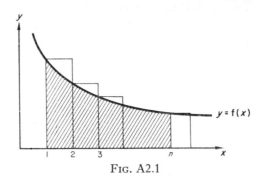

Fɪɢ. A2.1

$\int_1^n f(x)\,dx$ is the shaded area underneath the curve, which is obviously less than the area of the rectangles, thus making $u_n > 0$.

We now show that $u_{n+1} < u_n$. For we have

$$u_{n+1} - u_n = f(1) + f(2) + \ldots + f(n) + f(n+1) - \int_1^{n+1} f(x)\,dx$$

$$-f(1) - f(2) - \ldots - f(n) + \int_1^n f(x)\,dx$$

$$= f(n+1) - \int_n^{n+1} f(x)\,dx,$$

and from Fig. A2.2 we see immediately that this is negative.

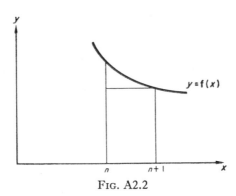

Fɪɢ. A2.2

Hence $u_{n+1} - u_n < 0$, i.e., $u_{n+1} < u_n$.

Thus the u_n constitute a decreasing sequence, every member of which is positive, and thus by a general principle the sequence must possess a limit as n tends to infinity. Hence $\lim_{n \to \infty} u_n$ exists.

The choice of $f(x) = 1/x$ will satisfy the conditions that $f(x)$ be continuous, positive and decreasing.

Then

$$u_n = 1 + \frac{1}{2} + \frac{1}{3} + \ldots + \frac{1}{n} - \int_1^n \frac{1}{x}\, dx$$

$$= 1 + \frac{1}{2} + \frac{1}{3} + \ldots + \frac{1}{n} - \ln n.$$

So we know that $\lim_{n \to \infty} \{1 + (1/2) + (1/3) + \ldots + (1/n) - \ln n\}$ exists. It is called Euler's constant and is usually denoted by γ. It may be shown that, correct to four decimal places, $\gamma = 0{\cdot}5772$.

3 DIFFERENTIAL EQUATIONS

Equation	Solutions	
$(1 - x^2)y'' - 2xy' + l(l+1)y = 0$	$P_l(x)$	Legendre polynomials
	$Q_l(x)$	Legendre functions of the second kind
$(1 - x^2)y'' - 2xy'$ $+ \left\{l(l+1) - \dfrac{m^2}{1-x^2}\right\}y = 0$	$P_l^m(x)$	Associated Legendre polynomials
	$Q_l^m(x)$	Associated Legendre functions of the second kind
$x^2y'' + xy' + (x^2 - n^2)y = 0$	$J_n(x)$	Bessel functions of the first kind
	$Y_n(x)$	Bessel functions of the second kind
	$\left.\begin{array}{l}H_n^{(1)}(x)\\ H_n^{(2)}(x)\end{array}\right\}$	Hankel functions
$x^2y'' + xy' - (x^2 + n^2)y = 0$	$\left.\begin{array}{l}I_n(x)\\ K_n(x)\end{array}\right\}$	Modified Bessel functions
$x^2y'' + (1 - 2\alpha)xy'$ $+ \{\beta^2\gamma^2 x^{2\gamma} + (\alpha^2 - n^2\gamma^2)\}y = 0$	$x^\alpha J_n(\beta x^\gamma)$ $x^\alpha Y_n(\beta x^\gamma)$	
$x^2y'' + 2xy' + \{x^2 - l(l+1)\}y = 0$	$\left.\begin{array}{l}j_l(x)\\ y_l(x)\end{array}\right\}$	Spherical Bessel functions

Equation	Solutions
$y'' - 2xy' + 2ny = 0$ $y'' + (\lambda - x^2)y = 0$	$H_n(x)$ Hermite polynomials $\Psi_n(x) = \exp\left(-\tfrac{1}{2}x^2\right)H_n(x)$ Weber–Hermite functions
$xy'' + (1 - x)y' + ny = 0$ $xy'' + (k + 1 - x)y' + ny = 0$	$L_n(x)$ Laguerre polynomials $L_n^k(x)$ Associated Laguerre polynomials
$(1 - x^2)y'' - xy' + n^2 y = 0$	$\left.\begin{array}{l} T_n(x) \\ U_n(x) \end{array}\right\}$ Chebyshev polynomials
$(1 - x^2)y'' - (2\lambda + 1)xy'$ $\qquad\qquad + n(n + 2\lambda)y = 0$	$C_n^\lambda(x)$ Gegenbauer polynomials
$(1 - x^2)y'' + \{\beta - \alpha - (\alpha + \beta + 2)x\}y'$ $\qquad\qquad + n(n + \alpha + \beta + 1)y = 0$	$P_n^{(\alpha,\beta)}(x)$ Jacobi polynomials
$x(1 - x)y'' + \{\gamma - (\alpha + \beta + 1)x\}y'$ $\qquad\qquad - \alpha\beta y = 0$ $x^2 y'' + (\beta - x)y' - \alpha y = 0$ $y'' + \left\{-\dfrac{1}{4} + \dfrac{k}{x} + \dfrac{\tfrac{1}{4} - m^2}{x^2}\right\}y = 0$	$_2F_1(\alpha, \beta; \gamma; x)$ $\qquad$ Hypergeometric function $x^{1-\gamma}\,_2F_1(\alpha + 1 - \gamma; \beta + 1 - \gamma; 2 - \gamma; x)$ $_1F_1(\alpha; \beta; x)$ $\qquad$ Confluent hypergeometric function $x^{1-\beta}\,_1F_1(\alpha - \beta + 1; 2 - \beta; x)$ $\left.\begin{array}{l} M_{k,m}(x) \\ M_{k,-m}(x) \end{array}\right\}$ Whittaker's confluent $\qquad\qquad$ hypergeometric functions

4 ORTHOGONALITY RELATIONS

Function	Relation
Legendre polynomials	$\displaystyle\int_{-1}^{1} P_l(x)P_m(x) = \frac{2}{2l + 1}\delta_{lm}$
Associated Legendre polynomials	$\displaystyle\int_{-1}^{1} P_l^m(x)P_{l'}^m(x)\,\mathrm{d}x = \frac{2(l + m)!}{(2l + 1)(l - m)!}\delta_{ll'}$ $\displaystyle\int_{-1}^{1} \frac{P_l^m(x)P_l^{m'}(x)}{1 - x^2}\,\mathrm{d}x = \frac{(l + m)!}{m(l - m)!}\delta_{mm'}$

Function	Relation
Bessel functions	$\int_0^a x J_n(\lambda_i x) J_n(\lambda_j x) \, \mathrm{d}x = \dfrac{a^2}{2} \{J_{n+1}(\lambda_i a)\}^2 \delta_{ij},$ where λ_i and λ_j are roots of $J_n(\lambda a) = 0$
Spherical Bessel functions	$\int_{-\infty}^{\infty} j_m(x) j_n(x) \, \mathrm{d}x = \dfrac{\pi}{2n+1} \delta_{mn}$
Hermite polynomials	$\int_{-\infty}^{\infty} \mathrm{e}^{-x^2} H_n(x) H_m(x) \, \mathrm{d}x = 2^n n! (\sqrt{\pi}) \delta_{nm}$
Weber–Hermite functions	$\int_{-\infty}^{\infty} \Psi_n(x) \Psi_m(x) \, \mathrm{d}x = 2^n n! (\sqrt{\pi}) \delta_{nm}$
Laguerre polynomials	$\int_0^{\infty} \mathrm{e}^{-x} L_m(x) L_n(x) \, \mathrm{d}x = \delta_{mn}$
Associated Laguerre polynomials	$\int_0^{\infty} \mathrm{e}^{-x} x^k L_m^k(x) L_n^k(x) \, \mathrm{d}x = \dfrac{(n+k)!}{n!} \delta_{mn}$
Chebyshev polynomials	$\int_{-1}^{1} \dfrac{T_m(x) T_n(x) \, \mathrm{d}x}{\sqrt{(1-x^2)}} = \begin{cases} 0 & m \neq n \\ \pi/2 & m = n \neq 0 \\ \pi & m = n = 0 \end{cases}$ $\int_{-1}^{1} \dfrac{U_m(x) U_n(x) \, \mathrm{d}x}{\sqrt{(1-x^2)}} = \begin{cases} 0 & m \neq n \\ \pi/2 & m = n \neq 0 \\ 0 & m = n = 0 \end{cases}$
Gegenbauer polynomials	$\int_{-1}^{1} (1-x^2)^{\lambda-\frac{1}{2}} C_m^\lambda(x) C_n^\lambda(x) \, \mathrm{d}x$ $\qquad\qquad = \pi \dfrac{2^{1-2\lambda} \Gamma(n+2\lambda)}{n!(n+\lambda)\{\Gamma(\lambda)\}^2} \delta_{mn}$
Jacobi polynomials	$\int_{-1}^{1} (1-x)^\alpha (1+x)^\beta P_m^{(\alpha,\beta)}(x) P_n^{(\alpha,\beta)}(x)$ $\qquad = \dfrac{2^{\alpha+\beta+1}}{2n+\alpha+\beta+1} \dfrac{\Gamma(n+\alpha+1)\Gamma(n+\beta+1)}{n!\Gamma(n+\alpha+\beta+1)} \delta_{mn}$

5   GENERATING FUNCTIONS

Function	Generating function $(R = (1 - 2xt + t^2)^{1/2})$
Legendre polynomial	$\dfrac{1}{R} = \displaystyle\sum_{n=0}^{\infty} t^n P_n(x)$
Associated Legendre polynomials	$\dfrac{(2m)!(1 - x^2)^{m/2}}{2^m m! R^{m+\frac{1}{2}}} = \displaystyle\sum_{r=0}^{\infty} t^r P_{r+m}^m(x)$
Bessel functions	$\exp\left\{\dfrac{x}{2}\left(t - \dfrac{1}{t}\right)\right\} = \displaystyle\sum_{n=-\infty}^{\infty} t^n J_n(x)$
Hermite polynomials	$\exp\,(2tx - t^2) = \displaystyle\sum_{n=0}^{\infty} \dfrac{t^n}{n!} H_n(x)$
Laguerre polynomials	$\dfrac{\exp\{-xt/(1-t)\}}{1-t} = \displaystyle\sum_{n=0}^{\infty} t^n L_n(x)$
Associated Laguerre polynomials	$\dfrac{\exp\{-xt/(1-t)\}}{(1-t)^{k+1}} = \displaystyle\sum_{n=0}^{\infty} t^n L_n^k(x)$
Chebyshev polynomials	$\dfrac{1 - t^2}{R^2} = T_0(x) + 2\displaystyle\sum_{n=1}^{\infty} t^n T_n(x)$
	$\dfrac{\sqrt{(1 - x^2)}}{R^2} = \displaystyle\sum_{n=0}^{\infty} t^n U_{n+1}(x)$
Gegenbauer polynomials	$\dfrac{1}{R^{2\lambda}} = \displaystyle\sum_{n=0}^{\infty} t^n C_n^\lambda(x)$
Jacobi polynomials	$\dfrac{2^{\alpha+\beta}}{R(1 - t + R)^\alpha(1 + t + R)^\beta} = \displaystyle\sum_{n=0}^{\infty} t^n P_n^{(\alpha,\beta)}(x)$

HINTS AND SOLUTIONS TO PROBLEMS

CHAPTER 1

(1) The general solution is $Ay_1(x) + By_2(x)$ in each case, where A and B are arbitrary constants and $y_1(x)$ and $y_2(x)$ are given by

(i) $y_1(x) = 1 + \displaystyle\sum_{n=1}^{\infty} \frac{1}{n!1.5.9\dots(4n-3)}x^n$,

$\quad y_2(x) = x^{3/4}\left\{1 + \displaystyle\sum_{n=1}^{\infty}\frac{1}{n!7.11.15\dots(4n+3)}x^n\right\}$,

valid for all x;

(ii) $y_1(x) = e^{-x}$,

$\quad y_2(x) = \ln x . e^{-x} - \displaystyle\sum_{n=1}^{\infty}(-1)^n\frac{1}{n!}\left(1 + \frac{1}{2} + \frac{1}{3} + \dots + \frac{1}{n}\right)x^n$,

valid for all x;

(iii) $y_1(x) = \displaystyle\sum_{n=3}^{\infty}(-1)^n\frac{1}{2n!(n-3)!}x^n$,

$\quad y_2(x) = y_1(x)\ln x + 1 + \frac{1}{2}x + \frac{1}{4}x^2 - \frac{1}{36}x^3 +$

$\qquad + \displaystyle\sum_{n=4}^{\infty}\frac{(-1)^n}{2n!(n-3)!}\left\{-2\left(1 + \frac{1}{2} + \frac{1}{3} + \dots + \frac{1}{n-3}\right.\right.$

$\qquad\qquad \left.\left. - \frac{1}{n-2} - \frac{1}{n-1} - \frac{1}{n} + \frac{3}{2}\right\}x^n\right.$,

valid for all x;

(iv) $y_1(x) = 1 + \displaystyle\sum_{n=1}^{\infty}\frac{1.4.7\dots(3n-2)}{3^n n!}x^n$

$\qquad = (1-x)^{-\frac{1}{3}}$,

$\quad y_2(x) = x^{7/3}\left\{1 + \displaystyle\sum_{n=1}^{\infty}\frac{8.11.14\dots(3n+5)}{10.13.16\dots(3n+7)}x^n\right\}$,

valid for $|x| < 1$;

(v) $y_1(x) = 1 + \displaystyle\sum_{n=1}^{\infty} \frac{(-1)(-3)\ldots(4n^2 - 14n + 9)}{(2n)!}x^{2n}$,

$y_2(x) = x + \displaystyle\sum_{n=1}^{\infty} \frac{(-3)(-1)\ldots(4n^2 - 10n + 3)}{(2n + 1)!}x^{2n+1}$,

valid for $|x| < 1$;

(vi) $y_1(x) = x^2$,

$y_2(x) = x^2 \ln x + x^2 \displaystyle\sum_{n=1}^{\infty} \frac{(-1)^n}{n.n!}x^n$,

valid for all x;

(vii) $y_1(x) = x$,

$y_2(x) = 1 + \dfrac{x^2}{2!} + \dfrac{x^4}{4!} + \displaystyle\sum_{n=3}^{\infty} \frac{3^2.5^2\ldots(2n - 3)^2}{(2n)!}x^{2n}$,

valid for $|x| < 1$;

(viii) $y_1(x) = \displaystyle\sum_{n=2}^{\infty} (-1)^{n+1}\frac{1}{3^{2n-1}(n - 2)!n!}x^{3n-1}$,

$y_2(x) = y_1(x) \ln x + x^{-1} + \tfrac{1}{9}x^2 + \tfrac{1}{324}x^5$

$+ \displaystyle\sum_{n=3}^{\infty}(-1)^{n+1}\frac{1}{3^{2n}(n-2)!n!}\left\{1 - 2\left(1 + \frac{1}{2} + \ldots + \frac{1}{n - 2}\right)\right.$

$\left. - \frac{1}{n - 1} - \frac{1}{n}\right\}x^{3n-1}$,

valid for all x;

(ix) $y_1(x) = 1 + \tfrac{1}{2}x^2 + \tfrac{1}{24}x^4 + \tfrac{1}{20}x^5 + \tfrac{1}{720}x^6 + \tfrac{13}{2520}x^7 + \ldots$,

$y_2(x) = x + \tfrac{1}{6}x^3 + \tfrac{1}{12}x^4 + \tfrac{1}{120}x^5 + \tfrac{7}{360}x^6 + \tfrac{41}{5040}x^7 + \ldots$,

valid for all x.

(2) (i) Impossible; (ii) impossible; (iii) possible.

(3) The general solution is $Ay_1(x) + By_2(x)$ where A and B are arbitrary constants, and $y_1(x)$ and $y_2(x)$ are given by:

(i) $y_1(x) = 1 + \displaystyle\sum_{n=1}^{\infty} \frac{2.7.16\ldots(2n^2 - n + 1)}{n!1.3.5\ldots(2n - 1)}\frac{1}{x^n}$,

$y_2(x) = x^{-1/2}\left\{1 + \displaystyle\sum_{n=1}^{\infty} \frac{4.11.22\ldots(2n^2 + n + 1)}{n!3.5\ldots(2n + 1)}\frac{1}{x^n}\right\}$;

(ii) $y_1(x) = 1 - \dfrac{2}{3x}$,

$$y_2(x) = x^{-1/2}\left\{1 + \sum_{n=1}^{\infty} \frac{(-3)(-1)\ldots(2n-5)}{n!\,1.3.5\ldots(2n-1)}\frac{1}{x^n}\right\}.$$

CHAPTER 2

(1) Use definition (2.1) of the gamma function with a suitable change of the variable of integration.

(2) Use theorem 2.5.

(3) Use theorem 2.5.

(4) (i) $B(\tfrac{5}{4}, \tfrac{3}{4}) = \dfrac{\pi}{2\sqrt{2}}$.

(ii) $\Gamma(a)$. (Make the change of variable $1/x = e^y$.)

(iii) $(b-a)^{m+n-1}B(m, n)$. (Make the change of variable
$$y = (x-a)/(b-a).)$$

(iv) $\dfrac{1}{n}B\left(\dfrac{m+1}{n}, p+1\right)$. (Make the change of variable $y = x^n$.)

(v) $\dfrac{1}{n}B\left(\dfrac{1}{n}, \dfrac{1}{2}\right) = \dfrac{\sqrt{\pi}}{n}\dfrac{\Gamma(1/n)}{\Gamma\{(1/n)+\tfrac{1}{2}\}}$. (Make the change of variable
$$y = x^n.)$$

(vi) $B(\tfrac{1}{2}, \tfrac{1}{2}) = \pi$. (Make the change of variable $u = 1/(1+t)$.)

(6) $\Gamma(-\tfrac{1}{2}) = -2\sqrt{\pi}$; $\Gamma(-\tfrac{7}{2}) = \tfrac{16}{105}\sqrt{\pi}$.

(7) Use theorem 2.12.

CHAPTER 3

(1) Use theorems 3.8(ii) and 3.5.

(2) Use theorems 3.8(vii), 3.8(ii) and 3.5.

(3) Consider $(x^2 - 1)^l$ as the product $(x-1)^l.(x+1)^l$.

(4) $c_r = \begin{cases} (-1)^{(r-1)/2}\dfrac{(r+\tfrac{1}{2})(r-1)!}{2^r\{(r+1)/2\}!\{(r-1)/2\}!} & \text{if } r \text{ is odd} \\ 0 & \text{if } r \text{ is even.} \end{cases}$

Use the result of Example 2.

(5) Differentiate the generating function for the Legendre polynomials m times and use definition (3.36).

(6) Use theorems 3.8(ii) and 3.5.

$$u_n = \begin{cases} 2/n & \text{if } n \text{ is even} \\ 0 & \text{if } n \text{ is odd.} \end{cases}$$

(7) Use theorem 3.8(i).
(8) Use theorem 3.8(ix).
(10) Use theorems 3.8(viii) and 3.16 and Example 5.
(11) Use definitions (3.61) and (3.36).
(12) Use theorems 3.2 and 3.15 and integrate by parts l times.

CHAPTER 4

(1) Use theorem 4.8(iii) and (iv).
(2) Use the infinite series for J_0 and J_1.
(3) Compare with Example 4.
(4) $Ax^{1/2}J_{2/3}(\frac{4}{3}(\sqrt{\lambda})x^{2/3})$ (with A an arbitrary constant). Use theorem 4.12.
(5) Use the infinite series for J_0.
(6) Use the fact that $1 = \exp\left[x\{t-(1/t)\}\right].\exp\left[-x\{t-(1/t)\}\right]$ and pick out the coefficient of x^0 on the right-hand side.
(7) Use theorems 4.8(ii), 4.21(i) and 4.22(i).
(8) Use the generating function.
(9) Use the generating function for the J_n.
(10) Show that both Bessel's equation and Bessel's modified equation may, by further differentiations, be written in the given form.

(11) $c_r = \dfrac{2}{a\lambda^3}\dfrac{\{(\lambda_r a)^2 - 4\}}{J_1(\lambda_r a)}.$

(12) $\displaystyle\int_{-\infty}^{\infty} j_m(x)j_n(x)\,\mathrm{d}x = 0 \quad (m \neq n).$

$\displaystyle\int_{-\infty}^{\infty} \{j_n(x)\}^2\,\mathrm{d}x = \dfrac{\pi}{2n+1}.$

(13) Take real and imaginary parts of the infinite series for $J_n(i^{3/2}x)$.

(14) Take real and imaginary parts of the integral $\displaystyle\int_0^x tJ_0(i^{3/2}t)\,\mathrm{d}t$; use theorem 4.8(i) to help evaluate the integral.

(15) Take real and imaginary parts of the asymptotic form of $J_0(i^{3/2}x)$, given by theorem 4.21(i).

CHAPTER 5

(1) Use theorem 5.6(ii) and 5.5.

(3) Use the fact that $2\displaystyle\int_0^{\infty} e^{-t^2}\cos 2xt = \int_{-\infty}^{\infty} e^{-t^2}\cos 2xt = \mathrm{Re}\int_{-\infty}^{\infty}$

$\exp(-t^2 + 2ixt)\,\mathrm{d}t.$

$$H_{2n+1}(x) = (-1)^n \frac{2^{2n+2}}{\sqrt{\pi}} e^{x^2} \int_0^\infty e^{-t^2} t^{2n+1} \sin 2xt \, dt.$$

(4) Using the result of problem 3 for both $H_n(x)$ and $H_n(y)$ gives

$$\sum_{n=0}^\infty \frac{H_n(x)H_n(y)}{2^n n!} t^n = \frac{1}{\pi} \exp(x^2 + y^2) \int_{-\infty}^\infty \int_{-\infty}^\infty \exp(-u^2 - v^2 + 2iux + 2ivy - 2uvt) \, du \, dv.$$

Performing the integrations gives the required result.

(7) (i) $2^n n! (\sqrt{\pi}) \delta_{mn}$.

(ii) $2^{n-1} n! (\sqrt{\pi}) \delta_{m,\,n-1} - 2^n (n+1)! (\sqrt{\pi}) \delta_{m,\,n+1}$.

CHAPTER 6

(3) Use equation (6.3) and integrate term by term.
(4) Use equation (5.3) and integrate term by term.
(5) Use theorem 6.9.
(6) Use theorems 6.11(ii) and 6.10.
(7) Use equation (5.3).

CHAPTER 7

(1–6) Make the substitution $x = \cos\theta$.
(8) Use the series solution method of Chapter 1, and remember that n is integral.

CHAPTER 8

(1) Use definition (8.2) or theorem 8.5.
(2) Use definition (8.2).
(3) Use theorem 8.5(ii).
(4) Use theorem 8.3(i).
(5) Use definition (8.2).
(6) Use theorem 8.1 and equation (3.17).

CHAPTER 9

(3) Use theorem 9.4.
(6) Use theorem 9.1.
(7) $(1/s)_2F_1(\alpha, 1; \beta; s)$. Use theorem 9.7.

CHAPTER 10

(1) Integrate by parts.

(2) Write $\displaystyle\int_0^\infty e^{-st} \, \text{Ci}\,(t) \, dt$ as a double integral and change the order of the integration.

(5) Integrate by parts.

(6) First prove the equality of the two integrals by making the substitution $y = (\pi/2) - x$ in the first. Then consider the second integral, and make the substitution $\cos x = \cos^2 u$.

(8) Make the substitution $x = \tan \theta$.

BIBLIOGRAPHY

ABRAMOWITZ, M., and STEGUN, I. A. *Handbook of Mathematical Functions*, Dover, New York (1965).

ARTIN, E. *The Gamma Function*, Holt, Rinehart and Winston, New York (1964).

ERDELYI, A., MAGNUS, W., OBERHETTINGER, F., and TRICOMI, F. G. *Higher Transcendental Functions* (Bateman Manuscript Project), Vols. 1–3, McGraw-Hill, New York (1953).

FLETCHER, A., MILLER, J. C. P., ROSENHEAD, L., and COMRIE, L. J. *An Index of Mathematical Tables*, Vols. 1 and 2, 2nd edn., Addison-Wesley, Reading, Mass. (1962).

HOBSON, E. W. *The Theory of Spherical and Ellipsoidal Harmonics*, Cambridge University Press, London (1931).

HOCHSTADT, H. *Special Functions of Mathematical Physics*, Holt, Rinehart and Winston, New York (1961).

JAHNKE, E., EMDE, F., and LÖSCH, F. *Tables of Higher Functions*, 6th edn., McGraw-Hill, New York (1960).

LEBEDEV, A. V., and FEDOROVA, R. M. *A Guide to Mathematical Tables*, Pergamon Press, Oxford (1960).

LEBEDEV, N. N. *Special Functions and their Applications*, Prentice-Hall, Englewood Cliffs, N.J. (1965).

MACROBERT, T. M. *Spherical Harmonics*, 2nd edn., Methuen, London (1947).

MAGNUS, W., OBERHETTINGER, F., and SONI, R. P. *Formulas and Theorems for the Functions of Mathematical Physics*, 3rd edn., Springer-Verlag, New York (1966).

MCLACHLAN, N. W. *Bessel Functions for Engineers*, 2nd edn., Oxford University Press, London, (1955).

RAINVILLE, E. D. *Special Functions*, Macmillan, New York (1960).

RELTON, F. E. *Applied Bessel Functions*, Blackie, London (1946).

SLATER, L. J. *Confluent Hypergeometric Functions*, Cambridge University Press, London (1960).

SNEDDON, I. N. *Special Functions of Mathematical Physics and Chemistry*, 2nd edn., Oliver and Boyd, Edinburgh (1961).

WATSON, G. N. *A Treatise on the Theory of Bessel Functions*, 2nd edn., Cambridge University Press, London (1931).

INDEX

Associated Laguerre polynomials 176
  definition of   176
  generating function for   177
  notation for   182
  orthogonality properties of   178
  recurrence relations for   178
Associated Legendre equation   62
Associated Legendre functions   62
  definition of   62
  orthogonality relations for   66
  properties of   65
  recurrence relations for   68

Bessel functions   92
  of the first kind   94
    asymptotic behaviour of   127
    definition of   94
    generating function for   99
    graph of   134
    integral representations for   101
    orthogonality properties of   137
    recurrence relations for   104
  of the second kind   97
    asymptotic behaviour of   127
    definition of   97
    explicit expression for   98
    graph of   134
    recurrence relations for   106
  of the third kind (*see* Hankel functions)
Bessel series   141
Bessel's equation   92
Beta function   23
  definition of   23

Chebyshev polynomials   187

definition of   187
  generating function for   190
  orthogonality properties of   192
  recurrence relations for   193
  series for   188
  special values of   192
Chebyshev's equation   189
Confluent hypergeometric equation 210, 212
Confluent hypergeometric function 203
  contiguity relations for   212
  definition of   203
  integral representation of   211
Cosine integral   219

Debye functions   224
Differential equations
  satisfied by various special functions 233
  solution of by Frobenius' method   1

Elliptic integrals   224
Error function   221
Euler's constant   231
Exponential integral   218

Fresnel integrals   221
Frobenius' method   1
  summary of   7

Gamma function   23
  definition of   23, 30
  graph of   31

Gauss's equation 207
Gegenbauer polynomials 197
  definition of 197
  differential equation satisfied by 198
  generating function for 197
  orthogonality properties of 198
  power series for 198
  recurrence relations for 198
Generating function 236
  for associated Laguerre polynomials 177
  for Bessel functions of the first kind 99
  for Chebyshev polynomials 190
  for Gegenbauer polynomials 197
  for Hermite polynomials 157
  for Jacobi polynomials 198
  for Laguerre polynomials 169
  for Legendre polynomials 46

Hankel functions 107
  asymptotic behaviour of 127
  definition of 107
  recurrence relations for 108
Hermite polynomials 156
  definition of 157
  generating function for 157
  orthogonality properties of 161
  recurrence relations for 162
  special values of 160
Hermite's equation 156
Hypergeometric equation 207, 208
Hypergeometric functions 203
  contiguity relations for 210
  definition of 203
  integral representation of 207
  relationship with other special functions 204

Incomplete gamma functions 218
Indicial equation 3
Integral representation
  of Bessel functions 101
  of confluent hypergeometric function 211
  of hypergeometric function 207
  of Legendre polynomials 49
  of modified Bessel functions 116

Integrals involving Bessel functions 141

Jacobi polynomials 198
  definition of 198
  differential equation satisfied by 199
  generating function for 198
  orthogonality properties of 199
  recurrence relations for 199
  series for 199

Kelvin's functions 120
  graphs of 137
Kummer function 204
Kummer's equation 210

Laguerre polynomials 168
  definition of 169
  generating function for 169
  notation for 182
  orthogonality properties of 172
  recurrence relations for 173
  special values of 171
Laguerre's equation 168
Laplace's integral representation 49
Legendre duplication formula 29
Legendre functions of the second kind 70
  graphs of 84, 85
  properties of 77
Legendre polynomials 42
  definition of 46
  generating function for 46
  graphs of 82, 83, 84
  Laplace's integral representation for 49
  orthogonality properties of 52
  recurrence relations for 58
  Rodrigues' formula for 48
  special values of 50
Legendre series 55
Legendre's associated equation 62
Legendre's equation 42
Leibniz's theorem 63
L'Hôpital's rule 39, 97
Logarithmic integral 219

Modified Bessel functions 110
  asymptotic behaviour of 128
  graphs of 135
  integral representations for 116
  recurrence relations for 113

Neumann functions (*see* Bessel functions of the second kind)
Neumann's formula 78

Orthogonality properties 234
  of associated Laguerre polynomials 178
  of associated Legendre functions 66
  of Bessel functions 137
  of Chebyshev polynomials 192
  of Gegenbauer polynomials 198
  of Hermite polynomials 161
  of Jacobi polynomials 199
  of Laguerre polynomials 172
  of Legendre polynomials 52
  of spherical harmonics 80

Pochhammer symbol 203

Rayleigh's formulae 126
Recurrence relations
  for associated Laguerre polynomials 178
  for associated Legendre functions 68
  for Bessel functions of the first kind 104

for Bessel functions of the second kind 106
for Chebyshev polynomials 193
for Gegenbauer polynomials 198
for Hankel functions 108
for Hermite polynomials 162
for Jacobi polynomials 199
for Laguerre polynomials 173
for Legendre polynomials 58
for modified Bessel functions 113
for spherical Bessel functions 122
Riemann's zeta function 223
Rodrigues' formula 48

Sine integral 219
Spherical Bessel functions 121
  asymptotic behaviour of 128
  graphs of 136
  Rayleigh's formulae for 126
  recurrence relations for 122
Spherical harmonics 78
  orthogonality properties of 80

Ultraspherical polynomials (*see* Gegenbauer polynomials)

Weber-Hermite functions 163
Whittaker's confluent hypergeometric functions 212

Zeta function 223